THEORY OF PSYCHOLOGICAL MEASUREMENT

SHAFFER AND LAZARUS *Fundamental Concepts in Clinical Psychology*
SIEGEL *Nonparametric Statistics: For the Behavioral Sciences*
STAGNER *Psychology of Personality*
TOWNSEND *Introduction to Experimental Method*
VINACKE *The Psychology of Thinking*
WALLEN *Clinical Psychology: The Study of Persons*
WATERS, RETHLINGSHAFER, AND CALDWELL *Principles of Comparative Psychology*
WINER *Statistical Principles in Experimental Design*
ZUBEK AND SOLBERG *Human Development*

John F. Dashiell was Consulting Editor of this series from its inception in 1931 until January 1, 1950, Clifford T. Morgan was Consulting Editor of this series from January 1, 1950 until January 1, 1959.

Theory of
Psychological Measurement

Edwin E. Ghiselli

Professor of Psychology
University of California
Berkeley, California

New York
San Francisco
Toronto
London

McGRAW-HILL BOOK COMPANY

Theory of Psychological Measurement

To

ROBERT C. TRYON

Friend and Teacher

Preface

The objective of this book is to present an elementary discussion of the basic problems of psychological measurement. Since I have taught a course in theory of psychological measurement for many years, it is natural, I suppose, for me to have developed certain ideas about what topics should be included and how the material should be presented. Unquestionably others will disagree with my approaches and developments. This is as it should be, since clarification of concepts emerges from the comparison of varying points of view about them.

The topics covered in the book are few. The initial discussion of the nature and types of variables leads up to the use and development of norms and the standardizing of scores. There follows an extended discussion of correlation, because it is my opinion that an understanding of the basis and nature of the Pearsonian coefficient is absolutely necessary if the student is to grasp the concepts of reliability and validity. In view of the fact that most scores are combinations of other scores, composite variables are examined in some detail. This also provides an opportunity to present item analysis and permits the development of formulae important in reliability and validity of measurement. In connection with reliability I have presented conceptual formulations other than the classical Yule-Spearman view. Thus a variety of interpretations of reliability are possible as well as differing evaluations of ways for estimating reliability. Similarly, differing notions of validity are presented, though more attention is given to predictive validity than to either content or construct validity.

At the end of each chapter is a list of selected readings. These were chosen with the idea of providing the more interested students some historical perspective and varying points of view.

Almost all formulae are developed in full. Many will not approve of this, especially in view of the fact that the developments are in painful detail. However, it seems to me that insofar as possible students must understand the logic which underlies the formulae they will be using. Perhaps if undergraduate majors in psychology were well prepared in mathematics, much of the detail would not be necessary—but in my experience they are not. I try to teach my students to read mathematical developments in much the same manner that they read a logical argument given in verbal terms.

In my classical education the blacks and whites of Dante's "Divina

Commedia" disturbed me. But among Pirandello's subtle variations of gray I was completely comfortable. I have no difficulty tolerating ambiguity, and indeed paradoxy seems to me to be the normal state of affairs. It will bother some that I do not take a position on such matters as the normalizing of distributions of scores, linearity and homoscedasticity in correlation, reliability, and validity. And that I fail to evaluate various points of view on these issues, painting one white and all the rest black, will seem the height of maleficence to many. But with Pirandello I prefer merely to present the contrasting notions and let the reader decide for himself which, if any, is the *real* truth—"Così è se vi pare."

Various portions of this book have gone through several mimeographed editions which I have used in my course in psychological measurement. To the many students who have tried to learn from these preliminary editions and who have made numerous helpful comments I am duly grateful. I also wish to express my appreciation to my colleague Professor Read D. Tuddenham, who kindly reviewed many of the chapters. I especially wish to thank Professor Edward Minium of San Jose State College, who spent so much time reviewing the manuscript in detail and made many constructive suggestions. Finally I should like to thank Drs. M. D. Davidoff and H. W. Goheen and the editors of *Psychometrika* for permission to reproduce Table 6-2, used in estimating the tetrachoric coefficient of correlation.

In dedicating this book to Professor Robert C. Tryon I wish to acknowledge at least in some small way the stimulation, support, and above all the warm friendship he has so freely given me. His enthusiasm, ingenuity, and wisdom invariably leave their marks on all who are associated with him. It was more than three decades ago, when we were both fledglings, that as a student I was first exposed to measurement theory in his course in individual differences. For twenty-five years we have been colleagues, and each day he has given me some new insight, a new idea to steal, a bit of wit to make life sparkle. Inasmuch as he has willingly continued to be my tutor, I could feel fully justified in holding him accountable for my errors and bad logic which appear in these pages. But some slight measure of the tolerance which so characterizes this gentle man has brushed off on me and so I forgive him the shortcomings of this text.

Edwin E. Ghiselli

Contents

chapter 1   Introduction

When we compare the characteristics of amoebae, sharks, cats, and human beings we see vast differences. The oozing locomotion of the amoeba, the graceful undulation of the shark, the loose easy pace of the cat, and the jerky walk of the human being are clearly dissimilar. Indeed, so vast are the differences between the various kinds of organisms that the differences among individuals of any one kind seem small and insignificant.

Yet if we direct our attention toward any one kind of creature we see quite significant differences. One amoeba flows along an undeviating path whereas another wanders aimlessly. One shark thrashes through the waters with a great commotion whereas another progresses with steady rhythmic oscillations. One cat boldly pursues a direct course whereas another furtively darts from one protective shelter to another. One man walks "ten feet tall" with shoulders back whereas another shuffles along with a slouch.

The differences among individuals of any one kind, then, are very real and substantial in magnitude. The task of the psychologist is to understand individuals. He is therefore interested in the sources of the differences and in the factors that in a given situation cause one individual to behave in one way and another to behave quite differently. He is interested, too, in the factors that cause changes in the individual—improvements in performance, reductions in ability, or cyclical variations in social adjustment.

1

THE PURPOSE OF PSYCHOLOGICAL MEASUREMENT

Obviously, before the factors determining the psychological character-istics of individuals can be systematically examined those very character-istics must be described. This is the purpose of psychological measure-ment. Measurement essentially is concerned with the operations designed to provide quantitative descriptions of the extent to which individuals manifest or possess specified traits. Therefore it is important that, as students of psychology, we understand something of the theory and problems of psychological measurement and of the nature and use of quantitative descriptions as given by the operations of measurement.

Many varied operations have been devised for measuring the numerous traits that psychologists see living creatures as manifesting or possessing. There are sundry tests of knowledge and of problem solving, question-naires wherein the individual reports his perceptions about himself, and rating procedures that require one individual to judge the traits of others. In one way or another all these devices yield descriptions of the extent to which individuals manifest or possess specified traits. These quantitative descriptions, or scores, given by the various operations of measurement differ widely in their utility and meaningfulness. Some are valuable as they stand, whereas others must be subjected to further operations, usu-ally of a mathematical nature, so that they can be transformed to other values or scores which are more meaningful and useful.

TOPICS IN PSYCHOLOGICAL MEASUREMENT
TO BE COVERED

Psychological measurement is a broad field, replete with both method-ological and theoretical problems. In this book we shall not cover all the basic problems, nor shall we even be able to present a complete discussion of those we do consider. Our principal concern will be with providing an introduction to some of the fundamental aspects of measurement and of the description of the differences among individuals.

We shall begin with a general consideration of some of the basic prob-lems in the psychological description of individuals, discussing such matters as the definition of psychological traits, the development of oper-ations designed to measure those traits, and the ways in which individuals differ from one another. This will lead us to a consideration of the use of distributions of scores, or norms, as a basis for giving some meaning to scores and for making scores on different traits comparable. Therefore we shall have to discuss ways and means for describing and dealing with dis-tributions of scores and for standardizing scores on distributions.

For many practical and theoretical problems, indices of the degree of relationship between traits are necessary. Such indices tell us about the similarity in the order of individuals on different traits, the accuracy with which we can distinguish one trait from another, and something of the factors that determine differences among individuals. Consequently we shall delve somewhat into the theory of correlation and shall examine ways for describing the degree of relationship between traits.

Many of the tests and other operations we use in measuring individuals are complex, being composed of a series of items, subtests, or other kinds of parts or components which are added together. Consequently we must examine the combination of components into composites, and the relationships between scores on different composites.

The instruments we use to describe individuals quantitatively in terms of various psychological traits never measure those traits with perfect precision. Some are highly reliable and others have a lesser degree of reliability. Reliability of measurement is a problem of fundamental importance, but one not easily stated. We shall consider the various theoretical approaches that have been made to the problem of reliability and shall discuss ways and means for estimating the degree to which a test gives reliable measurements.

We shall return to the problem of composite variables and consider ways in which the components forming a composite can be differentially weighted, along with the effects of such weighting. Differential weighting of variables has considerable importance with respect to the problem of prediction of an individual's standing on one trait from a composite of his scores on a series of other traits.

Finally, we shall discuss the problem of validity of measurement. Validity has to do with prediction and with the determination of the traits actually measured by a given test. As is the case with reliability of measurement, we shall see that there are differing views about the nature of validity of measurement. We shall examine these various approaches to validity in order to gain some insight into the problem.

THEORIES AND MODELS

It has so often been said that the world is complex that the import of this statement is frequently forgotten. Indeed, sometimes it seems that the complexity is so great that no one man or group of men will ever be able to understand it completely. We have a few bits of knowledge which we try to piece together to make some kind of a meaningful whole. Often, however, the facts available are not sufficient to make a total integrated picture. Furthermore, that which at one time appears to be a fact seems pure fantasy at another time. Once it was obvious that the sun revolved around the earth. Now we know that the reverse is true. Even if we do have a goodly number of facts, and they are facts which "stand still" and remain facts, the complexities of their relationships usually are so great that we are unable to grasp them.

Yet we must deal with the world and its inhabitants, and therefore some understanding of it is necessary. In order to integrate the fragments of knowledge we do have and to bring some comprehensible order into the chaos of ignorance and some understanding into the complexity, we often do a peculiar thing—we create a world in our minds and pretend it is the real world. When as scientists we create a substitute world, we term it a theoretical model.

A theoretical model, therefore, "stands in" for some phenomenon, that is, is a representation of it. In order to provide an integration of the partial knowledge we have about the phenomenon and to make it meaningful, the model must necessarily go beyond the known facts. Consequently the model describes features of the phenomenon which are not given directly by the facts. If the model is a good representation, the inferred features will be like those of the phenomenon; if it is a poor one, they will not.

Consider the ancients' view of the shape of the world. They noted, for example, that unless a surface is flat, objects placed on it slide off. Since people and things maintain their position on the surface of the earth and do not slide off, it seemed to the ancients that the surface of the earth necessarily must be flat. To be sure, there appeared to be some inconsistencies such as the fact that ships approaching from the distance appeared to rise out of the sea. But this could be explained away as being due to valleys and hills on the sea similar in nature to the valleys and hills on the land, irregular fluctuations from the basic plane of the earth.

In many instances where we are dealing with phenomena about which we have only fragments of information, we develop a theory or model into which the bits fit so as to organize them into a meaningful whole. Many of the features of our model are not given by the available facts, and we develop them by interpolations and extrapolations from those facts we do have, by inference, by plain "horseback" guess, and by nothing more nor less than our imagination. Thus the ancients' model of the flat earth had an edge, a top, and a bottom even though no one had ever seen the edge and the bottom, because they observed that all flat things like tabletops and coins have edges, tops, and bottoms. Since objects have to be supported by something or else they fall, the ancients decided that a giant must be holding up the earth.

Today it is obvious to us that the ancients' model of the world is incorrect. Yet in spite of their completely false notions they were able to accomplish some remarkable feats of navigation. In the time of the pharaohs the Egyptians were able to sail from the Red Sea to the far southern regions of Africa, and the Phoenicians were able to sail from their home ports in the Middle East to the distant land now called Spain.

Thus a model may be manifestly incorrect and still be useful as a description of a set of phenomena and useful for making predictions about them. Being more sophisticated and wiser than our ancestors, we realize that the world is round. If we wish to sail or fly from San Francisco to Singapore, we plot our course as an arc on a sphere. Nevertheless, if we were planning a short voyage or a flight—say from San Francisco to Los Angeles—we should probably not bother to use the more complicated spherical model but should be satisfied with the simpler flat model of the ancients. We should plot our course as a straight line on a plane as given by a Mercator projection rather than as an arc on a globe. For the relatively short distance involved, the error resulting from the use of the incorrect flat model rather than the more correct spherical model is, for all practical purposes, negligible. Practicality, then, may lead us to adopt a model which we know is incorrect but which nonetheless in restricted areas is useful for description and prediction.

Superior though our spherical model of the world may be compared with the flat model of the ancients, we must recognize that it, too, is not correct. Common observation indicates that the surface of the earth, pocked as it is with valleys and knobbed with mountains, is certainly not like the surface of a smooth sphere. If we use a sphere as a model it is only an approximate representation of the surface of the earth. The exterior of the earth obviously is a very complex surface, not a simple and smooth one like the surface of a true sphere. Nevertheless, we might say that it is not unreasonable to take a sphere as a representation of the earth. The differences between the surface of a sphere and the true surface of the earth are not great, and for practical purposes of planning a journey we do not introduce much error by pretending the world is spherical. As a matter of fact, recent evidence suggests that the earth is somewhat pear-shaped. The surface of a pear-shaped object is far more complex than that of a sphere and consequently more difficult to deal with. But if the "pearedness" of the earth is not too great, a spherical model may still serve with reasonable accuracy. If we believe the error is not too great, we should be willing to tolerate it for the sake of greater ease of comprehending and describing movements along the surface. Indeed, we do not know precisely what the shape of the world is. We do know that it is very complicated and that, while certainly not precisely spherical, it is nevertheless something like a sphere. Furthermore, the shape of the earth is not constant but in fact changes over time. Various celestial and terrestrial forces are at work, and even puny man changes the surface of the earth. A model might therefore be adopted to simplify a complex situation, to make it understandable and consequently "livable" even though the model is contrary to fact.

If we decide that we are going to consider the world as a sphere, then we can represent it by a physical model, perhaps by means of a ball. But the mathematical properties of a sphere are well known, so instead of a ball we could use as our model the various mathematical formulae which describe a sphere. There are formulae which permit us to calculate the total surface of a sphere or the various portions of it, the lengths of arcs on its surface, and the like. All these formulae are related to one another and provide ways for describing spheres. Knowing the characteristics of certain parts of a sphere, we can calculate the characteristics of other parts. In some instances, then, it is not necessary to have a physical model as a representation of a set of phenomena; instead, we can use a mathematical model, which gives us very precise descriptions and is more convenient.

As we consider the various problems of psychological measurement we shall find it helpful from time to time to talk about models. We shall find models not only very useful for purposes of description and prediction but also valuable for simplification of complex phenomena so that they become comprehensible. The models in many instances may be manifestly incorrect representations; nevertheless, they are useful when we are beset with incomplete facts and rendered helpless by a complexity beyond our understanding.

Suppose that, in order to describe the way in which intelligence is distributed among children, we administer an intelligence test to 50 children. We shall undoubtedly find that the distribution of scores is quite irregular. For instance, the number of children who have IQs of 99 and 101 may be greater than the number who have an IQ of 100. Since our facts are few, there being only 50 children, we are likely to ascribe the irregularity in the distribution to an insufficient number of cases. We should say that if we had a larger number of children the distribution would be quite smooth. We should therefore disregard certain of our facts and adopt as a model of the distribution of intelligence one which is smooth but has the same average and variability as our actual distribution.

When we give the same test many times to the same individuals we often find that the scores of each person change from time to time. The variations in an individual's scores are random, showing no systematic improvement or reduction. In order to understand these results we say that each person possesses a given true amount of the ability measured by the test but his score varies from time to time because of the effects of unsystematic and variable factors in the situation. On one occasion a person's score may be a little lower because he has a cold, and on another it may be a little higher because the lighting is extra bright and he can see what he is doing. We do not know that this actually occurs, but it is a reasonable explanation of the variation. So we can set up a simple mathematical model to explain and to understand test performance by saying that the score an individual obtains on a given administration of a test is his true ability plus an error.

So we see that it is sometimes helpful to use theoretical models to represent distributions of scores rather than the actual distribution itself, and to represent the factors that determine an individual's performance on a test. In this same way models are useful for dealing with other problems in psychological measurement when our facts are incomplete, when we have doubts about the adequacy of our measuring devices, and when the phenomena with which we deal are complex.

chapter 2   The Description
of Individual Differences

As we observe the world around us we see that the individual objects in it—be they things, animals, people, or social groups—differ among themselves in a variety of ways. Trees differ among themselves in height, animals in speed of locomotion, human beings in verbal facility, and social groups in homogeneity. Trees also differ among themselves in the nature of their foliage, animals in the ease with which they can be trained, human beings in the patterns of their personality traits, and social groups in their type of leadership. Not all individuals of a given kind, then, are the same with respect to some particular property. Rather, the rule is that individuals differ among themselves.

Sometimes the variation among individuals is qualitative, being in terms of kind; and in other instances it is quantitative, being in terms of frequency, amount, or degree. When we propose to study individual differences we must specify or define the property with which we are concerned. From this definition we can develop a series of operations that will permit us to describe individuals in terms of that property. Qualitative description is termed classification, and quantitative description is termed measurement. Measurement involves the use of numbers, that is, values which provide quantitative descriptions of individuals and which can be manipulated to give us further information about those individuals.

THE NATURE OF VARIABLES

The properties that individuals manifest may be such tangible characteristics as smoothness or size, or such intangible qualities as attitude toward war or the trait of sociability. Some properties may be manifested by all members of a particular population. Thus all living creatures possess the property of life, all books the property of pages, and all fish the property of being water dwellers. On the other hand, the members of a given population may differ with respect to a particular property. A property in which individuals differ among themselves is termed a *variable*. Thus shape is a property in which stones vary, weight a property in which people vary, and foreign policy a property in which political parties vary. There are various ways in which individuals may differ with respect to a property. They may differ qualitatively, as in kind, or quantitatively, as in amount. College students vary not only in kind in terms of their major subject but also in degree in terms of their academic performance. Furthermore, there are different types of quantitative variation. In some cases quantitative variables are discontinuous and show breaks or steps, such as the variable "number of boxcars in a freight train," where a fractional boxcar is a meaningless concept. In other cases quantitative variables are continuous, such as length, where the differences between individuals may be infinitesimally small or very great, and the variable is a continuum.

VARIABLES AS CONSTRUCTS

We have defined variables as characteristics or qualities in which individuals differ among themselves. In some cases this characteristic or quality is quite concrete and tangible. Thus if we are interested in the number of children per family, we can see, touch, and otherwise observe the property. But in other cases, particularly with psychological variables, this is not true. There is nothing tangible or concrete about the characteristic or quality itself, although the individuals being studied are quite concrete. In such cases we can term the variable an intellectual construct.

A construct is the product which results from the synthesizing or uniting of elements. A house is a physical construct, being a fabrication of wood, nails, bricks, and the like. Similarly, an intellectual construct is a fabrication, being made up of ideas. Unlike a physical construct, an intellectual construct is intangible. Since there is nothing concrete about an intellectual construct, its existence is in the world of conception rather than in the physical world.

What is length? It certainly is not the ruler by means of which we measure it. It is not a line drawn by a pencil. Rather, it is the distance along an imaginary line between two points. It is a concept—an intellectual construct. What is initiative? It is the capacity to develop new modes of attack on a problem under one's own power. It is not the number of new modes of attack that the individual writes down on a piece of paper, such as "things to try." It is not the dollar volume of new business the salesman brings in. It is a concept—an intellectual construct.

SIMPLE AND COMPLEX VARIABLES

The characteristic or quality with which we are concerned, our variable, may be either simple or complex. Height is a simple variable since it involves the differentiation of individuals on a single dimension or characteristic. Size, however, is a complex variable since it involves some combination of height and girth. Similarly, reaction time is a relatively simple variable since it merely involves quickness of sensation, perception, and response; whereas mechanical ability is a more complex variable since it is a combination of knowledge of tools and their use, dexterity in the use of the fingers and hands, capacity to deal with spatial relationships, understanding of mechanical movements, and a variety of other qualities. But be the variable simple or complex, it provides a series of categories into which all individuals of a specified sort can be placed.

VARIABLE AND CONSTANT PROPERTIES

If the individuals with whom we are concerned do not differ among themselves in a particular property, then for them it is a constant rather than a variable. Indeed, a given characteristic or quality may be a variable for one group of individuals and a constant for another. "A central nervous system" is a variable when all animals are considered. Some individuals such as mammals and fish possess a central nervous system, whereas others such as protozoa and jellyfish do not. However, if we consider only vertebrates then "a central nervous system" is a constant since all these individuals do possess a central nervous system.

A given characteristic or quality is a variable, then, because individuals manifest different kinds or amounts of it. However, for those individuals who manifest any one kind or amount, the property is a constant. Taking all human beings as a whole, sex is a variable. However, for men alone and for women alone it is a constant. Inasmuch as different individuals earn different scores on an arithmetic test, arithmetic ability is a variable. However, for individuals who earn any given score on the test, arithmetic ability is a constant. For people who earn a score of 42 on the test, arithmetic ability is a constant; for those who earn a score of 43, it is a constant; and for those who earn any other given score, it is also a constant.

QUALITATIVE VERSUS QUANTITATIVE VARIABLES

All variables can be classified into one or the other of two general types, those which are *qualitative variables* and those which are *quantitative variables.* When the variable is qualitative, individuals differ in kind or sort; and when it is quantitative, they differ in frequency, degree, or amount. With qualitative variables the categories into which individuals are placed are not ordered, whereas with quantitative variables the categories are ordered.

Occupation is an example of a qualitative variable. We can classify workers as management personnel, sales personnel, clerks, service workers, or industrial workers. In this system of categorization there is no natural ordering in the system itself. Any ordering either is purely arbitrary, such as alphabetical, or is accomplished on the basis of some characteristic other than that involved in the variable under consideration, such as the number of individuals in each category. Other examples of qualitative variables are "major in college," "type of psychiatric diagnosis," and "kind of experimental treatment."

With quantitative variables, on the other hand, there is a natural ordering of categories since the different categories represent different degrees, amounts, or frequencies of the property in question. The categories are ordered in terms of "moreness" of the property. Consider the variable "number of children in the family." With this variable we have a series of categories, 0, 1, 2, 3, etc., which naturally arrange themselves in order as determined by the frequency of the characteristic under consideration. Order is inherent in the categories themselves. Similarly, suppose we have height as a variable and have measured the heights of individuals to the nearest tenth of a foot. We have the categories 5.0, 5.1, and 5.2 ft, which arrange themselves in order naturally, with the categories having successively larger and larger numerical designations and containing individuals of greater and greater amounts of the trait under consideration. Other examples of quantitative variables are "strength of pull," "scholastic aptitude," and "emotional stability."

TYPES OF QUANTITATIVE VARIABLES

Quantitative variables can be subdivided into two types, *ranked variables* and *scalar variables*. Ranked variables merely provide an ordering of individuals, whereas scalar variables provide descriptions of frequency, degree, or amount. Position of the child in a family as first born, second born, etc., and final status in a race as first, second, etc., are examples of ranked variables. The weight of people and the number of dollars they earn per year are examples of scalar variables.

TYPES OF RANKED VARIABLES

Like qualitative variables, ranked variables provide a series of categories that are discrete and separate. However, unlike the categories of qualitative variables, those of ranked variables are ordered. These successive categories do not necessarily represent equal increments of the particular characteristic or quality, but merely more of it with the amount unspecified. When a person says he prefers vanilla ice cream to chocolate, and chocolate to strawberry, this does not mean that in terms of desirability he would place chocolate halfway between vanilla and strawberry. All it means is that if he cannot have vanilla he will take chocolate, and barring chocolate he will take strawberry.

The ranked variables just described are rankings of individuals because at each rank, that is, in each category, there is a single individual. It is also possible to have a ranking of groups. With this type of ranking we may have more than one individual at each rank or in each category. The food preferences of a person might be given by this type of variable. His first preference might be turkey, veal cutlets, or pot roast, and it does not matter which he gets. If he cannot have any of these he will take lamb chops or chicken, and again it does not matter which. If these also are ruled out he will take ham, meatballs, or pork chops. Similarly, the members of a particular society may regard themselves as being first-class citizens, second-class citizens, and third-class citizens. The differences between classes are in terms of properties such as rights, privileges, and the like, but the amounts of the differences between the groups are not specified. Finally, a teacher may find it convenient to divide her pupils into those who have a high interest in mathematics, those who are indifferent to mathematics, and those who dislike mathematics. She has, then, placed her pupils into three groups which are ranked in terms of the variable "interest in mathematics."

TYPES OF SCALAR VARIABLES—DISCONTINUOUS VERSUS CONTINUOUS SCALES

Scalar variables can be further subdivided into *discontinuous scales* and *continuous scales*. With discontinuous scales the categories are ordered but are discrete or separate from each other. An individual clearly falls into one category or another. In this characteristic, discontinuous variables are similar to qualitative and ranked variables, which also provide separate and distinct categories. With continuous scales there are no categories as such; rather, there is a continuum which represents gradually greater and greater amounts of the characteristic or quality. On such scales individuals can differ among themselves by very large amounts or by infinitely small degrees.

With discontinuous scales we have categories representing seriatim increasing amounts of some property. This is perhaps most easily illustrated by scales involving increasing frequency of some characteristic or quality. Individuals in the lowest category do not manifest the property at all, those in the next category manifest one of it, those in the next category manifest two of it, and so on. Examples of this type of scale are, for families, the number of children; for workers, the number of accidents; and for social groups, the number of members. A child either exists or it does not, so that a family has none, one, or two children but it cannot have a fraction of a child. An accident either happens or it does not, and a worker cannot have 3.2 accidents in a given period of time. A social group may have 10, 11, or 12 members, but it cannot have 10.5 or 11.5 members.

TYPES OF SCALAR VARIABLES—RATIO VERSUS INTERVAL SCALES

Scalar variables can be classified another way into what have been termed *ratio scales* and *interval scales*. Ratio scales are those where the absolute zero is known, and interval scales are those in which the absolute zero is not known.

In order to compare two or more individuals in terms of the relative amounts of some property they possess or manifest, we must measure that property on a scale on which the absolute zero is known. If we do not know the point on the scale which represents a complete absence of the property, then we cannot make statements about the ratio of one individual to another in terms of the amount of the property or about the proportion that one individual is to the other.

We can say that an individual who is 50 in. tall is two-thirds as tall as one who is 75 in. tall and that the latter is 50 per cent taller than the former, because the ruler by means of which we measure height has an absolute-zero point on the scale which indicates the complete absence of the property. Similarly, we can say that an individual who taps with his finger 500 times in 2 min taps only two-thirds as fast as one who taps 750 times and that the latter taps at a rate 50 per cent faster than the former, because on the scale of tapping, zero means no taps at all.

But suppose we are measuring arithmetic ability and use a test composed entirely of problems involving multiplication and division of three-digit numbers. We are not willing to say that an individual who fails to solve a single problem correctly has zero arithmetic ability, because we know it is possible that if we gave him simpler problems, say the addition of 2 and 2, he might be able to solve them. The zero on our test, then, does not represent an absolute zero or a complete absence of arithmetic ability. Consequently we cannot say that an individual who solves 50 multiplication problems correctly has two-thirds the arithmetic ability of one who solves 75 problems correctly and that the latter is 50 per cent superior to the former in arithmetic ability.

The ratios and proportions in situations such as this are meaningless because the magnitudes of the property are measured not in terms of "distance" from an absolute zero but only in terms of "distance" from an arbitrary zero. The zero is like the zero on a thermometer, which is arbitrarily established and has no particular reference to the absolute zero of temperature. It is as if we had a ratio scale and to all values on it some constant value of unknown magnitude had been added.

For many if not most psychological variables the scales are interval rather than ratio scales. The zero points on the scales are arbitrary points, not absolute zero representing a complete absence of the traits being measured. Consequently we are seldom able to say that as compared with one individual another manifests a certain proportion of a psychological trait or that one individual manifests a certain greater percentage of a trait than does another individual.

It may seem impossible for a scale to have any practical value if it does not have an absolute zero. However, we can easily show that it is possible. Suppose there are two towers on the same level field. By placing a ruler alongside each tower, or by using some comparable but less clumsy procedure, we can determine their heights. If we are interested in getting as far above sea level as possible, we merely climb to the top of the taller tower. We do not know how far above sea level the tops of the towers are, but we can say that the one is higher above it than is the other. Similarly, though we cannot say that the individual who earns a score of 75 on an arithmetic test is 50 per cent better in arithmetic ability than the individual who earns a score of 50, we do know that the former is superior to the latter.

THE PROCESS OF DETERMINING INDIVIDUAL DIFFERENCES ON A VARIABLE

When we set about studying individual differences, the first step is to define the variable in which we are interested. From among the multitude of characteristics and qualities manifested by the individuals with whom we are concerned, we abstract one particular property which we describe, specify, and differentiate from other properties. Our definition either explicitly or implicitly indicates the type of variable it is, whether qualitative or quantitative, and, if quantitative, which specific type. Having defined our variable we then devise a series of operations which permit us to observe similarities and differences among individuals. These operations involve a series of rules to be followed, stipulate the procedures and instruments that are to be used, and provide a categorization of individuals so that we have a description of them in terms of the variable.

These two steps are intimately related and, indeed, in many if not most instances are never completed. The definition of our variable determines the operations we set up, and the particular operations we devise may in turn force us to redefine our variable. Our decision to term our variable one particular type or another has a direct bearing upon the procedures and instruments we develop, and the particular categorization of individuals given by these procedures and instruments may cause us to change our views concerning the type of variable with which we are dealing.

The process of defining our variable and devising operations that we can use in the description of individual differences is a never-ending one. Not only is there an interaction between the definition and the devising of operations, but also the results obtained from our operations give us new insights into the nature of our variable so that we redefine it and modify our operations. The development of ways for describing individuals, then, is a dynamic process.

DEFINING VARIABLES

We define the variable in which we are interested in order to understand the nature of the property with which we are concerning ourselves and as a basis for developing the operations we shall use to obtain descriptions of individual differences in that property. Definition is never an easy task, so let us consider some matters that bear directly upon the definition of variables.

A good definition of a variable is precisely formulated. Specificity not only clarifies the nature of the property but also facilitates the development of the needed operations. As scientists we do not study individual differences just for the sake of studying them. Rather, we have some basis or framework from which we start, some theoretical or practical problem. We develop hypotheses, and these hypotheses direct our attention to some particular property or set of properties and to some particular kinds of individuals. Our definition of the variable is based not only upon our previous knowledge about the property and the individuals but also upon the concepts and theories we have about them.

IMPORTANCE OF PRECISELY FORMULATED DEFINITIONS

The clearer and more specific the definition of a variable the more useful it is. Not only does it describe the nature of the property, but it also differentiates it from other properties. It directly suggests the kinds of operations that should be employed in obtaining a categorization of individuals in terms of that property. A definition that is vague conveys only in a general way information about the nature of the variable and is of little value in providing guides for the development of appropriate operations.

Let us consider the variable "adjustment" so often used in psychodynamics. We speak of people as making good and poor adjustments; hence we are saying that there is some type of behavior in which individuals differ. By good adjustment do we mean the capacity to adjust leg length when walking on a hillside? Do we mean giving socially approved versus socially disapproved responses to frustrating situations? Do we mean tolerance of the actions of others? Do we mean ability to learn from experience? Do we mean all of these things or any of them? The term "adjustment" is so vague that we do not really know what is implied, and we do not know how it may be measured.

If we title the variable "emotional adjustment," as psychologists we shall have some notion of the limits of the property. We could specify it perhaps by saying that the property is the reaction to problem situations. We could delineate problem situations as those in which the individual is confronted by a conflict, and the reaction as behavior which does not meet with the approval of other members of his society. This definition is a considerable improvement. It more adequately circumscribes the property, and it suggests operations by means of which individual differences can be described, for example, by statements on the part of the individual's peers. Even so, our definition is not so precise as we might like, but at least it is a workable one. Further consideration of the problem, the results of studies of emotional adjustment, and greater refinement in theory will help us to further specify our definition.

TRAIT NAMES AND TRAIT DEFINITIONS

We name variables in order to identify them, the name of a variable providing a summary of the definition. Thus we may have a variable which we define as "the capacity of a member of a group to influence the other members with respect to the setting and achievement of group goals." Rather than identify the variable by means of this long and involved definition, we simply label it "leadership." The trait name "leadership," then, stands for the definition and is a more convenient label for the variable.

We choose a trait name which is appropriate, that is, a name which gives a reasonable representation of the definition. But because it is short and concise, the trait name in and of itself does not represent all the details and facets of the definition. Consequently one trait name may equally well represent several different definitions. The trait name "sociability" may be used to represent a trait defined as "the tendency to seek the company of others and to associate and interact with them" just as well as a trait defined as "the capacity to get along with others and to be understanding of and sensitive to the feelings, opinions, and motives of others."

The trait name comes from the definition, not vice versa. Therefore it would not be proper to say that either the one or the other is a better or more valid definition of "sociability." In these two definitions we have specified two different though perhaps related traits. The label "sociability" is attached to both because it appears appropriate to both. This does, of course, lead to confusion, and in the interests of clarity it would be better to attach different labels to the two variables. However, in a field such as psychology, in which basic ideas and concepts are so rapidly developing and changing, it is perhaps understandable that the same trait name is used with different connotations. One person may use a given trait name to identify a trait defined one way, and another to identify a trait defined differently. Indeed, one investigator may change his definition of a trait as he comes to understand it more and still retain the same trait name. As a consequence we must be exceedingly careful in comparing the results of different investigators or the findings with different psychological tests in which nominally the same trait is involved.

VARIABLES IN RELATION TO THE KINDS OF INDIVIDUALS

The kinds of individuals with whom we are concerned have an important bearing upon the way in which we define our variable. Variables defined in certain ways are not appropriate for certain kinds of individuals. A consideration of the nature of the individuals may require us to redefine the variable. Furthermore, the nature of the individuals may dictate the type of variable we conceive ours to be.

Suppose we take area as a variable and solid objects such as stones as individuals. Ordinarily we think of area as being the plane surface contained within boundary lines. If we wish to talk about area of solid objects, we shall have to retitle our variable as "surface area" and define it as the complexly shaped surface that is the outer boundary of the stone. Similarly, the variable "adequacy of nesting behavior" applies only to those animals who care for their young by building nests. If our interest lies in the behavior of all kinds of animals, we shall have to redefine our variable, perhaps as "protection of the young through use of physical shelter." The variable "type of personality disorder" implies that we are dealing with disturbed individuals alone. If our interest is broader in scope and includes all people, the normal as well as the disturbed, then we may redefine our variable as "type of personality structure."

The kind of individuals with whom we are concerned sometimes dictates the way in which we must consider the property as varying. For example, the variable "accuracy in aerial navigation" would seem obviously to be a continuous quantitative variable with individuals differing in the degree of accuracy with which they determine the location of their aircraft. However, while it may be true that some aerial navigators locate their aircraft with more accuracy than others, even the poorest navigator is considerably superior in aerial navigation to a person who has had no training whatsoever in that technology. Indeed, the latter would not even know how to begin the process of determining location, and the instruments would be completely unfamiliar to him. Therefore if we restrict ourselves to aerial navigators we shall certainly consider our variable to be a quantitative continuous one. On the other hand, if we take as our individuals everybody, we may prefer to think of it as a discontinuous quantitative variable with the two steps of "none" and "some" proficiency in aerial navigation.

CONCEPTS, THEORIES, AND KNOWLEDGE AS FACTORS IN DEFINING VARIABLES

The way in which we define a variable is a function of the concepts, the theories, and the knowledge we have about the property and the individuals for whom it is a variable. With one particular set of concepts, theories, and knowledge we might define a variable one way; whereas with different concepts, theories, and knowledge we might define it quite differently. As conceptualizations and theoretical formulations change and become more refined, and as our knowledge increases, our definitions of variables change so that what we once defined as a simple variable we now see is a complex variable, and what we had taken as five different variables we now see is one variable. Variables are not static, unchanging, universal truisms. They are modified, given up, and created as our concepts, theories, and knowledge grow and develop.

For example, we could define the height of people as the linear distance between the soles of their feet and the tops of their heads. In terms of present knowledge and concepts this is a perfectly adequate and useful definition. It indicates to us something about the nature of the variable, namely, that it is a quantitative and continuous variable. Furthermore, it suggests the operation that should be followed in describing individual differences, that is, the determination of the length of the straight line between the soles of the feet and the top of the head. However, it is based upon a particular set of concepts about space. It presumes that straight lines are the shortest distance between two points and that points have no extensity. Perhaps future developments will prove these postulates to be completely untrue. Even the casual reader of science fiction knows that 500 years from now we may realize that space is a twisted thing formed by blocks or chunks of what we now think of as time and that it is a qualitative and discontinuous variable. The way in which we define height now may appear as absurd to our distant descendants as the notions held before Columbus' time about the shape of the earth appear to us now.

It was once generally held that man possessed one single, general, all-important ability. This property, termed intelligence, was defined as quickness and accuracy of sensation and perception, ability to learn, and capacity to reason. Since intelligence was thought of as being a general capacity, the operations by means of which individual differences in it were to be indicated were obvious. Income, social status, rank, and position were taken as indices of intelligence. As more and more knowledge about individual differences and abilities was amassed, it seemed that man possessed not just one all-important ability which determined the degree of success achievable in such different activities as school performance and proficiency with a pick and shovel, but rather several different and perhaps independent abilities. The property that had been termed intelligence then was seen to be an aggregation of different properties. So the definition of intelligence was modified, and many psychologists specified it to include only those abilities involving judgment, reasoning, and the like, as exercised in abstract form and as manifested in verbal behavior and in response to verbal stimuli. Intelligence, then, was measured by tests involving questions requiring powers of analysis and synthesis, comparisons of similarities and differences, and the like. Today even this notion of intelligence is not uniformly held, and many would separate the property into smaller bits, defining each differently. As a consequence, today when we are concerned with ability we try to define the ability very specifically, seeking to differentiate it from other types of abilities.

It is possible that the future will show that there are 20 or 30 basic abilities possessed in different degrees by different individuals, or that there are thousands of them, or that ability is a completely erroneous concept. At the present time, however, we can define abilities in ways which at least currently are meaningful to us, and from our definitions we set up operations by means of which these abilities can be measured. We can employ the results of these operations in many useful ways for both theoretical and practical purposes, just as it was possible for the medieval traders to sail a ship from Venice to London by using navigational procedures based on the incorrect notion that the world is flat.

OPERATIONS AND THE DETERMINATION OF INDIVIDUAL DIFFERENCES

After defining our variable we are in a position to develop operations which permit us to observe individual differences in the property. These operations are set forth in rules which stipulate the procedures, instruments, and devices that are to be used, and to indicate the nature of the descriptions that will be given to individuals in terms of the property.

THE NATURE OF OPERATIONS

The definition of a variable provides the basis for the development of a series of operations that are to be performed in order to obtain descriptions of individuals in terms of the ways in which they manifest the particular property. The characteristics of the variable dictate the nature of the operations. With one variable there will be one series of operations, and with another variable a different series. The operations are outlined in a set of rules we prepare, the rules specifying the procedures that are to be followed, the instruments and devices that are to be used, and the nature of the final descriptions of individuals that will be given. These rules may be very restrictive, limiting the operations to one particular set; or they may provide for alternative kinds of procedures, instruments, or devices, and final descriptions of individuals. But in all cases the rules specify what should be done and how it should be done.

In the case of qualitative variables we term the operations *classification*, and in the case of quantitative variables we term them *ranking* for ranked variables and *measurement* for scalar variables. The processes of classification, ranking, and measurement, then, involve going through a prescribed set of operations according to a specified set of rules utilizing specified procedures, instruments, or devices which result in specified descriptions of individuals.

As a result of the operations we obtain a description of individuals in terms of some specified characteristic or property. The operations we employ in differentiating individuals in terms of the property "sex" place all individuals into one or the other of two categories, "male" and "female." Those used in measuring height place individuals at points on a continuum and provide such descriptions as 67.9 in. and 70.1 in. Because sex is a qualitative variable we have qualitative descriptions of individuals. Height being a quantitative variable, the operations give us quantitative descriptions.

In psychological measurement the quantitative description of an individual given by the operations is termed his *raw score*. If the instrument we use for measuring the proficiency of salesmen is the amount of their annual commissions, for a salesman who earns $6,000 during a year that is his raw score. If as a measure of aggression in preschool children we take the number of times a child strikes another during the 3-hr school period, a child who strikes another twice has as his raw score in aggression the value 2. An individual who is rated 4 on a 5-point scale of leadership has as his raw score on that scale the value 4. The individual who answers correctly 30 out of 50 questions on an arithmetic test has as his raw score on arithmetic ability the value 30.

In certain circumstances the numerical values given directly by the measuring instruments, the raw scores, are changed in one way or another to a different set of numerical values. The rules for the operations may specify that the raw scores be divided by some constant or changed in terms of some function. These new values are termed *transmuted scores*. Scores are transmuted to make the numerical values more convenient for recording or for arithmetic manipulation, or in order to provide more meaningful quantitative descriptions of individuals.

THE DEVELOPMENT OF OPERATIONS FROM THE DEFINITION OF THE VARIABLE

The particular operations developed and the rules which govern them stem directly from the definition of the variable. For example, we may define height of people as the linear distance between the soles of the feet and the top of the head. From this definition we can develop a series of rules to govern the operations appropriate for use in the measurement of height. The phrase "linear distance" indicates that we wish to obtain the shortest line between two points. One point falls at the soles of the feet, and therefore we shall stipulate that both feet shall be on the same plane. Linear distance implies a quantitative continuous variable, so our rules will stipulate a standard ruler marked either in inches or in centimeters. Height implies the upright body rather than some other posture such as sitting, so the rules also will stipulate that the individual shall be standing as erect as possible and perpendicular to the plane passing under the soles of the feet. The rules will go on to say that one end of the ruler, the end marked zero, shall be placed exactly on the plane on which the individual's feet rest. The ruler shall be perpendicular to this plane, and parallel to this plane another plane shall be established which just touches the top of the head. The point of intersection between this plane and the scale on the ruler shall be taken as the individual's height. The ruler shall be read to the nearest sixteenth of an inch or to the nearest millimeter; the decision as to which marker is nearest to the plane will depend entirely upon the judgment of whoever is doing the measuring.

The above example demonstrates how the operating rules stem from the definition of the variable and illustrates all the major elements that must be contained in the rules. They indicate procedures, instruments or devices, and the nature of the descriptions of individuals which result from the operations.

Simple as the process of measuring height might seem, these rules are rather lengthy. Even so, they are not sufficiently detailed and do not treat with many important problems. What is meant by a standard ruler? How does one determine whether the individual being measured is in fact standing completely erect? What does one do with people who have great masses of hair? These matters, too, could be dealt with by rules, but still further questions not covered by them would arise. Operating rules, then, never are complete. They are changed and improved as more and more experience is gained with them.

Let us take as another example the variable "arithmetic ability," which we may define as "proficiency in solving arithmetic problems quickly and accurately." This definition seems quite adequate as a basis for developing appropriate operations. It seems reasonable to conceive of the operations as involving a paper-and-pencil test on which appear a number of arithmetic problems, a quarter of which involve addition, a quarter subtraction, a quarter multiplication, and a quarter division. We shall have instructions to the subjects telling them what they are to do, how they are to record their answers, and so on. There will be additional instructions to the examiner delineating such matters as how these instructions are to be given to the subjects, the timing of the test, and the scoring procedure.

Helpful as this definition might seem as a basis for developing appropriate operations, it is not clear in certain important aspects. Why use a paper-and-pencil test? This type of device is not prescribed by the definition of the variable or even implied by it. We might just as well have used the oral examination method. Why should the problems be 25 per cent each of addition, subtraction, multiplication, and division? Why not some other proportions? Should the problems be simple or complex? Should they be presented in their barest form such as "2 + 2 = _____," or in some context such as "Two apples and two apples are how many apples?" How many problems should there be and how much time should be allowed to solve them? Instead of counting the number of correct answers the individual gets in a specified time, why not measure the amount of time it takes him to solve a given number of problems correctly?

PRACTICAL CONSIDERATIONS AS FACTORS DETERMINING SPECIFIC OPERATIONS

While the definition of the variable provides the basis for the development of the necessary operations, it is by no means a precise blueprint. The details of the operations and many of their major aspects are dictated by very practical considerations. Knowledge about the psychological processes, experience with operations previously used in obtaining descriptions of individuals on similar variables, and a substantial measure of wisdom, common sense, and indeed sheer intuition play a great part in the selection of specific rules, procedures, and instruments.

The psychologist knows that performance is a function of motivation and that the motivation of an individual varies from time to time. Hence when ability is being measured, steps must be taken to keep motivation constant, perhaps by attempting to maximize it during the measurement of ability. Social pressure prevents people from manifesting overtly and publicly certain traits such as aggressiveness. Therefore when these traits are being measured, people must be provided with means for disguising their socially undesirable responses. Sometimes an individual is not aware of the factors that stimulate him to action. Consequently, in many instances indirect means must be utilized to measure motivational variables, since the individual's reports of his own motivation are not sufficiently dependable.

The experienced test constructor knows that reliable descriptions are not obtained by short tests and yet if the test is too long, people will become tired or bored. In general, objective scoring of people's responses gives more reliable descriptions than those which involve others' judgments of them. Yet with certain kinds of responses such as "appropriateness of behavior in a social situation," and with certain traits such as "cooperativeness," only subjective evaluation may be possible.

Even though the definition may clearly indicate that the variable is a particular type, it may not be possible to utilize operations directly appropriate to that type. If we wish to measure attitudes of people toward many social issues, the time and effort to construct continuous scales measuring each of these attitudes may be prohibitive. Perhaps we may have to utilize some simple operations involving two-category discontinuous scales such as "approve" and "disapprove." Supervisors may be unwilling to devote the time to evaluating each of their subordinates on 10 different rating scales measuring different aspects of job performance but may be willing to rank the men in terms of their overall success. When faced with such realities of life, we are forced to make compromises in developing our operations, and by making certain assumptions about them we seek to bring the final operations closer in nature to what we would like them to be.

The operations we develop, then, while coming from the definition of the variable, are at least one stage removed from it. Hence they may or may not perfectly reflect that which is explicit or even implicit in the definition. Because we start with a particular definition of a variable it does not follow that the operations we develop in fact do what might be expected of them.

OPERATIONS AND THE DEFINITION OF THE VARIABLE

It therefore follows that in developing a specific set of operations we are in a very real sense redefining our variable, or at least further specifying its definition. The variable with which we are dealing, then, is that property on which individuals are differentiated by the particular operations, and the type of variable is that which is produced by the operations.

We might say that the variable is nothing more nor less than the result of the particular set of operations which we prescribed beforehand. Thus we should be forced to make such statements as "Emotional stability in these particular preschool children is what Miss Smithers, the nursery school teacher, says it is" and "Intelligence is that which is measured by test X." In a very real sense this is true, but it does not help us to understand our variables, to describe our intellectual constructs, or to develop hypotheses about our variables and how they are related to other variables. Hence while it is true that our variable is contained in the operations, we cannot completely divorce ourselves from the verbalizations that form the definition of the variable. These verbalizations, being more general and flexible, permit us to go beyond merely applying our operations here and there without any guideposts.

THE OPERATIONS OF CLASSIFICATION, RANKING, AND MEASUREMENT, AND THE USE OF NUMBERS

We have said that the end result of the operations we employ in differentiating among individuals in terms of a given property is some sort of description of those individuals in terms of how they manifest that property. These descriptions may be in verbal form, but—particularly with quantitative variables—they are also given by numbers. Therefore we need to examine something of the nature of numbers and their use as descriptions of individuals.

DESCRIPTIONS ASSIGNED INDIVIDUALS BY THE OPERATIONS

The final result of a set of operations is the assignment of individuals to categories or their placement on a continuous scale. In classification, individuals are assigned to categories which have no inherent order, and in measurement to categories which do have order. In classification, the categories usually are assigned verbal labels though sometimes other designations are used, including numerals. Thus leaders might be classified in terms of the type of leadership behavior they manifest as "democratic," "laissez-faire," or "autocratic." Or these types of behavior might be designated A, B, and C or 1, 2, and 3. With measurements we usually use numerals as descriptions of individuals in terms of the variable, but again we may use words or letters. On a rating scale of "emotional control," quantitative descriptions might be given by the terms 1, 2, 3, and 4; by the words "inferior," "fair," "good," and "excellent"; or by the letters D, C, B, and A. Because we are concerned with measurement and because numbers are of such special importance in measurement, we shall consider something about their nature.

SOMETHING ABOUT NUMBERS

It is by no means easy to define the term *number*. A number is an abstraction which stands for a class of individuals having the same numerosity, and it is symbolized by a numeral. When we classify individuals, all those who fall in the same group have some property in common. Therefore all cases to which the same number is applied have as their common property the same numerosity. Thus 5 applies to all cases having the property "five-ness." In this class fall groups composed of five individuals such as quintets and basketball teams, geometric figures such as pentagons and stars with five points, and 5-mile races, 5-ft-tall girls, and lathe operators rated 5 by their foremen on a scale of skill in lathe operation. In all instances numerosity in one or another characteristic or quality is 5.

Numbers have two important characteristics for measurement. First of all, they provide a means by which individuals can be classified or arranged in a systematic way in terms of the degree to which they possess some particular characteristic. All people who earn a score of 42 on an arithmetic test are placed in the same category; those who earn a score of 43, in another category; and those who earn a score of 44, in still another category. From these numbers we know that those in the first category possess less arithmetic ability than those in the second, and those in the second less than those in the third. From the very ordering of individuals given by the numbers, we sometimes immediately have further information about them. For example, we know that the first-born child enters a family devoid of children, whereas the fifth-born enters a family with considerable experience in dealing with infants.

A second characteristic of numbers is that they can be manipulated and combined by arithmetic processes to give more precise descriptions or other meanings. By averaging the numerical values given by repeated measurements on the same individual with the same measuring device, we obtain a quantitative description that is more precise in the sense that it is more reproducible if additional measurements of the same kind are taken. By averaging the ratings of aggressiveness assigned to a child by four nursery school teachers, we are more likely to have a value which will occur if additional ratings of the same trait are made by other teachers. By combining numbers indicative of the classes to which an individual belongs in terms of different variables, or by manipulating them in other ways, we may obtain somewhat different or new descriptions of the individual. The combination of an individual's scores on tests of knowledge of tools, capacity to deal with spatial relationships, and understanding of mechanical movements gives us a more general description of him which can be termed his mechanical aptitude. By dividing the score a child earns on an intelligence test with the average score earned by children of his same age, we can obtain an index of his relative intellectual retardation or acceleration.

THE USE OF NUMBERS WITH QUALITATIVE VARIABLES

When we are dealing with a qualitative variable, the operations we use assign individuals to one or another of two or more different categories or classes. Ordinarily we designate or "name" the classes in verbal terms so as to indicate the manner in which the members of each class manifest the particular property. For the variable "sex" we have the two designations "male" and "female," and for the variable "major in college" we have such designations as "economics," "history," "physiology," and "chemistry."

Sometimes, however, we may use letters or numbers as designations rather than words. When we use numbers in this fashion we use them because their symbols, the numerals, are simple, convenient, familiar, and unambiguous. We use them merely to identify or "name" classes or individuals so that they can be distinguished from one another. Hence when numbers are used in this fashion they are termed *nominal*. Football and basketball players carry numbers on their uniforms so that the spectators can tell one player from another. Numerals are used merely because they are more convenient than names.

However, when we use numbers in this nominal fashion we remove from them their characteristic of order and therefore their properties of combinability and manipulability. The numbers are assigned to individuals by operations that are quite different from those employed with quantitative variables. With "nominal" numbers the operations may be just random assignment or first come, first numbered.

THE USE OF NUMBERS WITH RANKED VARIABLES

When we are dealing with ranked variables, the operations we employ order individuals or groups in terms of the frequency, amount, or degree to which they manifest some property. The individual or group that manifests the property to the greatest extent is assigned the number 1, the individual or group that manifests it to the next greatest degree is assigned the number 2, etc. Numbers used in this fashion are termed *ordinal*. With ranking we avail ourselves only of the property of order in numbers and not of the properties of combinability and manipulability. The difference between individuals or groups ranked first and second is not "1" of the property but merely a difference in frequency, amount, or degree which is not specified. Consequently the difference, whatever it may be, is not necessarily the same as the difference between individuals or groups ranked second and third.

THE USE OF NUMBERS WITH DISCONTINUOUS QUANTITATIVE VARIABLES

Discontinuous quantitative variables provide a series of categories that are ordered. The individuals in successive categories differ in the frequency, amount, or degree of some property by equal increments of that property. Consider the scale "right-handedness" where the operations of measurement involve building a tower with 10 blocks and counting the number of blocks placed on the tower with the right hand. The lowest category in this scale contains individuals who never use their right hand but only their left hand, the next category those who place one block with the right hand and the rest with their left hand, the next those who place two blocks with their right hand, and so on. The difference between the individuals in any two neighboring categories is the same, being "1" of the property. Let us take another variable, "number of cents in paper money carried at the moment by the individual." Here the lowest category contains individuals who have no paper money, the next those who have 100 cents, the next those who have 200 cents, and so on. In this case the difference between individuals in any two neighboring categories is the same, but in this instance it is 100 of the property.

Numbers ordinarily are assigned to the different categories in such a way as to indicate the frequency, amount, or degree of the property manifested by the individuals in them. For the scale of "handedness" just described, the successive categories would be labeled "0," "1," "2," etc.; and for the scale of "cents," "0," "100," "200," etc. For convenience or to increase the meaningfulness, we may utilize other numbers. For example, for the scale of "handedness" we might express the numbers as percentages and label the categories "0 per cent," "10 per cent," "20 per cent," etc., of blocks placed with the right hand; and for the scale of money we might label the categories "$0," "$1," "$2," etc.

THE USE OF NUMBERS WITH CONTINUOUS QUANTITATIVE VARIABLES

With a continuous quantitative variable we have a continuum rather than a series of discrete categories. In order to provide descriptions of individuals we arbitrarily "mark off" intervals along the scale, the intervals representing equal amounts or degrees of the property. We "mark off" linear distance in inches, feet, and miles or in millimeters, centimeters, meters, and kilometers. We "mark off" weight in ounces, pounds, and tons or in milligrams, grams, and kilograms. Time we "mark off" in seconds, minutes, hours, days, weeks, etc. The markers, then, are "placed" on the scale in a systematic though arbitrary fashion, and there are specified operations we develop for placing them.

Numbers are assigned to these markers, and they are assigned in order to indicate equal increments in the property. Thus on a ruler the difference between the first-inch and the second-inch mark is 1 in., and this is also the difference between the twenty-fifth-inch and the twenty-sixth-inch mark. The position of the individual on the scale relative to these markers is taken as his quantitative description. An individual whose height falls at the sixty-seventh-inch mark on a scale of height is assigned the number 67, and one whose height falls halfway between the sixty-seventh-inch and the sixty-eighth-inch mark is assigned the number 67.5.

OPERATIONS AND CONTINUOUS SCALES

We have said that with continuous quantitative scales there is a continuum on which individuals can be placed in terms of the amount of some property they manifest. The difference between two individuals may be great or it may be small. Theoretically the difference may become smaller and smaller until it vanishes and both individuals are located at exactly the very same point on the continuum. In this way continuous scales are differentiated from discontinuous scales, in which individuals are placed in one or another of a series of ordered categories, the differences between all neighboring categories being some constant amount or frequency.

In a sense the difference between continuous and discontinuous scales is a difference not in kind but in degree. What we have termed continuous scales may be thought of as discontinuous scales with the categories being infinitely small. We might take a continuous scale and break it into sections or equal amounts of the property so that we have a series of intervals or categories. The individuals in any given interval or category differ among themselves in the amount of the property they possess, but all possess more than those in the interval or category immediately below and less than those in the interval or category immediately above. We could make these intervals or categories few and broad, or we could increase their number and make them narrower. As the categories increase in number and become narrower and narrower, we approach a true continuum.

In actual practice our operations never provide us with a continuous scale. What they give us in fact are measurements to some nearest imaginary marker. We measure height to the nearest quarter of an inch, and reaction time to the nearest hundredth of a second. In reading to the nearest marker we assign the same numerical description to all these individuals in a given range or class interval.

Therefore when a scale is continuous the quantitative description assigned to an individual never is precise but rather is an approximation. If the measuring device is crude the intervals may be few and broad, giving quite imprecise quantitative descriptions of individuals. If the measuring device is more refined it may divide the continuum into a large number of narrow intervals, thereby providing much more precise descriptions.

The particular operations we use may divide the continuum into equal intervals, or they unfortunately may divide it into intervals of unequal size. Indeed, we may have no direct information at all as to whether the intervals are or are not equally spaced along the continuum. Perhaps all we can do is to infer that they are or are not. If we have reason to suppose that they are not equally spaced, that is, if we believe that the units along the scale are not equal, then we can apply further operations in an attempt to equalize them. We can transmute the numerical values assigned to the individuals as quantitative descriptions to other numerical values which are equally spaced along the continuum. We shall consider such procedures later. Suffice it to say now that these procedures ordinarily involve assumptions, perhaps about the nature of the variable, the distribution of individuals in the variable, or the characteristics of the operations, assumptions that many are unwilling to make.

DICHOTOMOUS VARIABLES

With qualitative variables the operations of classification may separate individuals into only two categories. When we classify people according to sex we divide them into men and women. The forced-choice item of occupational interest, "prefer the job of bookkeeper—prefer the job of salesclerk," also results in a dichotomous classification of individuals as does the self-perception item, "Which best describes you, intelligent—sociable?"

Usually we think of the operations of measurement as providing a range of scores so that individuals are distributed among a wide variety of quantitative descriptions or categories which are ordered along a scale. However, quite often in psychological measurement we deal with tests which separate people only into categories that are two in number. The items in an objective test usually are of this kind, the responses being classified as correct or incorrect. On opinion and personality inventories the responses may be limited to two alternatives such as "like" or "dislike" and "yes" or "no." With certain rating devices only two steps of response are permitted. Thus with adjective checklists the individual is checked as being or not being "cheerful," "shy," and the like.

TYPES OF DICHOTOMOUS SCALES

We can distinguish two types of dichotomous scales, those which are based upon variables that are discontinuous and those which are based upon variables that are truly continuous or multistep discontinuous quantitative variables. In the discontinuous dichotomous scales the two categories are clearly different, even though they may form an order of more or less of some property. On the other hand, with the dichotomous scales based upon continuous or multistep variables we have variables along which individuals differ from one another perhaps by very small amounts, but the scale is divided into two portions or zones. There is some critical point on the scale, and all individuals who fall above it are placed in one category, the higher one, and those who fall below it are placed in the other category, the lower one.

DISCONTINUOUS DICHOTOMOUS SCALES

With discontinuous dichotomous scales the two categories represent classes of individuals who clearly are different. Workers may be classified as being either line workers or management personnel, and there are no intermediate degrees of occupational level. All workers are of one sort or the other. Men released from prison on parole either are successful parolees who do not break the rules covering their probation or are unsuccessful parolees who do break the rules. There may be doubt in a specific case as to whether a rule was broken, but this situation is the result of inadequate information rather than the representation of an intermediate degree of compliance with rules.

We are so used to thinking of psychological traits as being continuous variables that we overlook the many types of behavior and human characteristics that truly are discontinuous and dichotomous. Races are either won or lost. No matter how close behind the winner the losers are and how game a race they make of it, they do not win. We might say that all men in the race ran fast, but speed of running logically is a variable different from the variable "winning versus losing," even though the speed with which a man runs determines to a considerable extent whether or not he wins. There are no intermediate degrees of winning. Furthermore, speed of running and "winning versus losing" are measured by quite different sets of operations.

In a similar fashion an item in an intelligence test may be considered to represent a discontinuous variable. A problem is presented or a piece of information is called for, and the individual either does or does not solve the problem correctly or does or does not possess the needed bit of information. Hence either he answers the item correctly or he does not.

The two categories of a discontinuous dichotomous scale are ordered, for example, winning or losing a race, holding a position in a management or a line capacity, and answering an item correctly or incorrectly. Therefore the individuals in the higher category are assigned a score of 1 because they manifest the particular property under consideration, and those in the lower category a score of 0 because they do not.

DICHOTOMOUS SCALES BASED ON CONTINUOUS AND MULTISTEP SCALES

Sometimes the operations of measurement we adopt are of such a nature that they place the individuals into one or another of two categories even though the variable is a continuous or multistep one. The basic variable, then, is continuous or has many categories, but people are placed in one or the other of two zones of scores. Sometimes even though we actually have at hand the multistep scores, we deliberately divide individuals into classes on the basis of their scores. In other cases the operations we use are so crude that they differentiate only two degrees of the trait being measured.

The first type of dichotomization usually is done for some practical reason. The scale is deliberately divided into two zones by selecting a critical or cutoff score and placing all persons who obtain it or a higher score in one category and all who obtain lower scores in the other category. For example, a critical score may be set on an examination, and all who achieve it or a higher score are termed "passers" and all who earn scores lower than it are termed "failers." Similarly, with some measures of performance such as school grades and production on a job, individuals are divided into two classes, the successful and the unsuccessful, even though they distribute continuously along a scale and measurements of their precise positions on the scale are available. Usually this type of dichotomization is done when the scores are used for some administrative action such as accepting or rejecting candidates for admission or for a position, giving or not giving some therapeutic treatment, and presenting or not presenting some special award.

Sometimes our measuring device is so crude that it does not give us all the degrees of a trait we may desire. The ruler with which we measure the heights of individuals might have only a single mark, say the sixth-foot mark. When we place people against this ruler we can see whether or not their height exceeds this critical point. On this basis we classify people whose height falls above the mark as "tall" and those whose height falls below it as "short."

Similarly, we might wish to have people rated on a number of rating scales. Perhaps we should like to use scales with many steps ranging, say, from 0 to 100, which would give us a wide variety of scores. However, it is unlikely that people will be willing to take the time to make judgments of the specific degrees on a scale of 100 points to which, say, each of 50 people possesses 200 different traits. As a consequence we might resort to devices of a cruder nature that our raters would be willing to employ, such as a checklist of the 200 traits. With such a list the rater merely checks the individual as possessing or not possessing to a significant degree each of the traits. This second technique could be considered to be merely a crude form of the first refined rating scales.

In some cases we are willing to assume that a test which places individuals in only two categories really measures a continuous variable, even though we have no direct evidence that the variable is continuous. Thus intelligence may be conceived of as a continuous variable, and each item in an intelligence test is considered to measure this continuum. It is assumed that an item is merely a crude test which yields scores of 1 and 0 but that the trait itself is not discontinuous.

THE COMBINATION OF DICHOTOMOUS VARIABLES INTO MULTISTEP SCALES

Many tests used in psychological measurement consist of a series of items or questions each of which is scored in a dichotomous fashion. An individual's response to each item is classified as being correct or wrong, and on each he is given a score of 1 or 0. A total test score is computed by adding together the scores he obtains on the individual items, that is, by counting up the number of his responses that are classified as correct or of a particular kind.

Ordinarily the items of a test are created and put together on the basis of some rationale and are not mere random assemblages. For example, if the trait we wish to measure is analogical reasoning, we may develop a series of questions such as "Man is to mouth as bird is to (1) wing, (2) song, (3) beak, (4) food, (5) nest." Each item calls for the particular psychological process required by our definition of the variable we wish to measure. From this pool of items we select certain ones and list them together to form our test. The particular items we select are likely to be based on practical considerations. We may pretest the items by administering all of them to a preliminary group of subjects and eliminate those items which are not understood, are too difficult or easy, or are otherwise inadequate. The particular number of items we select, too, is dictated by the practicalities of having a sufficient number to be representative of the trait being measured but not so many that the subjects will rebel at taking the test.

Clearly, then, we conceive of our variable as a trait which can be measured by a variety of items which logically are similar in nature, and from this domain we select a sample for our particular operations of measurement. The total score on the test now is a composite variable which we say measures analogical reasoning. But now the question arises as to the nature of this variable. Obviously it is a quantitative variable, but is it a discontinuous or a continuous one? The answer to this question depends on how we regard the individual items. If we think of the items as being discontinuous scales, then our total scores form a discontinuous scale involving the frequency with which the individual manifests a particular property—the correct solving of a problem involving analogical reasoning. On the other hand, if we conceive of each item as being a continuous scale with the scores dichotomized because the items are crude measuring devices, then we say that the total scores represent points on a continuous scale.

But it may be that our items are dichotomous qualitative variables. For example, we might conceive of the trait of sociability as a qualitative variable, an individual preferring either activities involving interpersonal relationships or activities which are done by the individual himself. To measure this trait we might develop a series of questions such as "Which would you rather do, go to a party or read a book?" Again we have a set of items drawn from a domain of items which we assemble into a test. The items themselves are qualitative variables dividing people into either of two kinds, not into the categories of more or less of some trait. In each item we might assign the number 1 to the "social activity" choice and the number 0 to the "individual activity" choice. These numbers, of course, are purely nominal and do not indicate amount but only kind. The total score on such a test, however, is a quantitative variable and a discontinuous one. On this variable or total score, individuals differ in terms of how frequently they manifest one property rather than a counterpart property—social activity rather than individual activity. We could, if we wished, have assigned the number 1 to the "individual activity" choice and the number 0 to the "social activity" choice.

Summary

Individuals differ among themselves in a variety of ways. In some properties such as sex and occupation individuals differ in kind or in sort, and in other properties such as height and intelligence they differ in amount, degree, or frequency. We can therefore distinguish between those variables which are qualitative and those which are quantitative. Quantitative variables can be further classified into ranked variables and scalar variables. Ranked variables place individuals in order in terms of the amount, degree, or frequency with which they possess some property, and scalar variables place them into one or another of the categories of a multistep variable or place them at one or another point on a continuum.

When we wish to examine the differences among individuals on a variable the first step is to define that variable, describing and specifying it, and differentiating it from other variables. The way in which we define a variable is determined by the particular theories and concepts we have about it, together with whatever pertinent information there may be.

From the definition of the variable we develop operations by means of which we describe individuals on that variable. Operations are a series of rules to be followed in applying specified procedures and instruments which provide a categorization, and therefore a description, of individuals in terms of that variable. The operations are termed classification when the variable is qualitative, ranking when the variable is ranked, and measurement when the variable is scalar. Our concern will be with operations of measurement.

Even though the operations stem from the definition of the variable, many of the features of the actual operations we finally develop are dictated by practical considerations. In developing a test we are influenced by such factors as convenience in administration and scoring. Therefore, while the operations are based on the definition, they are at least one stage removed from it and in a very real sense redefine the variable.

The end result of the application of a set of operations is the assignment of individuals to categories or their placement along a continuum. Sometimes verbal labels are used to designate categories or points along a scale; but in measurement, numerals ordinarily are employed. Numbers are useful because they provide a way for the arrangement of individuals in terms of the degree, amount, or frequency with which they possess some property, and because numbers can be manipulated arithmetically to give more precise descriptions and new meanings.

In psychological measurement we frequently utilize operations which yield only a twofold classification of individuals. For example, the responses to the items of an objective test are scored as being correct or wrong. When the operations yield a twofold classification of individuals, depending upon our theoretical notions about the trait we may consider the two steps to represent either a truly discontinuous dichotomous variable or the two portions of a multistep or continuous scale arbitrarily dichotomized by crude operations of measurement. So our theoretical notions about the variable dictate the interpretation we put on the results obtained from the operations of measurement.

Selected Readings

Brogden, H.: New problems for old solutions, *Psychometrika,* **22**:301–309, 1957.
Campbell, N. R.: Symposium: Measurement and its importance for philosophy, Aristotelian Society, Supplement, vol. 17, 1938.
Comrey, A. L.: An operational approach to some problems in psychological measurement, *Psychological Rev.,* **57**:217–228, 1950.
Dantzig, T.: "Number, the Language of Science," Macmillan, 1939.
Feigl, H.: Operationism and scientific method, *Psychological Rev.,* **52**:250–259, 1945.
Guilford, J. P.: "Psychometric Methods," 2d ed., McGraw-Hill, 1954.
Gulliksen, H., and S. Messick (eds.): "Psychological Scaling," Wiley, 1961.
Stevens, S. S.: "Handbook of Experimental Psychology," Wiley, 1951.
Torgeson, W.: "Theory and Methods of Scaling," Wiley, 1958.

chapter 3   Some
Fundamental Aspects of
Psychological Measurement

In Chap. 2 we examined the nature of variables, separating them into qualitative and quantitative variables. The latter we further subdivided into ranked and scalar variables. The operations by means of which we obtain quantitative descriptions of individuals in terms of scalar variables we termed measurement. Since our primary interest is in the measurement of psychological traits, we must now direct our attention to some fundamental aspects of measurement, namely, the equality of units of measurement, the meaningfulness of scores, and the equivalence of measurements on different scales. Our logic, together with the circumstances we find with psychological variables, will lead us to the position that in many cases the raw scores yielded by the operations of measurement are meaningful and useful only when they are referenced to the distributions of scores earned by a number of individuals.

EQUALITY OF UNITS IN SCALAR VARIABLES

In order to be useful for measuring individuals, the successive categories of a discontinuous quantitative scale and the successive "markers" on a continuous quantitative scale must represent equal increments in the amount, frequency, or degree of the property being measured. If the difference in amount, frequency, or degree of the property between any two neighboring categories or markers is not the same as the difference between all other pairs of categories or markers, then we have a scale of unequal units and our measurements have very little precision. In this section we shall examine the necessity for equal units. We shall also inquire into the determination of equality of units and see whether there are any circumstances where inequality of units is not too serious.

THE NEED FOR EQUALITY OF UNITS

If we wish to examine individual differences on some variable, that is, to compare individuals in terms of the amount, frequency, or degree to which they manifest some property, the scale we use must have equal units. Suppose that the "inch" marks on a ruler are not truly 1 in. apart but some are as close together as ¼-in. and others are as far apart as 2 in. If this is the case then the difference between a "3-in.-long" object and a "4-in.-long" object cannot be said to be the same as the difference between a "6-in.-long" object and a "7-in.-long" object. Similarly, if we have a rating scale of "cooperativeness" with the four successive categories of "1—very poor," "2—poor," "3—fair," and "4—absolutely superb," we should not consider the difference in degree of cooperativeness between an individual rated 2 and another rated 3 to be the same as the difference between an individual rated 3 and another rated 4.

OPERATIONS FOR DETERMINING EQUALITY OF UNITS

With most devices that measure some physical property it is possible to ascertain through appropriate operations whether or not the units along a scale are equal. These operations are termed appropriate because they pertain to the variable under consideration and stem from certain conceptions we have about the property.

For example, if we set the points of a pair of dividers so that they exactly cover the distance between any two inch marks on a ruler, say the zeroth and the first, we can move the dividers to any other two markers such as the third and fourth or the tenth and eleventh and see whether the distance between them is the same. If the distances between all pairs of neighboring markers are exactly the same as the distance between the two points of the dividers, then we can say that by these operations all units along the scale have been demonstrated to be equal and consequently reflect the same amount of the property.

Note that these operations are based upon certain conceptions we have about space. We are presuming among other things that the shortest distance between two points is a straight line and that the distance between two points remains constant over time. The operations we use to demonstrate the equality of units, then, are based upon certain theories and certain conditions we take as given or we assume. Furthermore, the operations involve doing something in connection with linear distances.

As another example let us say we wish to develop a scale of weight. The theory of gravitation tells us that two objects of equal weight will exert downward force. We take a beam which we support exactly in the center and say that when two objects placed at the extremities of the beam exactly balance the beam they are equal in weight, and when they do not balance it they differ in weight. Now we take any object such as a stone and arbitrarily call it one unit of weight. We now find another stone which exactly balances our first stone. Operationally we say that the two stones are equal in weight, that is, are equal units representing equal amounts of the property of weight. In this fashion we can collect a number of stones of the same weight, each being considered to be a unit of weight. Now we wish to weigh a box. We place it at one extreme of the beam and place at the other extreme as many stones, units of weight, as are necessary to balance the beam. This number of units we term the weight of the box. It makes no difference on which arm of the beam we place the box or the stones, nor does it matter which particular stones we use. Thus operationally we say the weight of the box is so many units, and we have demonstrated by a series of operations which are pertinent to the variable and which derive logically from our basic conceptions about weight that the units are equal.

In psychological measurement, too, the operations we employ to ascertain whether the units on a scale do or do not represent equal amounts of the property, and the operations we employ to develop equal units, pertain to the variable and logically follow from some theoretical notions we have about the property and from assumptions about it we are willing to make. Let us take two examples to illustrate the point, one dealing with the typical mental test and the other with a measure of performance.

Suppose that we desire to measure reasoning ability and that we develop as an instrument a mental test comprised of a series of objective questions, each of which poses a problem to be solved by reasoning processes and each of which is answered either correctly or incorrectly. The specific questions which comprise the test are developed from our definition of the trait. Suppose further that on the basis of our theoretical notions about the variable, or empirical evidence of some sort, we decide that the ability is a continuous quantitative variable along which individuals distribute as shown in Fig. 3-1.

This being the case, we should conceive of each item as a crude device for measuring reasoning and one which merely separates individuals into two groups: those possessing a greater amount of the trait (who answer the item correctly) and those possessing a lesser amount of the trait (who answer it incorrectly). Some of the items may make the separation at high levels on the scale, whereas others make it at low levels. On this basis we should be forced to say that item A, which 70 per cent of a group of individuals answers correctly, measures a different amount of the trait than item B, which only 20 per cent of the group answers correctly. As can be seen from Fig. 3-1, these two items would not represent equal amounts of the ability.

Therefore if the items of a mental test differ in difficulty, we should have to conclude on the basis of this particular conceptualization that

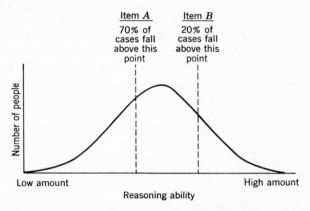

Figure 3-1 Hypothetical distribution of individuals on a continuum of reasoning ability.

the items in the test do not measure the same amount of the ability and therefore are not equal units. Consequently we should not be willing to say that the difference in ability between an individual who obtains a score of 12 and one who obtains a score of 15 is not necessarily the same as the difference in ability between an individual who obtains a score of 28 and one who obtains a score of 29.

As another illustration of the problem of equality of psychological units let us take a case where we wish to measure sales ability. We might measure the sales ability of men selling a given product by counting the number of dollars' worth of merchandise each man sells. If we do this we are in effect saying that one dollar of merchandise sold is exactly equivalent to any other dollar of merchandise sold. That is, the difference in dollars of sales between a man who sells $10,000 worth of merchandise and one who sells $20,000 worth reflects the same amount of sales ability as the difference between a man who sells $60,000 and one who sells $70,000.

Let us say that each salesman has his own area and that all areas are equivalent in the nature and numbers of potential customers. We might argue that people differ in their willingness to buy. The first sales, then, would be to those people who are quite ready to buy, and therefore such sales could be accomplished with little effort. However, later sales would be considerably more difficult to make. In other words, taking the difference between zero dollars and $1 of sales as reflecting a given amount of

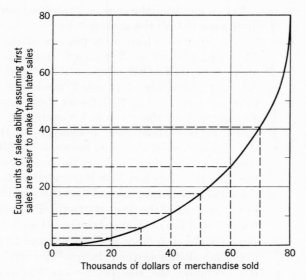

Figure 3-2 Hypothetical relationship between dollars' worth of merchandise sold and "sales ability."

sales ability, the difference in sales ability reflected by the difference between $1 and $2 of sales is greater than that, the difference in sales ability reflected by the difference between $2 and $3 is still greater, and so on. The situation would be like that shown in Fig. 3-2. If we take the curve in this figure as representing the relationship between "true" sales ability and dollars' worth of merchandise sold, then it is clear that the difference in sales ability reflected by the difference between $60,000 and $70,000 is about five times greater than the difference in sales ability represented by the difference between $10,000 and $20,000. Consequently if we adopt this point of view we shall have to conclude that dollars of merchandise sold is not a scale of sales ability on which the units are equal.

CIRCUMSTANCES IN WHICH THE UNEQUAL SIZE OF UNITS IS OF
LITTLE IMPORTANCE

Even though the operations we use to ascertain whether or not the units on a scale are equal may indicate that they are not, in some circumstances their inequality is of little importance. The situation in which the scale is applied may be such that for all practical purposes equal differences between scores can be taken as reflecting equal amounts of the property, or just about equal amounts.

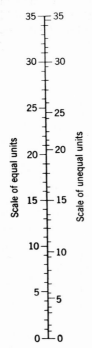

Let us consider the case of a ruler in which the inch marks are not all the same distance apart. Suppose we have a ruler on which some pairs of markers are only ½ in. apart, some are 1 in. apart, and some are 1½ in. apart. Let us further suppose that these "units" of different sizes are distributed randomly along the ruler as shown in Fig. 3-3. Under these conditions the average size of the "units" between, say, the zeroth and the fifteenth marker, is likely to be the same as the average size of the units between the fifteenth and the thirtieth marker. In the example shown in Fig. 3-3 this is in fact the case. Now it is true that, for example, the difference between 5 and 6 on this scale is not equal in the amount of the property to the difference between 6 and 7, and the difference between 19 and 20 is not the same as the difference between 20 and 21. However, over long distances these inequalities tend to average out. Suppose the size of the smallest object being measured was 200 units on the "true" scale and the size of the largest was 20,000 units. It is very likely that on the scale with unequal units any two objects measured as being, say, 400 units different in length would differ almost exactly by that amount on the "true" scale. Discrepancies between the two scales would be so small as to be insignificant, because differences in the sizes of the units would tend to average out.

Figure 3-3 Comparison of scales of equal and unequal units with the latter being randomly distributed along the scale.

Similarly, with a mental test we might be able to ignore the fact that the items do not represent equal units of the trait being measured. Suppose we have a test comprised of a number of items and the individual's score is the number he answers correctly within a specified time limit. Let us further suppose that items of all levels of difficulty are distributed randomly throughout the test. If the average difficulty of the items answered correctly by all individuals is the same, then we can say that the difference in ability reflected by the difference between scores of 50 and 100 is the same or very nearly the same as the difference in ability reflected by the difference between scores of 200 and 250.

There are many circumstances in psychological measurement where this situation occurs and the discrepancies in the size of the units would be expected to average out. Mental tests, personality and interest inventories, attitude questionnaires, and similar devices are comprised of a number of items arranged in such a fashion that inequalities in units are overcome by the sheer number of them and their randomness. However, this by no means always is the case, and it would be incorrect to assume that the averaging-out process invariably occurs. Sometimes, for example, in mental tests items are deliberately arranged in increasing order of difficulty so that the average difficulty of the items answered by one individual, who earns a low score, may be quite different from the average difficulty of those answered by another, who earns a high score.

There is a second circumstance where, even though we know the units of measurement are unequal, the situation is such that we can ignore the fact. We may have reason to believe, as in the case of sales ability, that a difference between two scores at one level—for example, low scores—may not reflect the same amount of ability as the difference between two scores at another level—for example, high scores. Thus the difference between $10,000 and $20,000 could not be taken to reflect the same amount of sales ability as the difference between $60,000 and $70,000. Let us grant this to be the case, but further suppose that the poorest salesman sells $50,000 worth of merchandise and the best $55,000. While, to be sure, the amount of sales ability as reflected by the difference between $50,000 and $51,000 is smaller than the amount reflected by the difference between $54,000 and $55,000, the difference between the two amounts of sales ability, as reference to Fig. 3-2 will show, is not great. In other words, we may be working in such a small range of the total possible scale that for all practical purposes the relationship between the scores yielded by the operations and the true amounts of the trait can be considered to be linear rather than curvilinear as in Fig. 3-2. As a parallel, even though we know the world is round, the distance between Philadelphia and Baltimore is so short that we should be willing to measure it in terms of the shortest straight line rather than the distance along an arc.

There are many similar cases in psychological measurement. If we were evaluating candidates for the Miss America title on a scale of beauty, examining the intellect of feebleminded individuals, or measuring the skill of master carpenters all of whom have had 20 or more years of experience, we probably should not worry much about the inequality of the units of measurement yielded by our operations if we believed them to be related in some nonlinear fashion to equal units on the true continuum, since the individuals we should be dealing with are so homogeneous that they would spread over only a small portion of the scale.

There are circumstances in which we should not be willing to ignore the differences. If the range of individual differences in the trait is broad—for example, the range of arithmetic ability of tenth-grade children or the learning ability of adults in general—then we probably should say that the differences in the sizes of the units are extremely important.

MEANINGFULNESS OF SCORES

As a result of the operations of measurement, an individual is assigned a number as a quantitative description, the number representing the frequency, amount, or degree to which he manifests some property. A meaningful quantitative description is one which is given in terms that directly convey some notion of the frequency, amount, or degree to which the individual manifests some property. That is, the scores are expressed in such a way that certain characteristics or qualities of the individual are immediately manifest in a quantitative sense.

REFERRING SCORES TO THE SCALE AS A SOURCE OF MEANING

The numbers assigned as a result of the operations of measurement sometimes are given in reference to the scale and sometimes are not. In the former case scores are given as so many or so much "something-or-anothers." The height of a tree is described as being 25 ft, the weight of a child as 67 lb, and the speed of response of a subject to a stimulus light as 0.28 sec. In the latter case scores are given merely as numbers with no direct reference at all to the scale. Indeed, the only reference is given to the measuring instrument that is used. Thus it is said that a patient received a score of 23 on the ABC Neurotic Inventory, a child attained a score of 247 on the XYZ Intelligence Test, and a worker was assigned a rating of 74 on the company's employee evaluation form.

In general, scores which are given in terms which refer to the scale itself convey more information than those which are not. Yet merely stating scores as so many "something-or-anothers" does not in and of itself ensure greater meaning. Unless the units in which the scale is expressed are familiar, the advantage is lost. Quantitative descriptions expressed in inches, dollars, hours, quarts, or pounds have considerable significance because we have frequently used them and have compared many different individuals in the properties they indicate. But scores expressed in cythi, cafiz, dha, lev, and koruny convey little or no information. Indeed, to say that a city is 3 farskh distant or that a man's wages are 20 abbasi tells us no more than a rating of 4 assigned to a nursery school child in need for security or a score of 59 earned by a boy on the Smithers test for mechanical aptitude.

In our earlier discussion we saw that the "markers" on a scale are established arbitrarily. The facts of the matter are that we can establish a unit as any amount of the property we want and can utilize as many different systems of units as we wish for the same continuum. We could say that a worker earns $12.50 per day or, equally well, that his earnings are 5,000 eyrir. The height of a girl could be given as 65.5 in. or as 2.5 alen. The weight of a bull could be stated as being 225 lb or 0.5 bahar. The time required by a student to solve a problem could be said to be 40 min or 1 candle. In cases such as these the units of the two systems pertain to the same scale and are merely different arbitrary systems of "markers." Therefore one system of units can be readily changed into the other system. By additional operations, then, it is possible to transmute scores which are expressed in unfamiliar terms to other values which are familiar and therefore meaningful. Transmutations of this sort are common. In the United States we express distances in terms of miles, and distances given in kilometers mean little to us. Miles and kilometers merely are two different sets of arbitrary "markers" on the same continuous scale of distance, and one resolves simply and directly into the other. Similarly we can transmute kilograms to pounds and liters to quarts.

It is unfortunate but true that with most psychological measuring devices, such as tests, inventories, rating scales, and questionnaires, the raw scores given directly by the operations of measurement seldom have a reference to a scale, and when they do the scale is very likely to be expressed in quite unfamiliar units. Scores on objective measuring devices are likely to be expressed only as so many "points" if they are given any reference at all. The information that a person made a score of 41 on an arithmetic test, a score of 215 on a sales interest inventory, a score of 3 on a rating scale of initiative, or a score of 84 on a sociability inventory tells us little or nothing about the individual in terms of how much of those particular properties he possesses. In some circumstances it is possible to transmute the values of the raw scores to other values which do have more meaning. This we shall discuss later.

REFERENCING AN INDIVIDUAL'S SCORE TO THOSE OF OTHERS OF HIS SAME GENERAL KIND AS A SOURCE OF MEANING

Suppose that instead of describing the worker's wages as $12.50 or 5,000 eyrir per day we said that they are equal to those of the lowest-paid worker. Suppose we reported the girl as being average in height instead of as being 65.5 in. or 2.5 alen. Suppose we said the bull is a dwarf instead of being 225 lb or 0.5 bahar. Suppose we said of the student that he took a little less than average time to solve the problem rather than saying he took 40 min or 1 candle. In no case should we know the absolute amounts of the properties the individuals manifested, but nevertheless we should have descriptions of them that are indeed quite meaningful and useful.

In many cases, then, if we know how the individual stands in the property relative to other individuals of his kind we have a quantitative description of him that is quite meaningful. If Fertaldig Ulderput, a man from Mars, is described to us as being 312 xlath (Martian units of height) tall, we really know nothing about him. But if we were told that Mr. Ulderput is 10 ft tall, unquestionably we should have some meaningful information. The description 10 ft is in terms which are quite familiar to us. Yet this quantitative description may not be sufficient. If Fertaldig were an earthman he would be a "whopper," but perhaps he is a runt among Martians. In addition to expressing the value of his height in units that are familiar to us, if that value also gives us some indication of how he compares in height with other Martians we have a quantitative description that is exceedingly meaningful.

It is meaningful to know that an object is 5 in. long. We can conceptualize it and get a "feel" of it. If in addition we know that the object is a mouse, our concept of the object is considerably richer. We now think of the object as "very large" because most mice are only about 2 or 3 in. long. However, if the object is a snake we think of it as "tiny" because most snakes are several feet long. These additional meanings come not from the scores themselves of the mouse and the snake but rather from the general knowledge we have of how mice and snakes run in length. "Very large" and "tiny" are not meanings we get directly from the quantitative description "5 in." In effect we recall the information we have gathered from various sources concerning the lengths of mice and snakes, and we reference the score of our individual to the scores of others of his kind. If a score tells us not only the amount of the property the individual possesses as measured on the scale but also where his score falls relative to the scores of others like him in kind, it does indeed provide a most valuable quantitative description. Later we shall see the extent to which this can be accomplished.

COMPARABILITY OF DIFFERENT SCALES

Sometimes we need to compare the similarities and differences among the traits of a given individual. For example, we might wish to ascertain whether an individual manifests greater clerical aptitude, mechanical aptitude, or sales aptitude. Or we may wish to determine whether a social group is most deficient in leadership, morale, cohesiveness, or internal structure. Only if the scores on the different scales are comparable can we say that an individual possesses more of one property than he does of another.

EQUIVALENCE OF UNITS AS A BASIS FOR THE COMPARABILITY OF DIFFERENT SCALES

When we make comparisons within the individual on different scales, we are asking whether he manifests more of one property than he does of another and, if he does, what the magnitude of the difference is. If we are to make comparisons of this sort, then the scores on the different scales must be comparable. For example, we can say that an automobile is wider than it is tall, because both scores are expressed in the same units, namely, units of length. We can say that a nursery school child evidences more acts of friendship than of aggressiveness, because both scores are expressed in terms of numbers of acts. We can say that a student's performance in English literature is better than his performance in mathematics, because both scores are expressed in terms of a standard grading system. We can say that a business establishment has more salesmen than clerks, because both quantitative descriptions are in terms of numbers of employees. In each of these cases the units in which the two variables are expressed are comparable.

However, on the same basis we cannot say that an automobile is wider than it is heavy, nor a child friendlier than he is tall, nor a student better in English than he is sociable; nor can we say that a business establishment has more salesmen than it has support from the public. We cannot make these comparisons, because the amounts of the two properties in each case are expressed in quite different terms. We could say for an automobile that the number of inches of width is greater than the number of pounds of weight. But for the same automobile we could say that the number of inches of width is less than the number of grams of weight. Comparisons of this sort are meaningless, because the markers on the scales are arbitrary and we can make as few or as many of them on the scales as we wish.

It is only when scores on the different scales are expressed precisely in the same terms that we can say they are comparable. We should have to conclude, then, that it is impossible to make comparisons within the individual on most psychological traits, because they are expressed in such quite different terms as number of seconds, number of items, number of units on a rating scale, and number of attempts. Only if by a series of further operations we can transmute the raw scores to other values which are equivalent will it be possible to make comparisons within the individual.

REFERENCING AN INDIVIDUAL'S SCORES TO THOSE OF OTHERS OF HIS
SAME GENERAL KIND AS A BASIS FOR THE COMPARABILITY OF
DIFFERENT SCALES

Let us pursue further the matter of comparisons within the individual,
that is, comparisons of the individual's scores on two or more different
variables. We have seen that in order to make this type of comparison it is
necessary for all scales to be expressed in the same type of units. Suppose
that students' academic performance is evaluated on a scale of $0 = F$ to
$4 = A$. A student whose grade-point average is 3.6 in literature courses
and 3.2 in courses in history apparently achieves greater superiority in
the former subject than in the latter. But let us suppose that when we
examine the grades earned by the thousands of students who have
attended this particular university we find that the highest grade average
attained by any student in literature courses is 4.0, whereas the highest
average attained by any student in history courses is 3.2. While it is
theoretically possible for students to earn grades as high as 4.0 in both
literature and history, the facts of the matter are that no student ever
does so in history. Therefore our particular student is not equal to the
best in literature, but he is equal to the best in history.

We might say, then, that two scores, each on a different variable, are
comparable if they represent the same standing in the same population
on those scales. If we are told that a man is 5 ft tall and weighs 250 lb we
immediately say of him that he is heavier than he is tall. We know that
the average height of men is somewhere between 5 and 6 ft and the
average weight somewhere between 100 and 200 lb. The man in question
clearly is below the average of other men in height and above the average
of other men in weight.

As another example, suppose that we know the range of scores of fifth-
grade children on a particular spelling test to be 75 to 150 points and on a
particular arithmetic test to be 10 to 40 points. A fifth-grade child who
earns a score of 145 on the spelling test and 11 on the arithmetic test
would be characterized as being better in spelling than he is in arithmetic.
Essentially what we are doing is to compare the child's scores with those
earned on the two tests by others of his kind, namely, fifth-grade children.
We ignore the descriptions of ability given by the raw scores in and of
themselves and take as descriptions of ability the positions of his scores
relative to those of other children. In a similar fashion we could say
that a worker is more deficient in amount of production than he is in
quality of production; a patient is as antisocial as he is depressed; the
morale of a social group is not up to the quality of its leadership; and as a
result of counseling, Harry's grades have improved more than his personal
adjustment. Comparability is attained not through rendering the units

on the various scales equal but rather through comparing the individual's scores on different variables with the distribution of scores earned by a population of individuals in his same general class. We shall discuss these problems again in the next section.

THE NATURE AND ESTABLISHMENT OF NORMS

In effect we have been saying that scores have more meaning and are more useful when they are referenced to the distribution of scores earned by a number of individuals. The distribution of scores earned by a specified group of individuals used as a basis for giving meaning to scores is termed a set of *norms*. In this section we shall consider various aspects of the problem of the establishment of norms.

TYPES OF GROUPS USED IN THE ESTABLISHMENT OF NORMS

Various types of populations are used as a basis for establishing norms. In actual practice, of course, we ordinarily do not have all members of a population but only a sample thereof. The selection of groups is a function of the purpose for which the measurements are being made. Thus the norms for a typing achievement test might be based on the scores earned by "trained typists in general" or "tenth-grade girls who have completed a one-semester course in typing," depending on the type of persons in whom we are interested.

One special group that is both useful and meaningful in the establishment of norms is the adult population. When norms based upon scores earned by this group are used, they are given separately for men and women when sex differences in scores are apparent. The samples of individuals utilized in the preparation of these norms can be examined in order to ascertain how representative they are by comparing their characteristics with those given for the population by the census figures.

ADEQUACY OF GROUPS USED IN THE ESTABLISHMENT OF NORMS

The adequacy of a group used in the establishment of norms obviously is a function of the number of cases involved and their representativeness. If the number of cases is small we cannot put much dependence on the norms, since another group consisting of the same number of persons might give quite different results. The larger the number of cases the more stable will be the norms.

Large numbers alone are not sufficient to ensure adequate norms. We must be sure that the individuals used in the sample are fully representative of the total group the norms are to represent. For example, college seniors would not be representative of college students in general, nor would bank managers be representative of the population of "business and industrial managers." In some instances where very special groups are involved, such as those in rare occupations such as sailmakers or those with special characteristics such as blindness, numbers of cases might have to be sacrificed in order to achieve representativeness. We should not add seamstresses to sailmakers nor partially blinded individuals to the totally blind merely to increase the numbers of cases.

THE SPECIFICATION OF GROUPS USED TO ESTABLISH NORMS

In addition to the administrative difficulties in securing adequate groups with respect to numbers and representativeness for the establishment of norms, a problem arises in connection with the definition of just what constitutes the total population the norms are supposed to describe. Too frequently it is supposed that a population is quite circumscribed and static. If our group used in the establishment of norms is carpenters, for example, we have to decide whether to include only master carpenters or to include journeymen and apprentices also. In addition, the question arises whether to include only those who are employed full time and those whose skill comes solely from formal training. The kinds of individuals entering or leaving a group may change. If the training of high school students in mathematics improves, then the scores of young people on a college aptitude test may well increase. If retirement rules in an industrial establishment are liberalized, the average level of skill of workers in the establishment may fall because of the retirement of the older and hence more skilled workers.

DESCRIBING DISTRIBUTIONS OF SCORES

If we are going to use the frequency distributions of scores earned by a particular group of individuals as frames of reference for giving meaning to scores, then we must be able to describe the nature of those distributions. Such descriptions are necessary so that we can ascertain the extent to which the scores earned by different groups on the same test provide the same frames of reference. There are a number of ways, mathematically and otherwise, for making such comparisons. However, we shall deal here only with certain ones, statistical devices which are particularly pertinent to our present discussion and for our later developments.

WAYS IN WHICH FREQUENCY DISTRIBUTIONS OF SCORES DIFFER

Let us compare the two distributions of scores given in Fig. 3-4. First of all we see that by and large the scores in distribution A are lower than those in distribution B. Therefore we want some way of indicating the general level of a set of scores, that is, their average. Secondly, when we examine the two distributions it is apparent that the scores in the two distributions vary among themselves in different degrees. The scores in distribution A tend to cluster together rather closely, whereas those in distribution B tend to scatter or spread out more. Hence we need an index of the degree to which scores vary among themselves. Thirdly, we can see that the distribution of scores in B is symmetrical whereas the scores in A are distributed in an asymmetrical, lopsided, or skewed fashion. Therefore an index of skewness is necessary. Fourthly, it is obvious that distribution A is sharply peaked or leptokurtic while distribution B tends to be flat or platykurtic. Finally, then, we want an index of kurtosis.

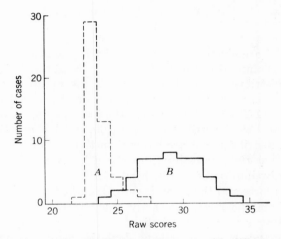

Figure 3-4 Examples of two distributions of scores with different characteristics.

THE MEAN

One kind of average of a set of values is their *arithmetic mean*. The mean of a set of scores is defined as their sum divided by their number. Therefore the formula for the arithmetic mean is

$$\bar{X} = \frac{X_a + \cdots + X_n}{n} = \frac{\Sigma X}{n} \tag{3-1}$$

where $\bar{X}$ is the mean and X represents the raw scores earned by the a to n individuals so that ΣX represents the sum of all the raw scores. In computing the mean we simply add together or sum (Σ) the scores of all individuals and divide by the number of individuals (n). Let us say that there are m different values of X, that is, X_1 is the lowest score and X_m the highest score. If there are several individuals earning the same given score, we can simplify the computation by first multiplying that score by the frequency f with which it occurs. We then can write the formula for the mean as

$$\bar{X} = \frac{fX_1 + \cdots + fX_m}{n} = \frac{\Sigma fX}{n} \tag{3-2}$$

For example, suppose the scores earned by six persons are respectively 9, 8, 8, 7, 7, and 6. The mean by Eq. (3-1) is

$$X = \frac{9 + 8 + 8 + 7 + 7 + 6}{6} = \frac{45}{6} = 7.5$$

By Eq. (3-2) it is

$$\bar{X} = \frac{(1)(9) + (2)(8) + (2)(7) + (1)(6)}{6} = \frac{9 + 16 + 14 + 6}{6} = \frac{45}{6} = 7.5$$

In Table 3-1 are given the frequency distributions of the scores shown in Fig. 3-4. In column 1 of this table there are listed the various scores (X) in the two distributions, and in column 2 the numbers of persons (f) earning each score. In column 3 the values of fX have been computed, and their sum (ΣfX or ΣX) is given at the foot. The mean of distribution A is 23.60 and that of distribution B is 29.00, which shows that in general the scores in distribution A are lower than those in distribution B.

The mean has the interesting property of being a sort of point of balance in the distribution of scores. First of all, the sum of the differences between the scores and the mean is zero. That is, the sum of the positive differences from the mean is exactly equal to the sum of the negative differences. Raw scores are symbolized by X, and the difference between the raw score and the mean, called a deviation score, is symbolized by x. The deviation score for any one individual is

$$x = X - \bar{X} \tag{3-3}$$

Let us now sum the deviation scores for all individuals:

$$\Sigma x = \Sigma(X - \bar{X})$$

If there are a total of n individuals, that is, a to n individuals, we can write the above equation as

$$\Sigma x = (X_a - \bar{X}) + (X_b - \bar{X}) + \cdots + (X_{n-1} - \bar{X}) + (X_n - \bar{X})$$

Rearranging terms gives

$$\Sigma x = X_a + X_b + \cdots + X_{n-1} + X_n - \bar{X} - \cdots - \bar{X}$$
$$= \Sigma X - \Sigma \bar{X}$$

The term $\Sigma \bar{X}$ involves adding the mean, a constant, to itself n times, the number of cases there are. Summing a constant, an unvarying value, to itself a given number of times is the same as multiplying that constant by

TABLE 3-1.   Computation of $\bar{X}$, σ, Sk, and Ku for Two Frequency Distributions A and B

(1)	(2)	(3)	(4)	(5)	(6)	(7)	(8)	(9)	(10)
X	f	fX	x	x^2	fx^2	x^3	fx^3	x^4	fx^4

Distribution A

X	f	fX	x	x^2	fx^2	x^3	fx^3	x^4	fx^4
27	1	27	+3.4	+11.56	+11.56	+39.30	+39.30	+133.63	+133.63
26	2	52	+2.4	+ 5.76	+11.52	+13.82	+27.64	+ 33.18	+ 66.36
25	4	100	+1.4	+ 1.96	+ 7.84	+ 2.74	+10.96	+ 3.84	+ 15.36
24	13	312	+0.4	+ 0.16	+ 2.08	+ 0.06	+ 0.78	+ 0.02	+ 0.39
23	29	667	−0.6	+ 0.36	+10.44	− 0.22	− 6.38	+ 0.12	+ 0.39
22	1	22	−1.6	+ 2.56	+ 2.56	− 4.10	− 4.10	+ 6.55	+ 3.48
Σ	50	1,180			+46.00		+68.20		+225.97

$$\bar{X} = \frac{1,180}{50} = 23.60$$

$$\sigma^2 = \frac{46}{50} = 0.92$$
$$\sigma = 0.96$$

$$\text{Sk} = \frac{68.20/50}{(0.96)^3} = \frac{1.36}{0.88} = 1.55$$

$$\text{Ku} = \frac{225.97/50}{(0.96)^4} - 3 = \frac{4.52}{0.85} - 3 = 5.32 - 3 = +2.32$$

Distribution B

X	f	fX	x	x^2	fx^2	x^3	fx^3	x^4	fx^4
34	1	34	+5	+25	+ 25	+125	+125	+625	+ 625
33	2	66	+4	+16	+ 32	+ 64	+128	+256	+ 512
32	4	128	+3	+ 9	+ 36	+ 27	+108	+ 81	+ 324
31	7	217	+2	+ 4	+ 28	+ 8	+ 56	+ 16	+ 112
30	7	210	+1	+ 1	+ 7	+ 1	+ 7	+ 1	+ 7
29	8	232	0	0	0	0	0	0	0
28	7	196	−1	+ 1	+ 7	− 1	− 7	+ 1	+ 7
27	7	189	−2	+ 4	+ 28	− 8	− 56	+ 16	+ 112
26	4	104	−3	+ 9	+ 36	− 27	−108	+ 81	+ 324
25	2	50	−4	+16	+ 32	− 64	−128	+256	+ 512
24	1	24	−5	+25	+ 25	−125	−125	+625	+ 625
Σ	50	1,450			+256		0		+3,160

$$\bar{X} = \frac{1,450}{50} = 29.00$$

$$\sigma^2 = \frac{256}{50} = 5.12$$
$$\sigma = 2.26$$

$$\text{Sk} = \frac{0/50}{(2.26)^3} = \frac{0}{11.54} = 0$$

$$\text{Ku} = \frac{3,160/50}{(2.26)^4} - 3 = \frac{63.33}{26.09} - 3 = 2.43 - 3 = -0.57$$

the number. In other words,

$$\Sigma \bar{X} = n\bar{X}$$

Hence

$$\Sigma x = \Sigma X - n\bar{X}$$

Substituting for the mean $\bar{X}$ from Eq. (3-1) gives

$$\Sigma x = \Sigma X - n\frac{\Sigma X}{n}$$
$$= \Sigma X - \Sigma X$$
$$= 0 \tag{3-4}$$

If we divide both sides of Eq. (3-4) by n we can see that the mean of the deviation scores also equals zero:

$$\bar{x} = \frac{\Sigma x}{n} = \frac{0}{n} = 0 \tag{3-5}$$

Furthermore, the sum of the squares of the differences between the raw scores and the mean, Σx^2, is smaller than the sum of the squares of the differences between the raw scores and any other point on the scale. So in this sense, too, the mean is a sort of point of balance. Let us take A as some point on the scale which is different from the mean. Then $A \neq \bar{X}$. Let us symbolize the difference between A and the mean as B. Then

$$A - \bar{X} = B$$
$$A = \bar{X} + B$$

Let us symbolize the difference between a raw score and A as d, just as we have symbolized the difference between a raw score and the mean as x. Then

$$d = X - A$$
$$= X - (\bar{X} + B)$$
$$= X - \bar{X} - B$$
$$= (X - \bar{X}) - B$$
$$= x - B$$

Squaring both sides of the equation gives

$$d^2 = (x - B)^2$$
$$= x^2 - 2xB + B^2$$

The above equation holds for any one individual. Now let us sum these equations for all cases:

$$\Sigma d^2 = \Sigma(x^2 - 2xB + B^2)$$
$$= \Sigma x^2 - \Sigma 2xB + \Sigma B^2$$

Since 2 and B are constants we can write the term $\Sigma 2xB$ as $2B\Sigma x$. In this term we have x, which differs for different individuals, and 2 and B, which are the same for all individuals. For each person we multiply the three values by each other $(2xB)$ and then sum the products for all individuals $(\Sigma 2xB)$. We can obtain the same final sum if we merely sum the variable for all individuals (Σx) and then multiply that sum by the two constants $(2B\Sigma x)$. Since B is a constant squared and summed to itself a given number of times, we can write the term ΣB^2 as nB^2. Making these substitutions, we have

$$\Sigma d^2 = \Sigma x^2 - 2B\Sigma x + nB^2$$

From Eq. (3-4) we know that $\Sigma x = 0$. Therefore the entire term $2B\Sigma x = 0$. Consequently

$$\Sigma d^2 = \Sigma x^2 + nB^2 \tag{3-6}$$

In Eq. (3-6) we have proof that the sum of the squared differences between the raw scores and any point on the scale other than the mean (Σd^2) is greater than the sum of the squared differences between the raw scores and the mean (Σx^2). Hence it is said that the mean is the point of least squares. Σx^2, then, is a minimum value and is always smaller than Σd^2 no matter from what point on the scale, A, other than the mean the deviations are computed. If we wished, we could compute the mean of the squares of the deviation scores. To do this we should divide both sides of Eq. (3-6) by n, the number of cases:

$$\frac{\Sigma d^2}{n} = \frac{\Sigma x^2}{n} + \frac{nB^2}{n} = \frac{\Sigma x^2}{n} + B^2 \tag{3-7}$$

Thus we can see from Eq. (3-7) that the mean of the squared deviations from the mean of the distribution also is a minimum value. Therefore the mean of a set of scores is that point on the scale which is a center point in a least-squares sense.

THE STANDARD DEVIATION AND VARIANCE

The mean of the squares of the deviation scores, the value we just discussed, has the interesting property of varying with the extent to which the scores in a distribution cluster together or spread out. Hence the mean of the squares of the deviation scores, or its square root, is commonly used as an index of the variability of scores. The square root of the mean of the squares of the deviation scores is termed the *standard deviation:*

$$\sigma_x = \sqrt{\frac{\Sigma x^2}{n}} \tag{3-8}$$

or

$$\sigma_x = \sqrt{\frac{\Sigma f x^2}{n}} \tag{3-9}$$

The square of the standard deviation, that is, the mean of the squared deviations itself, is termed the *variance:*

$$\sigma_x{}^2 = \frac{\Sigma x^2}{n} \tag{3-10}$$

or
$$\sigma_x{}^2 = \frac{\Sigma f x^2}{n} \tag{3-11}$$

For computing the standard deviation by Eq. (3-8) or (3-9) we need the values of the scores in deviation form, x. These are given in column 4 of Table 3-1 for the two distributions in Fig. 3-4. In column 5 the deviation scores are squared, and column 6 gives the values of fx^2. The sum of these values ($\Sigma f x^2$ or Σx^2) is given at the foot of column 6, and the computations of the variances and standard deviations are shown for each distribution. The standard deviation of distribution A is 0.96 and that of distribution B is 2.26, which proves what is obvious in Fig. 3-4—that the scores in distribution A cluster closely together whereas those in distribution B scatter out more.

Simple though Eqs. (3-8) and (3-9) appear, they are not very convenient for computation since they require that the raw scores first be transformed into deviation scores. Let us therefore derive a formula that is more practical for computational purposes:

$$\sigma_x{}^2 = \frac{\Sigma x^2}{n}$$

But $x = X - \bar{X}$. Therefore

$$\begin{aligned}
\sigma_x{}^2 &= \frac{\Sigma (X - \bar{X})^2}{n} \\
&= \frac{\Sigma (X^2 - 2X\bar{X} + \bar{X}^2)}{n} \\
&= \frac{\Sigma X^2 - \Sigma 2X\bar{X} + \Sigma \bar{X}^2}{n}
\end{aligned}$$

Remembering that 2 and $\bar{X}$ are constants, we get

$$\begin{aligned}
\sigma_x{}^2 &= \frac{\Sigma X^2 - 2\bar{X}\Sigma X + n\bar{X}^2}{n} \\
&= \frac{\Sigma X^2}{n} - 2\bar{X}\frac{\Sigma X}{n} + \frac{n\bar{X}^2}{n} \\
&= \frac{\Sigma X^2}{n} - 2\overline{X}\overline{X} + \bar{X}^2 \\
&= \frac{\Sigma X^2}{n} - 2\bar{X}^2 + \bar{X}^2 \\
&= \frac{\Sigma X^2}{n} - \bar{X}^2 \tag{3-12}
\end{aligned}$$

$$\sigma_x = \sqrt{\frac{\Sigma X^2}{n} - \bar{X}^2} \tag{3-13}$$

The standard deviation of scores is precisely the same in raw-score form as it is in deviation-score form. We can see this in Eq. (3-12). If we used deviation scores rather than raw scores, then the term $\bar{X}^2$ would be zero because the mean of deviation scores is zero, and the term $\Sigma X^2/n$ would be written as $\Sigma x^2/n$ without changing the value of σ. When we use deviation scores, obviously all we are doing is to subtract a constant $\bar{X}$ from all scores [Eq. (3-3)] and therefore we do not change the nature of the distribution or its shape. Hence for the standard deviation of a set of scores we can write either σ_X or σ_x.

SKEWNESS

A distribution of scores can be symmetrical, as with distribution B in Fig. 3-4, or skewed, as with distribution A. As may be seen in Fig. 3-5,

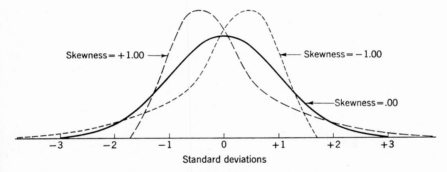

Figure 3-5   Examples of frequency distributions differing in skewness.

distributions can vary both in the direction and in the degree of skewness. It just so happens that the mean of the cubes of deviation scores $(\Sigma x^3/n)$ is related to both the direction and the degree of skewness. When the distribution of scores is symmetrical, the mean of the cubes of the deviation scores is zero. When the distribution of scores is positively skewed (the long "tail" of the distribution pointing toward the higher score values as with distribution A in Fig. 3-4), the mean of the cubes of the deviation scores is positive. When the distribution of scores is negatively skewed (the long "tail" of the distribution pointing toward the smaller score values), the mean of the cubes of the deviation scores is negative. Furthermore, the larger the mean of the cubes of the deviation scores, the greater the degree of skewness.

In order to compare the skewness of the two distributions of scores we should be sure the variation among the scores is the same in both cases. Therefore, rather than using the mean of the cubes of the deviation scores as an index of skewness, we refer it to the standard deviation of the distribution. The index of skewness, then, is

$$\text{Sk} = \frac{\Sigma x^3/n}{\sigma_x{}^3} = \frac{\Sigma f x^3/n}{\sigma_x{}^3} \tag{3-14}$$

To compute the index of skewness we need the deviation scores cubed. These values are given in column 7 of Table 3-1 for the two distributions in Fig. 3-4. In column 8 are computed the values of fx^3. The indices of skewness show what is apparent in Fig. 3-4, that distribution A is highly skewed positively ($\text{Sk} = +1.55$) and distribution B is symmetrical ($\text{Sk} = 0$).

KURTOSIS

In some distributions which are called leptokurtic there is a heavy piling up of scores in one region of the scale, whereas in others which are

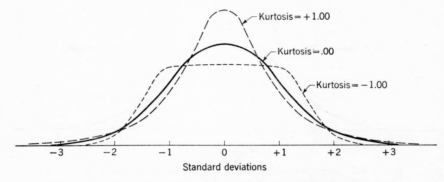

Figure 3-6   Examples of frequency distributions differing in kurtosis.

called platykurtic the scores tend to distribute more or less evenly throughout. Figure 3-6 shows some examples of distributions which differ in degree of kurtosis. Just as the mean of the cubes of the deviation scores is related to skewness, so the mean of the deviation scores to the fourth power ($\Sigma x^4/n$) is related to kurtosis. Again for an index we wish to hold the variation of scores constant and therefore reference the mean of the deviation scores to the fourth power of the standard deviation. The ratio of the mean of the deviation scores to the fourth power, to the fourth power of the standard deviation, is quite a satisfactory index of kurtosis. However, by convention we subtract 3 from this ratio for reasons which will be clear when we discuss the normal frequency distribution. Our index of kurtosis, then, is

$$\text{Ku} = \frac{\Sigma x^4/n}{\sigma_x{}^4} - 3 = \frac{\Sigma f x^4/n}{\sigma_x{}^4} - 3 \tag{3-15}$$

When this value is positive the distribution of scores is leptokurtic, and when it is negative the distribution is platykurtic.

The computations of the indices of kurtosis for the two distributions in Fig. 3-4 are shown in columns 9 and 10 of Table 3-1. Ku for distribution A is $+2.32$, indicating that it is very leptokurtic; and for distribution B it is -0.57, indicating that it is somewhat platykurtic.

THE NORMAL FREQUENCY DISTRIBUTION AND ITS CHARACTERISTICS

It is apparent that distributions of scores vary widely in their shape, manifesting different degrees and combinations of skewness and kurtosis. It therefore would be well to establish one particular distribution as a frame of reference for comparison purposes. If possible, this distribution should be so commonly found as to be characteristic, or nearly so, of the distributions of scores on a wide variety of qualities. Such a distribution does exist, and it is termed the normal frequency distribution.

The normal frequency distribution is symmetrical and bell-shaped. It is found for a variety of both physical and psychological traits. This is not to say that the frequency distributions of these traits always, or indeed ever, have precisely the characteristics of a normal frequency distribution, but rather that very often they quite closely approximate it

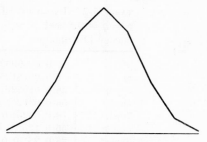

Figure 3-7 Expansion of the binomial $(p + q)^N$, where $p = q = 0.5$ and $N = 8$, to illustrate the normal frequency distribution.

in shape. The normal frequency distribution also has been termed the curve of error because it is closely approximated in those situations where a "score" is determined by a large number of factors which operate under conditions of equal likelihood of having an effect. For example, if one tossed a thousand coins a million times, counting up the number of heads occurring on each toss, and made a frequency distribution of these "scores," the distribution would be very similar in shape to that of a normal distribution.

The normal frequency distribution can be precisely stated mathematically. One statement is that it is the expansion of the binomial $(p + q)^N$, where $p = q = 0.5$ and N is an infinitely large number. By way of illustration, this binomial is expanded to the eighth power in Table 3-2. This particular expansion gives us a frequency distribution of nine steps or score values and is plotted as a frequency polygon in Fig. 3-7. If N is an infinitely large number, then the number of steps along the scale is infinitely large and the curve becomes smooth and does not have the "corners" we see in the distribution in Fig. 3-7. A normal frequency distribution has a skewness of zero (Fig. 3-5) and a kurtosis of zero (Fig. 3-6).

The normal frequency distribution is defined by a particular formula and is a theoretical curve. Its tails (see Table 3-2 and Fig. 3-7) never reach the base line; rather, they approach it asymptotically so that in a true normal frequency distribution there can never be a score value with a frequency of zero. Consequently it is never correct to say of any distribution of actual scores that the distribution is normal, even if both its skewness and its kurtosis are zero. Distributions of actual scores may have characteristics which closely approximate those of a normal frequency distribution, but they never have all of them. When we say that a distribution of scores is normal we really mean that its characteristics

TABLE 3-2.   Expansion of the Binomial $(p + q)^N$, where $p = q = 0.5$ and $N = 8$, to Illustrate the Normal Frequency Distribution

p^8	$1(0.00390625)$	0.00390625
$8p^7q$	$8(0.0078125)(0.5)$	0.03125000
$28p^6q^2$	$28(0.015625)(0.25)$	0.10937500
$56p^5q^3$	$56(0.03125)(0.125)$	0.21875000
$70p^4q^4$	$70(0.0625)(0.0625)$	0.27343750
$56p^3q^5$	$56(0.125)(0.03125)$	0.21875000
$28p^2q^6$	$28(0.25)(0.015625)$	0.10937500
$8pq^7$	$8(0.5)(0.0078125)$	0.03125000
q^8	$1(0.00390625)$	0.00390625
Σ		1.00000000

are very similar to those of a normal distribution. A normal frequency distribution, then, is purely a theoretical frequency distribution.

We can see from Table 3-2 that it would be possible to calculate the proportion of cases falling between any two points in such a distribution. This has been done mathematically so that the properties of the distribution are well known. The proportions of cases falling below various score values in a normal frequency distribution are given in the Appendix.

THE NORMAL FREQUENCY DISTRIBUTION AS A MODEL

For one reason or another we may believe that the particular distribution of scores given by the operations of measurement does not reflect the true distribution of the trait being measured. In some instances the individuals being measured may be drawn not from one but from two or more different populations, for example, men and women or apprentices and masters of a trade. But in many instances, even though the group does constitute a representative sample of the population with which we are concerned, we may be led to reject the distribution of their scores as being descriptive of the way in which the trait is distributed in the population.

It may be that we suspect there is some artifact in the measuring device or in the measuring situation. For example, suppose we find that on a particular test most people make low scores and relatively few people earn high scores. We might argue that this particular positively skewed distribution of scores resulted from the fact that the items in the test were too difficult for the group. Had we happened to develop somewhat easier items the distribution of scores would have been different. Similarly, if we have parents rate their children on some trait such as intelligence, probably most children will be assigned high ratings and relatively few will be assigned low ones. This negatively skewed distribution might be expected, because in general parents are likely to be lenient in judging their offspring. The distribution of scores as it stands would be rejected because it represents a mutilation of the true distribution of the trait due to an error of leniency on the part of the raters.

Furthermore, if we do not believe that the units along our scale are equal we do not expect the distribution of scores as given by our operations of measurement to mirror the way in which the trait actually is distributed among individuals. For example, we might have a situation such as that in Fig. 3-2 where successive units along the scale represent greater and greater amounts of the trait. A "unit" at the lower end of the scale represents a smaller amount of the trait than one at the higher end. Under such circumstances it would not be surprising to find that the upper end of the distribution is "pushed" down and a negatively skewed distribution of scores results.

Now it may be that we are perfectly happy with the distribution of scores given by our operations of measurement. We believe that the distribution is not affected by artifacts in the measuring instrument or measurement situation, or if there are any such effects they are of such a minor nature that they can be ignored. On the other hand, if we have reason to believe that the distribution of scores gives a distorted picture of the distribution of the trait, we are faced with some decisions.

Perhaps the most common decision is to admit that the distribution of scores given by our operations of measurement does not correctly reflect the distribution of the trait. We are unable to state the extent to which the distribution of scores gives a distorted picture of the distribution of the trait, because we have no idea of what the latter is like. In effect we throw up our hands and admit defeat but go ahead and use the scores anyway.

From theoretical considerations of one sort or another we might have an idea of the way in which the trait is distributed. Thus from our notions about hemispherical dominance in the brain we might decide that measures of preference for use of the right and left hands should be bimodal. That is, we should be saying that on a scale of hand preference there should be a large proportion of individuals toward one end of the scale (those who prefer to use the right hand), another substantial proportion at the other end of the scale (those who prefer to use the left hand), and few falling in the middle of the scale (those who have no hand preference). We develop, then, a model of the distribution of the trait from our theory. Clearly the adequacy of our model is a direct function of the adequacy of our theoretical considerations. If the theory is faulty so will be our model.

Once we make up our minds about the model of the distribution of the trait, that is, the shape of the frequency distribution of scores, we must make a further decision. First of all, we can attempt to design operations of measurement which yield scores that distribute in the same manner as our model. If the scores do not distribute in the way desired, the operations will be modified or discarded and new ones developed. Secondly, we can transmute our raw scores to other values of such a nature that the new transmuted scores do distribute in accordance with the model. Finally, we can say that the distribution of scores of the particular sample of individuals we have does possess the characteristics of the model even though it does not.

There are, of course, a wide variety of differently shaped distributions that could be adopted as the theoretical model of the distribution of psychological traits. Of all the possible distributions there appears to be more basis for choosing the normal frequency distribution. We have seen that if we measure the properties of large and representative populations of living things with a wide variety of measuring devices, particularly devices which measure physical properties, the distributions of scores tend to be shaped more like a normal distribution than any other type of distribution. This is not to say that the empirically obtained distributions of scores ever precisely fit a normal distribution, but rather that in many instances there is a very close approximation. Indeed, to many it seems that the bulk of the distributions of scores are simply chance variations from a normal distribution.

Frequently as we increase the numbers of cases the shape of the distribution of scores more and more closely approaches that of the normal frequency distribution. By way of example, the top diagram of Fig. 3-8 gives the distribution of scores earned on a test by 50 individuals. For comparison purposes a theoretical normal curve is superimposed on the empirical distribution. Clearly, the shape of the distribution of scores of this small sample of individuals is quite different from that of a normal distribution. The middle diagram in Fig. 3-8 shows the distribution when the number of cases is increased to 100, and in the lower diagram the distribution includes the scores of 1,000 individuals. It is apparent that in this instance, as in many others, as we increase the numbers of cases the shape of the distribution of scores comes closer and closer to that of a normal frequency distribution. Thus if we had just the 50 cases we might be willing to say that the distribution of the trait is normal even though the scores of our sample clearly are not normally distributed. We should use the mean and standard deviation of our empirical distribution to describe the mean and standard deviation of our normally distributed

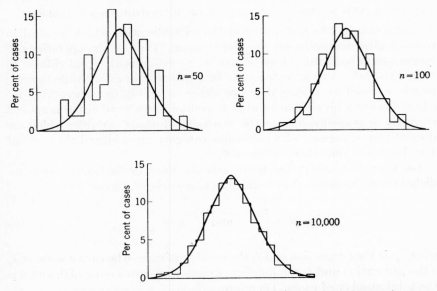

Figure 3-8   Illustration of how increasing the number of cases results in some instances in a distribution of scores that more and more closely approximates a normal frequency distribution.

trait and attribute to our empirical distribution the characteristics of a normal distribution.

The fact that the shapes of so many frequency distributions of scores approach that of a normal frequency distribution has been sufficient justification for some psychologists to hold that the normal frequency distribution of traits is the rule. Their position is strengthened by the ease of "explaining away" frequency distributions which are not normal as resulting from the use of poorly devised measuring instruments or small or nonrepresentative samples of individuals. For other psychologists the normal frequency distribution appears to be a reasonable hypothesis to be adhered to in "appropriate" circumstances. Finally there are those who completely reject the normal frequency distribution as a "law." They prefer to hold to whatever shape of distribution of scores the measuring device happens to yield. Apparently they have more faith in their capacity for devising satisfactory operations of measurement than in their capacity for theorizing. The decision of whether or not to adopt a normal distribution as a model seems to depend largely upon one's particular biases and inclinations. Often the decision appears to be reached on intuitive rather than explicit grounds, and certainly the entire matter is discussed with more heat than light.

THE MEAN AND STANDARD DEVIATION OF DICHOTOMOUS VARIABLES

As we saw in Chap. 2, many of the variables with which we deal in psychological measurement are dichotomous. That is, the operations of measurement sometimes merely give us an assignment of individuals to one of the other of two categories. In a question in an attitude survey, people respond by saying they are either favorably or unfavorably inclined toward a given issue, and in a spelling test a word either is spelled correctly or is spelled incorrectly. With dichotomous variables which are discontinuous, persons who fall in one category are assigned the score of 1 and those in the other a score of 0.

Let us now consider the mean and standard deviation of scores on dichotomous variables. For a dichotomous variable we can write

$$p = \frac{f_1}{n} \quad \text{and} \quad q = \frac{f_0}{n} \tag{3-16}$$

where p is the proportion and f_1 the number of cases who earn a score of 1, q the proportion and f_0 the number of cases who earn a score of 0, and n is the total number of cases. Therefore

$$p + q = 1 \quad p = 1 - q \quad q = 1 - p$$

From Eq. (3-2) we know that the mean of a set of scores is

$$\bar{X} = \frac{fX_1 + \cdots + fX_n}{n}$$

Since with a discontinuous dichotomous variable we have only two possible scores, 0 and 1, we can write this formula as

$$\bar{X} = \frac{f_0 X_0 + f_1 X_1}{n}$$

But $X_0 = 0$ and therefore the first term in the numerator is zero and drops out. Furthermore $X_1 = 1$ and therefore the second term in the numerator is $f_1 1$ or simply f_1. Hence

$$\bar{X} = \frac{f_1}{n} = p \tag{3-17}$$

That is, with a discontinuous dichotomous variable the mean is simply the proportion of persons falling in the upper category. Thus if 48 out of 200 cases fall in the upper category the mean is $^{48}\!/_{200}$ or 0.24.

From Eq. (3-11) we know that the variance of a set of scores is

$$\sigma_x^2 = \frac{\Sigma f x^2}{n}$$

Remembering that a deviation score is the raw score minus the mean, we have for a dichotomous variable

Raw scores	Deviation scores
$X_1 = 1$	$x_1 = 1 - p = q$
$X_0 = 0$	$x_0 = 0 - p = -p$

For a dichotomous variable, therefore, the variance is

$$\begin{aligned}
\sigma_x^2 &= \frac{f_0 x_0^2 + f_1 x_1^2}{n} \\
&= \frac{f_0(-p)^2 + f_1 q^2}{n} \\
&= \frac{f_0 p^2}{n} + \frac{f_1 q^2}{n} \\
&= \frac{f_0}{n} p^2 + \frac{f_1}{n} q^2 \\
&= q p^2 + p q^2 \\
&= pq(p + q) \\
&= pq(1) \\
&= pq \tag{3-18} \\
\sigma_x &= \sqrt{pq} \tag{3-19}
\end{aligned}$$

The standard deviation of scores on a dichotomous variable, then, is equal to the square root of the product of the proportions of individuals who fall in the two categories. Thus the proportion of cases falling in the upper category is 0.24, the proportion falling in the lower category is 0.76, and the standard deviation is $\sqrt{(0.24)(0.76)} = \sqrt{0.1824}$ or 0.43.

Summary

For measurements to be useful, the successive categories of a discontinuous multistep scale, and the successive "markers" on a continuous scale, must represent equal increments in the amount, frequency, or degree of the property being measured. That is, the units along a scale must be equal. With many measuring devices it is possible through appropriate operations to determine whether or not the units are equal. The operations are termed appropriate because they pertain to the variable under consideration and follow logically from the particular theoretical conceptions we have about the nature of the variable.

In certain situations, even though we may be certain that the units of measurement are not equal, such inequality is of little practical importance and can be ignored. If the units are unequal but the various sizes are distributed randomly throughout the scale, their differences will tend to average out, particularly when a large number of them are involved. There may be a curvilinear relationship between scores on the scale and the actual amounts of the trait being measured, so that units at one end of the scale reflect small amounts of the trait and those at the other end reflect large amounts. However, if we are dealing only with a small portion of the entire scale the discrepancies may be so small as to be unimportant.

To be useful, a quantitative description or a score must be meaningful. A meaningful score is given in terms that directly convey some notion of the amount, degree, or frequency of the property that the individual possesses. Most scores on psychological traits are expressed merely in terms of "points," without any reference to the trait being measured or to a frame of reference such as an absolute zero. Relating an individual's scores to the distribution of scores by other individuals does provide something of a frame of reference, and therefore does give more meaning to scores.

Sometimes we wish to make comparisons within the individual so that we can know in which traits he is strong and in which he is weak. Comparisons of this sort can be made only if the scores on the different variables are expressed in the same terms. That is, only when scores on different variables are comparable can we say an individual possesses more of one property than he does of another. Referencing an individual's score on each variable to distributions of scores on those variables does provide a kind of comparability among variables. At least it permits us to say that relative to other individuals this person is higher on certain traits than he is on others.

A distribution of scores used as a frame of reference to make scores meaningful and comparable is termed a set of norms. Since distributions of scores are so useful, it is necessary to describe them. Distributions differ from one another in many ways, but when they are used as norms the most useful descriptions of them are the mean and variation of the scores, and the shape of the distribution as given by the skewness and kurtosis.

Inasmuch as there are substantial variations in the shapes of distributions of scores, it would be useful to have one particular distribution as a frame of reference. The shape of this distribution should be characteristic, or nearly so, of the shapes of the distributions of a wide variety of properties. Such a distribution does exist and is termed the normal frequency distribution. This distribution is symmetrical and is shaped like a bell. The distributions of scores closely approximate the normal distribution in so many instances that it is useful as a theoretical model of distributions of scores.

Selected Readings

Boring, E. G.: The logic of the normal law of error in mental measurement, *Am. J. Psychol.*, **31**:1–33, 1920.
Cronbach, L. J.: "Essentials of Psychological Testing," 2d ed., Harper, 1960.
Lewis, D.: "QuantitativeMethods in Psychology," McGraw-Hill, 1960.
Lorge, I.: The fundamental nature of measurement, in E. F. Lindquist (ed.), "Educational and Psychological Measurement," American Council on Education, 1951.
Nunnally, J. C.: "Tests and Measurements," McGraw-Hill, 1959.
Torgeson, W.: "Theory and Methods of Scaling," Wiley, 1958.

chapter 4   Standardizing

Scores

In Chap. 3 we saw that under many circumstances measurements of human characteristics cannot utilize an absolute zero as a reference point and that equal differences between raw scores may have to be rejected as being indicative of equal differences in the trait being measured. Furthermore, we saw that the units in scales of psychological traits are not likely to be expressed in meaningful ways in the sense that they immediately convey a notion of the amount of some property that the individual possesses or manifests. Finally, we saw that the comparability of scores on different scales poses a number of problems. We also saw that if we use the distribution of scores earned by a representative group of individuals on the variables in which we are interested, most of these problems are given some resolution. Using distributions of scores as frames of reference or norms provides a basis for giving scores meaning and for making statements about the comparability of scores on different variables.

In this chapter we shall consider percentile ranks and standard scores, since they provide ways for referencing scores directly to a distribution. We shall also describe ways for transmuting raw scores to other values which are normally distributed. Since the members of some desired population may not be available in establishing norms, we shall present a procedure for estimating the distribution of scores on a given test for that population. Finally, we shall deal with the problem of combining scores from different samples.

PERCENTILE RANKS

In everyday communication one of the common ways for describing both people and things is to state the proportion of other individuals that a particular individual exceeds in the characteristic or quality under consideration. While we may not state the proportion with any degree of exactness, it nevertheless is implicit in our statement. We say, "There are few desserts I like better than strawberry shortcake." That is, we are saying that if we had available a random sample of all sorts of desserts we should reject the very large bulk of them, perhaps 95 per cent, in favor of strawberry shortcake. Similarly we say, "One-round Smith is about as poor a welterweight fighter as they come." We mean that if a representative sample of welterweight prize fighters were matched with Mr. Smith, in our opinion he could beat very few of them, perhaps only 3 or 4 per cent. Hence if a person is described as exceeding 99 per cent of his fellows in height, we immediately know that he is tall; if he is described as exceeding 50 per cent in leadership, we know that he is average in this trait; and if he is described as exceeding only 3 per cent in intelligence, we know that he is a dull fellow, indeed. Statements of the percentages of persons exceeded, then, are a familiar means of quantitative description and are immediately meaningful.

THE NATURE OF PERCENTILE RANKS AND PERCENTILES

The *percentile rank* of a score is the percentage of persons in the reference group who earn lower scores. Therefore if an individual earns a raw score of 217 on a given test and his score is superior to the scores earned by 70 per cent of the persons in the norming group, it is said that his percentile rank is 70. The raw score of 217, then, is the 70th percentile.

It will be recalled that when we are dealing with a continuous scale, a score represents a region or interval of the scale rather than a point on it. Consequently, by convention we say that the score of 217 occupies the interval of 216.5 to 217.5 and assume that individuals who obtain the score of 217 are distributed equally throughout this interval. More correctly, then, we should say that the raw score of 216.5 is the 70th percentile.

COMPUTATION OF PERCENTILE RANKS

In developing percentile ranks we simply determine the percentage of cases falling below the lower limit of each raw-score interval. Table 4-1 illustrates the computational process. One person or 0.7 per cent of the cases ($\frac{1}{150}$ = 0.007 or 0.7 per cent) earns scores less than 57.5, five people or 3.3 per cent of the cases ($\frac{5}{150}$ = 0.033 or 3.3 per cent) earn scores less than 58.5, etc. In order to obtain the percentile rank of an actual score we have to interpolate between the percentile ranks of its lower and upper limits. For example, the percentile ranks of the lower and

TABLE 4-1.   Computation of Percentiles and Percentile Ranks

Raw score	Lower limit of raw score "interval"	Frequency	Number of cases earning lower scores	Percentile rank
71	70.5	0	150	100.0
70	69.5	1	149	99.3
69	68.5	3	146	97.3
68	67.5	10	136	90.7
67	66.5	14	122	81.3
66	65.5	10	112	74.7
65	64.5	20	92	61.3
64	63.5	15	77	51.3
63	62.5	25	52	34.7
62	61.5	23	29	19.3
61	60.5	6	23	15.3
60	59.5	12	11	7.3
59	58.5	6	5	3.3
58	57.5	4	1	0.7
57	56.5	1	0	0.0
56	55.5	0	0	0.0

Total number of cases = 150

upper limits of a raw score of 60 (59.5 and 60.5) are 7.3 and 15.3. Now assuming as we have that individuals who earn a score of 60 are actually distributed equally throughout this interval and recalling that the score is taken to be in the middle of the interval, half the distance above the lower limit, we can calculate the percentile rank of the score of 60 as follows:

$$7.3 + 0.5(15.3 - 7.3) = 11.3$$

We should therefore say that 11.3 per cent of the cases fall below a raw score of 60 and that an individual who earns a score of 60 has the percentile rank of 11.3.

Rather than calculate the percentiles arithmetically it is easier to determine them graphically by plotting the percentile ranks of the lower limits of each score interval and then reading the appropriate values from the graph. Such a graph is given in Fig. 4-1 for the data in Table 4-1. In this graph the lower limits of the raw scores are plotted against the percentile ranks, as is shown by the circles. From the solid line which connects these points we could read off the percentile rank of any raw score. It will be noted that the line plotted exactly through the circles is somewhat irregular. Such irregularities ordinarily are attributed to sampling error, the implication being that if the sample contained many more cases than the 150 used here the line would show a regular and smooth progression. As a consequence, frequently a trend line is drawn through the points as is shown by the dotted line in Fig. 4-1. Percentile ranks are

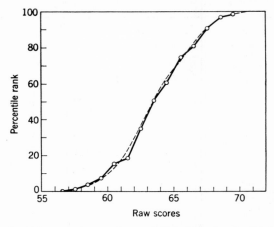

Figure 4-1   Graph of the percentage of cases falling below each raw score to illustrate the determination of percentile ranks.

taken from the trend line rather than the line that exactly connects the points. Thus the percentile rank assigned to a person earning a score of 62 would be taken as 30 rather than as 26. Clearly, when this smoothing process is employed, the distribution of actual raw scores is considered to be an inaccurate description of the distribution of scores of the population. We take the smooth curve as a model which we believe to be more descriptive of the population than the irregular curve drawn exactly through the points.

THE NATURE OF THE UNITS IN PERCENTILE RANKS

When raw scores are transmuted into percentile ranks, the units within a test and between tests are made comparable—at least after a fashion. The units are expressed not in terms of equal amounts of some psychological trait but rather in terms of numbers of people. We are dealing with a counted rather than a scalar function. As a consequence it cannot be said that differences between percentile ranks can be used to indicate amounts or degrees of differences in traits.

Suppose the percentile ranks of three individuals A, B, and C on a particular test are, respectively, 70, 60, and 50. While it is apparent that A is superior to B and B is superior to C, we cannot say that the difference between A and B in the property being measured is the same in magnitude as the difference between B and C. What we can say is that the number of persons by which A exceeds B is the same as the number by which B exceeds C.

As another example suppose that the percentile ranks of one person on three different tests X, Y, and Z are, respectively, 70, 60, and 50. We can say that compared with other people he is better on X than he is on Y and that he is better on Y than he is on Z. But we cannot say that the difference between his abilities as measured by tests X and Y is the same as the difference between his abilities as measured by tests Y and Z. Again what we must talk about are the differences in numbers of persons exceeded.

CHARACTERISTICS OF THE DISTRIBUTION OF PERCENTILE RANKS

The frequency distribution of percentile ranks earned by the group on which they are determined necessarily is rectangular in shape. That is, 10 per cent of the cases fall below the percentile rank of 10, another 10 per cent fall between that rank and the percentile rank of 20, etc. Therefore all distributions of percentile ranks have the same shape and hence the same averages and variabilities. The use of percentile ranks forces scores into a particular shape of distribution—rectangular; hence implicitly the shape of the distribution of raw scores is discarded and is considered to be unimportant.

STANDARD SCORES

In Chap. 3 we saw that it is possible to describe mathematically certain characteristics of a frequency distribution in terms of the average of and variation among the scores. Since we wish to reference an individual's raw score to the total distribution of scores, we should be able to accomplish this mathematically by taking into account the mean and standard deviation of the total distribution. This is in fact accomplished by means of standard scores.

THE NATURE OF STANDARD SCORES

We can obtain some notion about an individual's standing on a given test if we know whether his score exceeds or falls below the mean score of his particular group and the magnitude of the difference. However, the information given by this difference alone is limited. If the scores of other individuals in general do not differ much from the mean, then a given difference might be considered quite large; whereas if the scores of others in general differ greatly from the mean, then that difference would be considered to be relatively small.

The standard deviation provides a quantitative description of the extent to which the scores earned by a group of individuals cluster around the mean value or depart from it. Therefore we can use it as an index of the extent of variation among scores. Knowing the difference between an individual's score and the mean, together with the direction of the difference, we can make statements about the relative value of the score by comparing the difference, which is the deviation score, with the standard deviation. We can then say that relative to other scores this particular score tends to be high or low, and we can at the same time give some information about where in the distribution the score falls.

A *standard score*, symbolized by z, is computed by the formula

$$z = \frac{X - \bar{X}}{\sigma_x} = \frac{x}{\sigma_x} \tag{4-1}$$

From this formula we can see that a standard score expresses an individual's score in units which are given as standard deviations of the distribution of scores of his group.

CHARACTERISTICS OF THE DISTRIBUTION OF STANDARD SCORES

When the scores in a distribution are transformed into standard scores, the mean of the standard scores, $\bar{z}$, necessarily is zero, and the variance σ_z^2 and the standard deviation are 1.00. These propositions are easily demonstrated as follows:

$$\bar{z} = \frac{\Sigma z}{n} = \frac{\Sigma(x/\sigma_x)}{n} = \frac{(1/\sigma_x)\Sigma x}{n} = \frac{1}{\sigma_x}\frac{\Sigma x}{n}$$

Since we know from Eq. (3-5) that $\Sigma x/n = 0$,

$$\bar{z} = \frac{1}{\sigma_x}0 = 0 \tag{4-2}$$

The variance of standard scores is

$$\sigma_z^2 = \frac{\Sigma z^2}{n}$$
$$= \frac{\Sigma(x/\sigma_x)^2}{n} = \frac{\Sigma(x^2/\sigma_x^2)}{n} = \frac{(1/\sigma_x^2)\Sigma x^2}{n} = \frac{1}{\sigma_x^2}\frac{\Sigma x^2}{n}$$

Since $\Sigma x^2/n = \sigma_x{}^2$ we can write

$$\sigma_x{}^2 = \frac{1}{\sigma_x{}^2}\,\sigma_x{}^2 = 1 \qquad\qquad (4\text{-}3)$$

Since the standard deviation is the square root of the variance and the variance of standard scores is 1, the standard deviation of standard scores also is 1. In view of the fact that the mean of standard scores is zero, they are, of course, deviation scores. Indeed, we can think of standard scores as being deviation scores which have a standard deviation of 1.

The transformation of raw scores into standard scores does not change the shape of the distribution of scores. This is obvious from the formula for standard scores, (4-1), which clearly indicates that all that is done is to subtract one constant (the mean) and divide by another constant (the standard deviation). Every score is treated exactly in the same manner and therefore the relationship between raw and standard scores is linear and, of course, perfect. This is readily observable in Fig. 4-2, which shows both raw and standard scores for three distributions.

If we use standard scores we are presuming that the particular shape of the distribution of raw scores given by the test is important inasmuch as it is retained. With some tests the distribution of scores may be positively skewed and with others it may be negatively skewed; and with some the kurtosis may be positive and with others it may be negative. This means that we should be forced to conclude that in some traits there are many persons who stand high while in others there are few. While this might not be an unreasonable state of affairs to expect, nevertheless the situation is confusing since tests that apparently measure the same abilities or traits sometimes show quite different-shaped distributions of scores even when administered to the same group of subjects. Furthermore, removing or adding easy or difficult items in a test will result in a significant shift in the shape of the distribution of scores earned by one group of individuals.

STANDARD SCORE UNITS

Transformation of raw scores into standard scores necessarily assumes that the units of measurement as given by the raw scores are all equal. This is obvious since all that is done, as we indicated above, is to subtract one constant from each score and to divide by another.

The use of standard scores further assumes that the units of different tests are made comparable merely by equating their variabilities, that is, their standard deviations. The difference between a standard score of $+1$ and $+2$ on a test of ability to comprehend spatial relations is held to be the same amount of spatial relations ability as the amount of finger dexterity given by the difference between standard scores of, say, -1 and 0 on a test of finger dexterity.

STANDARDIZING SCORES WITH SET MEANS AND STANDARD DEVIATIONS

A difficulty with standard scores, though perhaps a minor one, lies in the fact that they are given in both positive and negative values, and as fractional numbers. These characteristics make them somewhat difficult to deal with arithmetically and lead to computational errors.

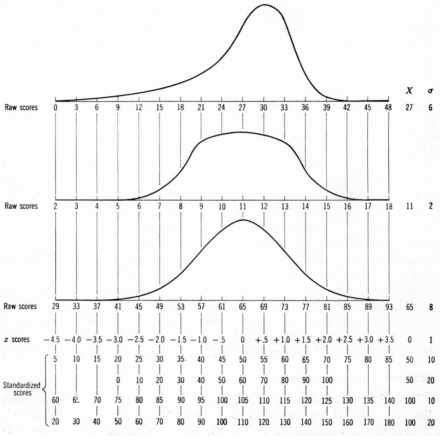

Figure 4-2 The relationships among raw, standard, and standardized scores for three frequency distributions.

In order to overcome the arithmetical difficulties involved in standard scores, sometimes transformations are made using values other than zero for the mean and 1.00 for the standard deviation. The mean can be set at any convenient value such as 50 or 100, and the standard deviation at 10 or 20. *Standardized scores* of this sort frequently are symbolized as Z, which may be taken as parallel to z, the symbol for standard scores. For three different distributions the relationships between raw scores, standard scores, and various commonly employed sets of standard scores are shown in Fig. 4-2.

Whatever presuppositions are made with respect to standard scores also hold for these various standardized scores. Of the various standardized scores, the one employing a mean of 50 and a standard deviation of 10 probably is the most convenient since in the very large majority of cases all scores will be two digits. Use of a mean of 100 leads to values that are sometimes confused with IQs.

NORMALIZING SCORES

If we wish to adopt the normal frequency distribution as a model but find the operations of measurement yield scores which are distributed in another fashion, then it is necessary to transmute the raw scores to other values which are normally distributed. A number of techniques have been developed for normalizing a set of scores. Essentially these techniques can be reduced to four: (1) taking some function of the raw scores such that the distribution becomes normal, (2) transmuting rankings into scale values in a normal distribution, (3) normalizing by means of areas corresponding to base-line intervals of equal size, and (4) normalizing by means of areas corresponding to base-line intervals of unequal size.

TAKING A FUNCTION OF RAW SCORES SUCH THAT TRANSMUTED SCORES FORM A NORMAL FREQUENCY DISTRIBUTION

When scores on a test are skewed, it is sometimes possible to render the distribution normal or to change it so that it closely approaches the shape of a normal distribution by taking some function of the scores. Thus the square, square root, logarithm, reciprocal, or some other function of the raw scores may yield values which are distributed normally. Such a transformation does not alter the order of individuals in terms of their scores but merely changes the magnitude of the differences among them. In some instances, if a direct function of the scores does not give satisfactory results, the addition or subtraction of a constant from the scores before applying the function may give the desired result.

By way of example, Table 4-2 (column f and A) gives the distribution of scores on a test, the distribution being positively skewed. Table 4-3 permits a comparison of the distribution of these raw scores with a normal distribution. In columns 1 and 2 of Table 4-3 a normal distribution in class intervals of half a standard deviation is given for convenience in making comparisons. Columns 3 and 4 of Table 4-3 show the distribution of raw scores in comparable class intervals. Thus the interval 56 to 68

TABLE 4-2. Distributions of Raw and Normalized Scores

f	A	B	C	D	E	f	A	B	C	D	E	f	A	B	C	D	E
1	142	11.0	1	99.5	76	1	101	9.0	8	92.5	64	1	60	6.3	42	58.5	52
0	141	11.0				0	100	8.9				2	59	6.2	43.5	57.0	52
0	140	11.0				1	99	8.9	9	91.5	64	2	58	6.2	45.5	55.0	51
0	139	10.9				0	98	8.8				2	57	6.1	47.5	53.0	51
0	138	10.9				0	97	8.8				4	56	6.0	50.5	50.0	50
0	137	10.8				1	96	8.7	10	90.5	63	2	55	5.9	53.5	47.0	49
0	136	10.8				0	95	8.7				2	54	5.8	55.5	45.0	49
1	135	10.7	2	98.5	72	0	94	8.6				2	53	5.7	57.5	43.0	48
0	134	10.7				1	93	8.5	11	89.5	63	1	52	5.7	59	41.5	48
0	133	10.6				0	92	8.5				0	51	5.6			
0	132	10.6				1	91	8.4	12	88.5	62	1	50	5.5	60	40.5	48
0	131	10.5				0	90	8.4				2	49	5.4	61.5	39.0	47
0	130	10.5				0	89	8.3				2	48	5.3	63.5	37.0	47
0	129	10.4				1	88	8.3	13	87.5	62	1	47	5.2	65	35.5	46
0	128	10.4				1	87	8.2	14	86.5	61	3	46	5.1	67	33.5	46
0	127	10.3				1	86	8.2	15	85.5	61	2	45	5.0	69.5	31.0	45
0	126	10.3				0	85	8.1				1	44	4.9	71	29.5	45
0	125	10.2				2	84	8.0	16.5	84.0	60	3	43	4.8	73	27.5	44
0	124	10.2				2	83	7.9	18.5	82.0	59	0	42	4.7			
0	123	10.1				1	82	7.9	20	80.5	59	2	41	4.6	75.5	25.0	43
0	122	10.1				0	81	7.8				1	40	4.5	77	23.5	43
0	121	10.0				1	80	7.7	21	79.5	58	1	39	4.4	78	22.5	42
1	120	10.0	3	97.5	70	1	79	7.7	22	78.5	58	2	38	4.2	79.5	21.0	42
0	119	9.9				0	78	7.6				3	37	4.1	82	18.4	41
0	118	9.9				0	77	7.5				2	36	4.0	84.5	16.0	40
0	117	9.8				1	76	7.5	23	77.5	58	2	35	3.9	86.5	14.0	39
0	116	9.8				1	75	7.4	24	76.5	57	0	34	3.7			
0	115	9.7				0	74	7.3				2	33	3.6	88.5	12.0	38
1	114	9.7	4	96.5	68	2	73	7.3	25.5	75.0	57	1	32	3.5	90	10.5	37
0	113	9.6				1	72	7.2	27	73.5	56	1	31	3.3	91	9.5	37
0	112	9.6				1	71	7.1	28	72.5	56	2	30	3.2	92.5	8.0	36
0	111	9.5				2	70	7.1	29.5	71.0	56	0	29	3.0			
0	110	9.5				3	69	7.0	32	68.5	55	2	28	2.8	94.5	6.0	34
1	109	9.4	5	95.5	67	2	68	6.9	34.5	66.0	54	1	27	2.6	96	4.5	33
0	108	9.3				1	67	6.9	36	64.5	54	0	26	2.4			
0	107	9.3				2	66	6.8	37.5	63.0	53	1	25	2.2	97	3.5	32
1	106	9.3	6	94.5	66	0	65	6.7				1	24	2.0	98	2.5	30
0	105	9.2				1	64	6.6	39	61.5	53	1	23	1.7	99	1.5	28
0	104	9.2				1	63	6.6	40	60.5	53	0	22	1.4			
1	103	9.1	7	93.5	65	1	62	6.5	41	59.5	52	1	21	1.0	100	0.5	24
0	102	9.1				0	61	6.4									

f = number of cases
A = raw scores
B = normalized scores through the transformation: score = $\sqrt{X - 20}$
C = ranks
D = per cent position
E = normalized standardized scores through transformation from ranks, $\bar{X} = 50$
    and $\sigma = 10$

TABLE 4-3. Distributions of Raw and Normalized Scores

Theoretical normal distribution		Original raw scores		Normalized scores when score = $\sqrt{X}-20$		Scores normalized from ranks		Scores normalized through area equivalents					
								11-point scale			9-point scale		
Standard scores	% of cases	Raw scores	% of cases	Normalized scores	% of cases	Normalized scores	% of cases	Raw scores	Standardized scores	% of cases	Raw scores	Standardized scores	% of cases
(1)	(2)	(3)	(4)	(5)	(6)	(7)	(8)	(9)	(10)	(11)	(12)	(13)	(14)
+2.75 and above	0	132 and above	2	10.7 and above	2	73 and above	1	139 and above	10	1	112 and above	9	4
+2.25−+2.74	1	119–131	1	9.7–10.6	2	68–72	3	112–138	9	3	92–111	8	7
+1.75−+2.24	3	107–118	2	8.7–9.6	6	63–67	7	92–111	8	7	76–91	7	12
+1.25−+1.74	7	94–106	5	7.6–8.6	12	58–62	12	76–91	7	12	63–75	6	17
+0.75−+1.24	12	82–93	10	6.6–7.5	18	53–57	17	63–75	6	17	50–62	5	20
+0.25−+0.74	17	69–81	13	5.6–6.5	19	48–52	20	50–62	5	20	40–49	4	17
−0.25−+0.24	20	56–68	19	4.5–5.5	18	43–47	17	40–49	4	17	33–39	3	12
−0.75−−0.26	17	44–55	19	3.5–4.4	13	38–42	12	33–39	3	12	26–32	2	7
−1.25−−0.76	12	32–43	19	2.5–3.4	6	33–37	7	26–32	2	7	25 and below	1	4
−1.75−−1.26	7	19–31	10	1.5–2.4	3	28–32	3	22–25	1	3			
−2.25−−1.76	3	7–18	0	1.4 and below	1	27 and below	1	21 and below	0	1			
−2.75−−2.26	1	6 and below	0										
Total	100		100		100		100			100			100
Mean	0.0		62.54		6.04		50.01			5.00			5.00
σ	1.0		24.95		2.06		10.33			2.00			1.96

ranges from a quarter of a standard deviation above the mean to a quarter of a standard deviation below it. A comparison of the distribution of raw scores with the normal distribution shows that the former are markedly skewed in a positive direction.

In order to transmute the raw scores to other values which are distributed in accordance with a normal frequency distribution, a function of them was taken as follows:

$$\text{Normalized score} = \sqrt{X - 20}$$

These values are given in column B of Table 4-2. For example, in transmuting the raw score of 101 to the new value, 20 was subtracted, yielding a value of 81, the square root of which is 9.0, which is the transmuted score.

We might well wonder how this particular curious function (normalized score equals $\sqrt{X - 20}$) was reached. The answer is that it was arrived at through an extensive trial-and-error process. While procedures have been developed for arriving at approximations of the best function, to utilize their solutions may well leave the distribution still differing significantly from a normal distribution. Ultimately, therefore, one will seek an appropriate function through such tedious trial and error that the result is not worth the labor. As a consequence, unless a ready function such as a square, logarithm, or reciprocal can be applied directly to raw scores and will yield a normal distribution without adding or subtracting a constant from the raw scores, some other procedure for normalizing scores is well advised.

TRANSMUTING RANKS INTO SCALE VALUES IN A NORMAL FREQUENCY DISTRIBUTION

Sometimes the quantitative descriptions of individuals on some trait are given not in the form of scores on a continuous scale but rather as ranks. Even if the quantitative descriptions are scores on a continuous distribution, the individuals can be ranked on the basis of their scores. In either case it is possible to transmute ranks into values in a normal distribution.

When we transmute ranks to other values that are scores which are normally distributed on a continuous scale, we consider each person as occupying a particular area of a normal frequency distribution. Suppose, for example, we have five individuals. Each person, then, constitutes 20 per cent of the total group. We take the person ranked 1 as occupying the top 20 per cent of the area of a normal frequency distribution, the person ranked 2 as occupying the next 20 per cent, etc. Reference to the table for a normal frequency distribution (see the Appendix) will show that in a normal frequency distribution the highest 20 per cent of the cases fall above a standard score of +0.84, the second 20 per cent between +0.84 and +0.25, the third 20 per cent between +0.25 and −0.25, the fourth 20 per cent between −0.25 and −0.84, and the lowest 20 per cent below −0.84. This is shown graphically in the top diagram of Fig. 4-3. If we had eight individuals ranked, then each person would be taken as occupying 12.5 per cent of the area of a normal frequency distribution as is shown in the lower diagram of Fig. 4-3.

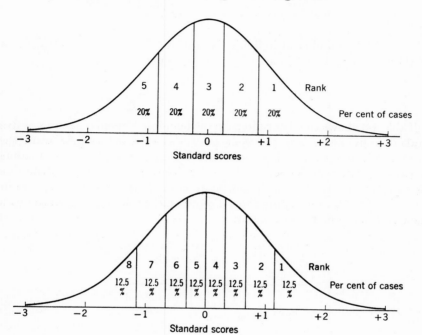

Figure 4-3 The assignment of individuals by rank to portions of the normal frequency distribution.

On the basis of an individual's rank, then, we can describe his position in a normal frequency distribution by the range he occupies on the base line. Thus as we just saw, when five individuals are ranked, each one is taken to occupy 20 per cent of the area of the distribution, and the person ranked 2 occupies the range of standard scores from +0.84 to +0.25. For convenience we should like to describe his position not by a range of scores but rather by a single value. We could do this by determining the standard score of his midpoint. For example, in the case of the person assigned the rank of 2 in a group of 5, there are three people below him plus the half of him below his midpoint. That is, there are 3.5 people below his midpoint. Since there are five people in the group, his per cent position in the group is 3.5/5 or 70 per cent. Reference to the table for a normal frequency distribution (see the Appendix) tells us that in a normal frequency distribution 70 per cent of the cases fall below a standard score of $+0.52$. This standard score of $+0.52$ we take as descriptive of him rather than his range of $+0.84$ to $+0.25$ standard scores. The per cent position of any individual can be determined by the following formula:

$$\text{Per cent position} = 100 \frac{(n - \text{rank}) + 0.5}{n}$$

where n is the number of individuals ranked. Thus the per cent position of the person ranked 4 in a group of five people is

$$100 \frac{(5 - 4) + 0.5}{5} = 30 \text{ per cent}$$

Table 4-4 shows the determination of the normal standard scores of five ranked individuals. The per cent positions were determined from the formula given above, and the standard scores were obtained by reading the appropriate values from the table for a normal frequency distribution given in the Appendix. It should be apparent that we could use one or another of the various standardized scores rather than standard scores if such values are more convenient.

TABLE 4-4.   Transmuting Ranks into Scores That Are Normally Distributed

Rank	Per cent position	Normalized standard scores
1	90	$+1.28$
2	70	$+0.52$
3	50	0.00
4	30	-0.52
5	10	-1.28

In the event of a tie in rank, the mean of the "disputed" ranks is assigned. For example, if two individuals tie for first, they are both assigned the rank of 1.5 and the third individual is assigned the rank of 3. If three individuals tie for first, they are all assigned the rank of 2 and the fourth individual is given the rank of 4.

When there are many ties in rank, the distribution of transmuted scores is not precisely normal in shape. Hence when many individuals obtain the same raw score this procedure should not be used. Another shortcoming of the ranking method stems from the use of very few cases. When there are very few individuals who are being ranked, the standard deviation of their normalized standard scores is less than 1. For example, when only five cases are ranked the standard deviation of their normalized standard scores is 0.88. As the number of cases used increases, the standard deviation more and more closely approaches a value of 1. But it is not until about 40 cases are involved that a close approximation of 1 is reached.

An illustration of the transformation of ranks to normalized scores with a mean of 50 and a standard deviation of 10 is given in Table 4-2. In column C of this table, ranks have been assigned to individuals on the basis of the raw scores they obtained; and in column D are shown the corresponding per cent positions. In column E the equivalent normalized Z scores are given, being read for the per cent positions from the table for the normal frequency distribution given in the Appendix. The normalized scores have been assembled by class intervals in Table 4-3. Comparison of the distribution of these scores with a theoretical normal distribution shows that a very close approximation of a normal frequency distribution has been obtained.

NORMALIZING SCORES BY MEANS OF AREAS CORRESPONDING TO BASE-LINE INTERVALS OF EQUAL SIZE

Columns 1 and 2 of Table 4-3, which give the theoretical normal distribution in class intervals of half a standard deviation, suggest that we might normalize scores by assigning cases in proportion to the areas of a normal frequency distribution covered by these intervals. In Table 4-2 it will be observed that the best person earns a score of 142 and he is followed by three people who earn scores of 135, 120, and 114. In a normal distribution 1 per cent of the cases earn standard scores of $+2.25$ and above. Therefore since there are 100 cases, we might assign this person who represents the highest 1 per cent of the cases to the standard-score interval of $+2.25$ and above. The next three people, representing 3 per cent of the cases, could be assigned to the next highest interval of $+1.75$ to $+2.24$ since the next 3 per cent of cases fall here in a normal distribution. This has been done for all the cases represented in Table 4-2, and the resulting distribution is shown as columns 9 to 11 of Table 4-3. The 11 intervals have been arbitrarily assigned score values ranging from 0 to 10. The mean of this distribution is 5.00 and the standard deviation is 2.00.

The raw scores that define these intervals and the areas are shown in column 9 of Table 4-3. As noted above, the best four persons earned raw scores of 142, 135, 120, and 114. The top interval is given as 139 and above, splitting the difference between 142 and 135. Similarly, the second interval is given as 112 to 138, the value 112 splitting the difference between the fourth and fifth highest scores.

The normalized score values of 0 to 10 that were assigned are, as indicated, completely arbitrary. Values ranging from 95 to 105 could have been assigned just as easily. Except from a computational point of view it makes little difference what particular numbers are used. Obviously it is easier to deal arithmetically with small numbers; hence they are to be preferred.

Furthermore, there is no need to use intervals of half a standard deviation. In some instances intervals of one standard deviation or of a quarter of a standard deviation might be more useful. Appropriate areas for such intervals can be determined from a table for the normal frequency distribution.

For further simplification, sometimes only nine intervals are used as is shown in columns 12 to 14 of Table 4-3. The advantage is that all scores are single digits, which makes them particularly easy to record and to manipulate arithmetically. All that has been done is to add together the two intervals at both extremes as given in column 9 of Table 4-3. Scores of this kind have been termed stanines (standardized-nine).

NORMALIZING SCORES BY MEANS OF AREAS CORRESPONDING TO BASE-LINE INTERVALS OF UNEQUAL SIZE

The foregoing method of normalizing requires that the scores can be grouped precisely into predetermined and exact percentages. These percentages are such that the percentages of cases in all groups occupy portions of a normal distribution that cover exactly the same distance, except for the highest and lowest portions. Thus stanines call for the lowest category to contain 4 per cent of the cases, the next category 7 per cent, etc., with the cases in each interval covering half a standard deviation. Consider the distribution in Table 4-5. In this distribution three, or 2.7 per cent, of the cases earn scores of 58 and below; and seven, or 6.3%, of the cases earn the score of 59 and below. It is therefore impossible to obtain a bottom category, a stanine of 1, with exactly 4 per cent of the cases. The discrepancy between 2.7 per cent or 6.3 per cent of cases and the required 4 per cent of cases might not be considered to be too great, but as we proceed up the distribution the discrepancies become more serious.

It is therefore apparent that in some instances the distribution of raw scores is such that it is impossible to obtain the exact percentages required. A very large range of raw scores such as that in Table 4-2 is required. With a circumstance such as that in Table 4-5 it is not feasible to effect the desired transformation by the method of base-line intervals of equal size.

In the normalizing procedure we have just described, equal intervals are set along the base line of a normal distribution, and raw scores are grouped into categories or percentages representing the areas of a normal distribution corresponding to those intervals. Except for mere neatness there is no good reason for having equal intervals. The intervals along

TABLE 4-5. Illustration of the Method for Normalizing Scores by the Method of Base-line Units of Unequal Size

Raw score	f	Per cent of cases	Number of cases earning lower scores	Number of cases in each interval falling below the median	Number of cases earning scores below each median	Per cent of cases earning scores below each median	Normalized standard scores
71	0	0.0	110				
70	1	0.9	109	0.5	109.5	99.4	+2.51
69	3	2.7	106	1.5	107.5	97.6	+1.98
68	7	6.4	99	3.5	102.5	93.0	+1.48
67	9	8.2	90	4.5	94.5	85.7	+1.07
66	8	7.3	82	4.0	86.0	78.1	+0.77
65	16	14.5	66	8.0	74.0	67.2	+0.44
64	13	11.9	53	6.5	59.5	53.2	+0.08
63	19	17.3	34	9.5	43.5	39.5	−0.27
62	16	14.5	18	8.0	26.0	23.6	−0.72
61	4	3.6	14	2.0	16.0	14.5	−1.06
60	7	6.4	7	3.5	10.5	9.5	−1.31
59	4	3.6	3	2.0	5.0	4.5	−1.70
58	2	1.8	1	1.0	2.0	1.8	−2.10
57	1	0.9	0	0.5	0.5	0.5	−2.58
56	0	0.0	0				

Total number of cases = 110

the base line could just as well be unequal in size, provided the base line itself is in terms of equal units.

Consider the diagram in Fig. 4-4a. Here we have a normal distribution with the cases divided into groups on the basis of equal intervals of half a standard deviation along the base line of a normal distribution. Now consider the diagram in Fig. 4-4b. Here the base line is divided into intervals of unequal size. In the preceding section we saw how the diagram in Fig. 4-4a could be constructed. Now let us see how the diagram in Fig. 4-4b can be developed.

We shall use the data in Table 4-5 to illustrate the method for developing normally distributed scores by the method of unequal base-line units.

We can see from the third column of this table that 0.9 per cent of the cases earn the lowest score of 57. This will be the lowest category in our distribution. In a theoretical normal distribution the curve representing ordinates approaches the base line asymptotically but never reaches it. Consequently we cannot determine the lower limit of the lowest interval.

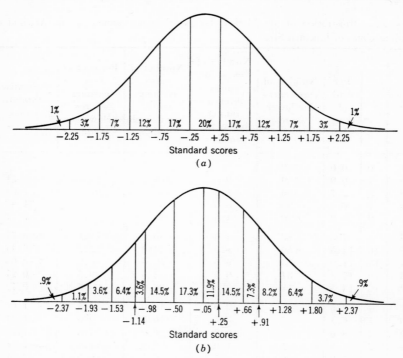

Figure 4-4 Normal frequency distributions divided into portions on the basis of (*a*) equal base-line intervals and (*b*) unequal base-line intervals.

We can, however, determine the upper limit of the interval of the lowest category. Reference to the table for a normal frequency distribution will show that in such a distribution 0.9 per cent of the cases fall below a standard score of −2.37. This, of course, is also the upper limit of the next category, those two or 1.8 per cent of cases earning raw scores of 58. Now 0.9 per cent + 1.8 per cent, or 2.7 per cent of the cases, earn scores of 58 and below. Again referring to the table for a normal distribution we find that the lowest 2.7 per cent of cases fall below a standard score of −1.93. This value, then, is the upper limit of the second category and the lower limit of the third category. In a similar fashion the upper and lower limits for the distribution as shown in the diagram of Fig. 4-4*b* were determined.

Now what single standard-score value shall we assign to the cases in each interval? One obvious value is the average, and we shall use the median because it is a value determined by counting individuals and we are assigning individuals to various portions of a normal distribution by counting them. The median of an interval is that point on the scale above and below which fall 50 per cent of the cases in that interval. Thus two people earn scores of 58 and one falls below and one above the median of that interval. Seven people earn the score of 60, so we say that 3.5 of them fall below the median of that interval and 3.5 above it. The number of persons falling below the median of each score interval for the data in Table 4-5 are given in the sixth column.

The process of normalizing scores by the method of base-line intervals of unequal size is accomplished as follows (see Table 4-5):

1. Determine the number of cases falling below each score (column 4).
2. Determine the number of cases falling below the median of each raw-score interval (column 5).
3. Determine the number of cases falling below the median of each score interval (column 6, the values being obtained by adding together the values in columns 4 and 5).
4. Divide the number of cases falling below the score-interval medians by the total number of cases. This gives the percentages of cases falling below each score-interval median (column 7).
5. Determine the normal standard (or standardized) score for each score-interval median by reference to the table (see the Appendix) for a normal frequency distribution (column 8).

Occasionally we have operations which assign individuals to one or another of several groups, the groups being ordered in terms of the degree to which they possess or manifest some trait. For example, we may have a rating procedure for the trait of cooperativeness, and individuals are assigned to one or another of the following five categories in terms of our judgment of the extent to which they manifest cooperativeness: excellent, superior, good, fair, poor. For one reason or another we may believe that these five categories do not represent equal steps along a scale, that is, they are not equal units. All we are willing to say is that the group in the top category stands higher in the trait than those in the second highest category, those in the second category stand higher in the trait than those in the third highest category, and so on. We have, then, a ranking of groups. If we are willing to assume that the distribution of individuals on the trait is normal, then we can use the procedure just outlined for developing normalized scores by means of areas corresponding to base-line intervals of unequal size.

Consider the example in Table 4-6. Here we have 50 individuals assigned to one or another of five categories in terms of the extent to which they manifest some trait. We are willing to rank the categories but are not willing to say that they represent equal steps along a scale. In the highest ranked category there are 11 of the 50 individuals, or 22 per cent; in the second highest category there are 9 of the 50 individuals, or 18 per cent; and so on. We have here exactly the same situation we had in Table 4-5, a series of ordered groups. Just as we did in Table 4-5, in our present case we can consider the 11 individuals in the top category to occupy the top 22 per cent of the area of a normal frequency distribution, the 9 in the second highest category to occupy the next 18 per cent of the area and so on. As before, we can assign to the individuals in each category the standard or standardized score corresponding to the proportion

TABLE 4-6. Illustration of the Method for Obtaining Normalized Scores by the Method of Base-line Intervals of Unequal Size when Groups of Individuals Are Ranked

Rating	Rank of group	Number of people in each group	Number of cases falling below each rank	Number of cases in each rank falling below the median	Number of cases falling below each median	Per cent of cases falling below each median	Normalized standard scores
Excellent......	1	11	39	5.5	44.5	89	+1.22
Superior.......	2	9	30	4.5	34.5	69	+0.49
Good.........	3	3	27	1.5	28.5	57	+0.18
Fair.........	4	12	15	6.0	20.0	42	-0.20
Poor.........	5	15	0	7.5	7.5	15	-1.04

Total number of cases = 50

of individuals falling below the median in each category. The details of the computations given in Table 4-6 for determining normal standard scores with ranked groups will be seen to be precisely the same as those in Table 4-5 when groups are ordered in terms of their raw scores.

SAMPLING AND NORMALIZING

Obviously the normalizing of scores is done on a sample of individuals. Usually we wish to apply the transmuted scores to other individuals not in the particular sample. Thus we apply our measuring device to a sample of individuals and on the basis of their raw scores set up the function which normalizes the scores or set up the appropriate score intervals, depending upon which method we are using. This establishes our norms, and we proceed to apply these norms to individuals tested on other occasions or in other situations.

The adequacy of such normalized and standardized scores clearly is a direct function of the representativeness of the sample and of the number of cases in it. This dependence upon sampling is, of course, not peculiar to this particular type of norm. It is more likely to be forgotten, however, because we have used a theoretical model as a basis for transmuting scores, which suggests quite incorrectly that the raw scores have now somehow been made absolute and true.

ESTABLISHING NORMS ON ONE TEST FROM THOSE ALREADY ESTABLISHED ON ANOTHER

We have seen that norms provide the basis for giving meaning to scores and for comparing the scores earned by different individuals on the same test or the scores earned by one individual on different tests. The adequacy with which scores can be interpreted, then, is a direct function of the adequacy of the norms. Therefore the group on which the norms are established is a matter of considerable importance. Sometimes, however, we have a test on which it is desired to obtain norms of a particular sort, but a representative sample of individuals of the kind required is not available or is very difficult to obtain. Under such circumstances we might be forced to use the distribution of scores of some nonrepresentative group as norms, and as a consequence our capacity to interpret and compare scores is impaired.

For example, suppose we have developed a test of achievement in mathematics for use with tenth-grade children and have available as a standardization group only tenth-grade children known to be superior in intellect. Such children obviously are different from tenth-grade children in general; hence norms developed on them would not be adequate as a basis for interpreting the scores of all types of tenth-grade children.

Sometimes a new form of a test is developed and it is desired to equate the scores with those of the original form. Occasionally we may wish to change the time limits of a test and will want to equate the scores on the two time limits. Finally, we may have a battery of tests yielding a total composite score and may wish to change the weights of the component tests, or it may be necessary to drop out one of the component tests or to add a new one. We should like to equate scores on the new composite with those on the old composite, but we do not have available the original standardization group or a comparable group.

Situations such as the foregoing are not uncommon, and typically the solution is to use the distribution of scores of a nonrepresentative group as norms. Obviously when this is done a considerable error is introduced in the interpretation of scores, and such interpretations therefore may have little value. Rather than use clearly inadequate norms we could attempt to estimate the desired norms, the distribution of scores of a representative group. What we wish is a table or graph such as Tables 4-1 and 4-2 or Figs. 4-1 and 4-2, relating scores on the test to the percentile ranks or standard or standardized scores of the particular group of individuals we believe constitute the group on which norms should be established. However, that group is not available to us, so we need to obtain the best estimate we can of that table or graph. In other words, we wish to transmute scores from the raw-score scale to a scale of percentile ranks or standard or standardized scores of a particular group, but we cannot do this directly by giving the test to that group.

A BASIS FOR ESTABLISHING NORMS ON ONE TEST FROM THOSE ESTABLISHED ON ANOTHER

Suppose we have as measures of linear distance a scale of inches and a scale of glubs and we wish to transmute height as described by the second scale to that as described by the first. Further, suppose it is not possible to place the two rulers side by side so that "scores" on the one scale can be transmuted to "scores" on the other. If we had the heights of a number of individuals on both scales, we could plot scores on one scale against those on the other and by running a line through the points we should have a graph which would permit us to transmute scores in glubs to scores in inches. If we did not have any very short or tall people we should have to extrapolate our line beyond our points.

Let us say that we do not have the pair of scores on each person but know only the number earning various scores on both scales, height being measured to the nearest glub and to the nearest inch. The distributions of glub and inch scores for 18 individuals each of whom was measured on both scales are given in Table 4-7. In this table we can see that four individuals are less than 21.5 glubs in height, 21.5 being the lower limit of the score interval of 22. We also note that four individuals are less than 65.5 in. in height, 65.5 being the lower limit of the score interval of 66. Since both scales are measuring precisely the same property, linear distance, their scores must be perfectly correlated. That is, the individual who has the lowest glub score must have the lowest inch score, the individual who has the next highest glub score must have the next highest inch score, etc. Consequently the four individuals who are less than 21.5 glubs in height must be the same four individuals who are less than 65.5 in. in height. Therefore we can say that a score of 21.5 glubs is comparable to a score of 65.5 in. Similarly, we can see from Table 4-7 that six individuals fall below 22.5 glubs and six also fall below 67.5 in. Again these six individuals who have the lowest glub scores are the same as the six who have the lowest inch scores. So we should say that a score of 22.5 glubs is comparable to a score of 67.5 in. By determining the number of cases falling below each glub score, we should obtain in this fashion a number of pairs of comparable scores on the two scales. We could plot these on a graph, and by running a line through them we should have a graph which would permit us to transmute glubs to inches or, if we wished, inches to glubs.

We have ascertained the number of cases falling below each glub score and have found the inch scores below which the same numbers fall. But we could just as well do the reverse. Thus we see in Table 4-7 that two individuals fall below an inch score of 64.5. Because four individuals earn the lowest glub score we shall have to split the score interval in order to get a point on the glub scale below which two individuals fall. For the glub score of 21 we say the interval is 20.5 to 21.5 since people have been measured to the nearest whole number. In the present instance we wish to

TABLE 4-7.   Distribution of the Heights of 18 Individuals Measured Both on a Hypothetical Scale of Glubs and on a Scale of Inches

Glubs	Lower limit of score interval	Number of cases	Number of cases earning lower scores	Inches	Lower limit of score interval	Number of cases	Number of cases earning lower scores
26	25.5	0	18	74	73.5	0	18
25	24.5	2	16	73	72.5	1	17
24	23.5	6	10	72	71.5	1	16
23	22.5	4	6	71	70.5	3	13
22	21.5	2	4	70	69.5	3	10
21	20.5	4	0	69	68.5	2	8
				68	67.5	2	6
				67	66.5	1	5
				66	65.5	1	4
				65	64.5	2	2
				64	63.5	2	0

obtain the point in the interval below which fall two out of the four individuals who have a glub score of 21. We shall have to assume that the individuals who earn a particular score are evenly distributed throughout the score interval. Hence we wish to proceed $2/4$ or 0.5 of the distance up through the interval. Therefore we should say that $20.5 + 0.5$, or 21.0, is the point on the glub scale below which two individuals fall. Consequently 64.5 in. is comparable to 21.0 glubs. In order to determine further pairs of comparable scores we should proceed up the inch scale finding comparable glubs. The ultimate resulting graph will be the same whether we ascertain the inch values comparable to given glub values or ascertain glub values comparable to inch values.

The procedure just described is more cumbersome than just placing the two rulers side by side or plotting pairs of scores of individuals, but the ultimate result is precisely the same. By all these procedures we should obtain the same transmutation of glubs to inches. But note that in this last procedure of cumulative frequencies we make no direct comparison between the two scales. We neither have the scales side by side nor utilize the pairs of scores of individuals as pairs plotted on a graph. All we utilize are the distributions of scores on the two scales, determining comparability of scores by determining points on both scales below which the same numbers of cases fall. We can take such points as comparable scores because we know that scores on both scales are perfectly correlated. In other words, both scales measure precisely the same property and are merely different systems of arbitrary markers on a continuous scale.

A PROCEDURE FOR ESTABLISHING NORMS ON ONE TEST FROM THOSE
ESTABLISHED ON ANOTHER

Now suppose we have two psychological tests, test A and test B, both of which measure precisely the same traits. We know they measure precisely the same traits because scores on the two tests are perfectly correlated. From the graph resulting from this procedure we could transmute scores on test B to those on test A just as we transmuted glubs to inches. Let us say that by this procedure we found the score of 66 on test A to be comparable to the score of 24 on test B. We could say that had he been given test B he would have obtained the score of 24. Similarly, if an individual were given test B and obtained the score of 24 we could say that had he been given test A he would have obtained the score of 66.

If test A had been previously administered to a representative group, we should already have a table by means of which we could transmute raw scores on test A to percentile ranks or standard or standardized scores in terms of the performance of that group on test A. If the score of 66 on test A is the 30th percentile we could then say that had the representative group been given test B, 30 per cent of them would have fallen below the score of 24 on test B, and the score of 24 on test B would be the 30th percentile of the representative group. In a similar fashion we could determine for raw scores on test B other percentile ranks for the representative group. Obviously we could concern ourselves with standard or standardized scores as well as percentile ranks.

By this means we can establish norms on one test, test B, from those already established on another test, test A. The individuals to whom we give the two tests need not be the ones for whom we have established the norms on test A. All we need is to have the norms on test A already established, and from whatever individuals are now available we can establish the comparability of scores on the two tests.

An example is given in Table 4-8. Here we have the percentile ranks and the standard-score equivalents of raw scores on test A as determined

TABLE 4-8. Illustration of the Establishment of Norms on One Test, Test B, from Norms Already Established on Another Test, Test A

		Test A				Test B				Comparable scores		
Percentile rank	Standard score	Raw score	Lower limit of score interval	Number of cases	Number of cases earning lower scores	Raw score	Lower limit of score interval	Number of cases	Number of cases earning lower scores	Test A	Test B	Number of cases earning lower scores
100.0	+3.5	74	73.5	0	29	35	34.5	0	29	73.5	34.5	29
99.9	+3.0	73	72.5	2	27	34	33.5	2	27	72.5	33.5	27
99.4	+2.5	72	71.5	3	24	33	32.5	2	25	71.5	32.0	24
97.7	+2.0	71	70.5	5	19	32	31.5	3	22	70.5	30.5	19
93.3	+1.5	70	69.5	5	14	31	30.5	3	19	69.5	29.0	14
84.0	+1.0	69	68.5	4	10	30	29.5	4	15	68.5	27.5	10
69.1	+0.5	68	67.5	3	7	29	28.5	2	13	67.5	26.0	7
50.0	0.0	67	66.5	2	5	28	27.5	3	10	66.5	24.5	5
30.0	-0.5	66	65.5	1	4	27	26.5	2	8	65.5	23.5	4
15.9	-1.0	65	64.5	3	1	26	25.5	2	6	64.5	20.5	1
6.7	-1.5	64	63.5	1	0	25	24.5	1	5			
2.3	-2.0	63	62.5	0		24	23.5	1	4			
0.6	-2.5	62	61.5	0		23	22.5	1	3			
0.1	-3.0	61	60.5	0		22	21.5	1	2			
						21	20.5	1	1			
						20	19.5	1	0			
						19	18.5	0				

previously from the performance of a large and representative group on that test. Since the group or one equivalent to it is not now available to us, in order to establish for test B the same type of norms we have for test A, we have given both tests to 29 individuals who happen to be available to us. Reference to Table 4-8 will show that these 29 individuals are quite different from the original group, tending to have somewhat higher scores. Only 7 per cent of them earn scores lower than 67, the mean of the original group.

As we did with glubs and inches, we proceed with the cumulative frequencies on these tests to determine comparable scores. On test A, one person earns a score below 64.5; and on test B, one person earns a score below 20.5. So we take 64.5 and 20.5 to be comparable scores. On test A, four people earn scores below 65.5; and on test B, four people earn scores below 23.5. So 65.5 and 23.5 are taken as comparable scores. In a similar fashion we proceed up the various scores on test A determining comparable scores on test B. As pointed out earlier, we could have done the reverse, proceeding up the various scores on test B and finding the comparable scores on test A, and the ultimate results would have been the same. We can do whichever is more convenient, and by doing both we have a check on our computations.

In Fig. 4-5 we have plotted the pairs of comparable scores on the two tests. It will be noted that they do not exactly fit on a straight line. This is because our assumption that individuals are distributed equally throughout a score interval is not correct. For our purposes, however, it is close enough since our line represents the trend through all the points. As we can see from this chart, we can now transmute raw scores on test B into percentile ranks or standard scores of the representative group even though this group was not actually given test B.

If the units on test B are not equal along the scale, then the line through the points representing pairs of comparable scores will be curved rather than straight. For the data in Fig. 4-5 it might be that a curved line would give a better representation of the points than a straight line.

LIMITATIONS OF THE PROCEDURE FOR ESTABLISHING NORMS ON ONE TEST FROM THOSE ESTABLISHED ON ANOTHER

The key circumstance in the procedure just described is the relationship between the scores on the two tests. As we outlined the procedure we saw that it presumes that both tests measure precisely the same properties and therefore that their scores are perfectly correlated with the scores on the two scales, being merely different arbitrary systems of markers along a continuous scale such as inches and centimeters.

One of the many unfortunate facts of life for those concerned with psychological measurement is that scores on any two psychological tests never are perfectly correlated. Therefore it can never be said of any two tests that they measure precisely the same properties. The best we can expect are two tests measuring very nearly the same properties and having scores which are highly but not perfectly related. Consequently the procedure of cumulative frequencies gives only an approximation of the desired norms. The higher the relationship between scores on the two

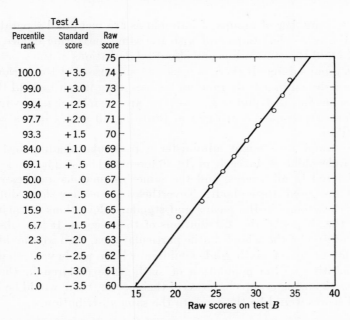

Test A		
Percentile rank	Standard score	Raw score
		75
100.0	+3.5	74
99.0	+3.0	73
99.4	+2.5	72
97.7	+2.0	71
93.3	+1.5	70
84.0	+1.0	69
69.1	+ .5	68
50.0	.0	67
30.0	− .5	66
15.9	−1.0	65
6.7	−1.5	64
2.3	−2.0	63
.6	−2.5	62
.1	−3.0	61
.0	−3.5	60

Raw scores on test B

Figure 4-5   The establishment of norms on one test, test *B*, from norms already established on another test, test *A*.

tests, the better is the approximation of the desired norms. But even at the very best all we have is an approximation, and consequently it should be clear that this process is never so good as actually establishing norms on a large and representative group. However, an approximation is better than nothing at all, and the approximated norms may be far superior to norms established on a nonrepresentative group.

COMBINING SCORES FROM DIFFERENT SAMPLES

Occasionally a measuring device has been administered to a number of different samples all drawn from the same population and it is desired to combine the scores of all cases into a single distribution. When this situation arises, either of two conditions may hold:

1. All groups are measured under the same conditions with exactly the same measuring device.
2. Different groups are measured under different conditions and/or with different forms of the measuring device.

MEASURING UNDER THE SAME CONDITIONS WITH THE SAME MEASURING DEVICE

When a number of groups of individuals are measured separately but under the same conditions and with the same measuring device, we are likely to find that the means and standard deviations of the scores of the various groups differ. If there is reason to suppose that the various samples were drawn in a truly random fashion, then it can be held that differences in the distributions of scores are merely chance variations. Therefore we should be justified in throwing all scores into a common distribution.

For example, we might administer a particular reading test to the sixth-grade children in each of 10 different schools. The same test is administered to all groups, and the same instructions and testing conditions are used throughout. Nevertheless, we may find differences among the groups in the means and standard deviations of their scores and in the shapes of the distributions of their scores. If the schools are representative of the schools in the particular area, then we should expect the total group of sixth-grade children whom we have tested to be representative of the population of sixth-grade children in that area. Differences among groups in terms of their scores, then, would be ignored and all scores would be thrown into the same distribution.

MEASURING UNDER DIFFERENT CONDITIONS AND/OR WITH DIFFERENT FORMS OF THE MEASURING DEVICE

Under these circumstances we are likely to find differences among the means and standard deviations of the scores of the various groups and differences in the shapes of the distributions of scores. However, in this case we do not think we can account for the differences on the basis of sampling error. Rather, it appears to us that these differences arise out of differences in conditions or in measuring devices.

Some examples will clarify the problem. Suppose we administer a typing test to 50 typists who use brand A typewriter and the same test to 50 other typists who use brand B typewriter. Any differences in scores that occur between these groups might well be the result of using different types of machines, that is, being tested under different conditions. If for each group we transform the scores to standard or standardized scores, equalize their means and standard deviations and hence differences in measured performance due to differences in testing conditions. Similarly, suppose two elementary school teachers rate the students in their classes in emotional adjustment. Differences between the ratings assigned the two groups may occur not because the groups differ in degree of emotional adjustment but because one rater is more lenient in assigning ratings than is the other. By transmuting each set of ratings separately to

TABLE 4-9. Illustration of the Method of Combining Scores of Groups Tested under Different Conditions or with Different Forms of the Same Test by Transmuting the Scores of Each Group to Standard Scores

| | Transmutation of scores | | | | | | Distribution of standard scores | | | | |
| | Group A | | Group B | | Group C | | | | | | |
X	f	z	f	z	f	z	z	Group A	Group B	Group C	Total
27	1	+1.90					+2.25-+2.74	...	...	1	1
26	2	+1.26	1	+1.91	1	+2.29	+1.75-+2.24	1	1	...	2
25	3	+0.63	1	+1.48	...	+1.98	+1.25-+1.74	2	1	2	5
24	4	0.00	2	+1.06	1	+1.68	+0.75-+1.24	...	2	2	4
23	3	-0.63	2	+0.64	1	+1.37	+0.25-+0.74	3	2	6	11
22	2	-1.26	3	+0.21	2	+1.07	-0.24-+0.24	4	6	8	18
21	1	-1.90	3	-0.21	3	+0.70	-0.25--0.74	3	2	6	11
20			2	-0.64	3	+0.46	-0.75--1.24	...	2	2	4
19			2	-1.06	4	+0.15	-1.25--1.74	2	1	2	5
18			1	-1.48	4	-0.15	-1.75--2.24	1	1	...	2
17			1	-1.91	3	-0.46	-2.25--2.74	...	...	1	1
16					3	-0.70					
15					2	-1.07					
14					1	-1.37					
13					1	-1.68					
12					...	-1.98					
11					1	-2.29					
n	16		18		30		n	16	18	30	64
$\bar{X}$	24.00		21.50		18.50		$\bar{z}$	0.00	0.00	0.00	0.00
σ_x	1.58		2.36		3.28		σ_z	1.00	1.00	1.00	1.00

standard scores we eliminate differences due to using different forms of the same measuring device, that is, two different raters.

The combination of scores of groups tested under different conditions or with different forms of the same measuring device is illustrated in Table 4-9. If the distributions of scores of the different groups vary in shape, they too may be made the same by normalizing the scores within each group.

In essence, what is being suggested is that differences in means and standard deviations of the scores of the various groups be eliminated through the use of standard or standardized scores, and differences in the shapes of the distributions of scores eliminated through normalizing procedures. The following assumptions therefore are being made:

1. There are no differences among the scores of the various groups that can be accounted for on the basis of sampling error, and the true distribution of the trait being measured is exactly the same in all groups. That is, if the same measuring device were administered to all groups and under exactly the same conditions, the distributions of scores of all groups would be exactly the same.
2. There is a perfect correlation between measurements taken under different conditions or with different forms of the measuring device. That is, if there were several groups tested under different conditions or with different forms of the measuring device, an individual would have the same standing in any group with which he was tested, regardless of the group.

Neither of these assumptions is ever completely valid. Different forms of a test never do measure quite the same properties, different conditions of testing introduce different factors which affect performance, and variations in sampling are always with us. Therefore transmuting the scores of all groups to standard or standardized scores actually introduces an error. However, as we have seen, in some cases it also reduces error. Consequently it is a matter of judgment, or perhaps of faith, whether the errors introduced by this procedure are greater or lesser than those which are eliminated.

Summary

In this chapter we considered ways for standardizing scores, that is, referencing them to a distribution of scores. Standardizing scores involves transmuting raw scores to other values which are more meaningful and which, at least after a fashion, make scores on different variables comparable.

One way of referencing a score to a distribution of scores is to determine the percentage of individuals who have lower scores than that one. Such a percentage, termed a percentile rank, is meaningful because it immediately tells how an individual stands relative to other individuals. Percentile ranks on different variables are comparable in the sense that they indicate those traits in which the individual stands high relative to other individuals, and those in which he stands low.

A second way of referencing an individual's score to a distribution of scores is to divide his deviation score by the standard deviation of the distribution. These transmuted values, termed standard scores, have a mean of 0 and a standard deviation of 1. Consequently, when standard scores are used all distributions have the same mean and standard deviation. Since standard scores are expressed in terms of the mean and standard deviation of the distribution, they tell where an individual falls in it. In this sense they are meaningful and are comparable from one variable to another.

Standard scores are difficult to deal with arithmetically because they are given in positive and negative values, and as fractional numbers. For convenience, sometimes raw scores are transmuted to values which have a mean other than 0 and a standard deviation other than 1. For example, standardizing scores with a mean of 50 or 100 and a standard deviation of 10 or 20 gives scores all of which are positive and whole numbers.

If the normal frequency distribution is adopted as a model, then scores which are distributed in a different fashion must be transmuted to other values which are distributed normally. One way of accomplishing this is to find some function of the raw scores, such as their square root or logarithm, which does give a normal distribution. In most instances this is not a useful method, because it is difficult to find the exact function.

A second way to normalize scores is to rank them and compute the percentage of individuals falling below each score. By referring to the table for a normal frequency distribution we can find for each raw score that normal standard score below which the same percentage of individuals fall. However, there are significant distortions in transmuted scores when many ties in rank occur and when there are only a few individuals being ranked.

A normal frequency distribution can be divided into areas which vary in size but occupy equal intervals on the base line. From the table for a normal frequency distribution we can determine the percentage of individuals falling into each area. If raw scores are arranged into the same percentage distribution, then the distribution is normalized. Any convenient set of successive numbers can be assigned to the successive base-line intervals, and they are the transmuted normalized scores.

In the final method, the percentages of individuals earning each raw score are computed. By reference to the table for a normal frequency distribution, the base-line intervals where each percentage falls are determined. Since the distribution of raw scores is not normal, the base-line intervals differ in size. The midpoint of each interval is taken as the score for all individuals who fall in it.

Sometimes we wish to obtain test norms on a particular group, but that group is not available for testing. If scores on the test are highly correlated with those on another test for which norms have been established on the desired group, it is possible to estimate norms for the first test by administering both tests to some other group. The lower the correlation between the two tests the poorer will be the estimated norms.

Occasionally we wish to establish norms on a test when different groups have been tested under somewhat different conditions or with different forms of the test. If it is assumed that there are no differences among the groups in the trait being measured, and there is a perfect correlation between measurements taken under the different conditions or with different forms of the test, then standard scores can be determined for each group separately and all scores can be thrown together in the same distribution.

Selected Readings

Anastasi, Anne: "Psychological Testing," 2d ed., Macmillan, 1961.
Bingham, W. V.: "Aptitudes and Aptitude Testing," Harper, 1927.
Burros, R. H.: Three rational methods for the reduction of skewness, *Psychological Bull.*, **48**:505–511, 1951.
Hull, C. L.: "Aptitude Testing," Harcourt, Brace & World, 1928.
McCall, W. A.: "How to Measure in Education," Macmillan, 1922.
Nunnally, J. C.: "Tests and Measurements," McGraw-Hill, 1959.

chapter 5   The Concept of

Correlation

Inasmuch as many of the problems in psychological measurement involve the degree to which scores on different variables are related, correlation is a concept of utmost importance. When we speak of correlation we are referring to the extent to which scores on one variable go hand and hand with scores on another. In other words, we are referring to the extent to which the order of individuals on one variable is similar to the order on another variable, or the extent to which an individual has the same standing on two variables.

Essentially there are two general types of problems for which we need a quantitative description of the relationship that exists between scores on two variables. One is the accuracy with which scores on one variable can be predicted from scores on another, and the second is the extent to which individual differences in two variables can be attributed to the same determining factors. In the first case we are concerned with predicting or forecasting one kind of behavior from another, and in the second we are seeking some understanding of the factors that determine the differences among individuals in their behavior.

Ordinarily the first of these problems arises from practical considerations. For example, we might be interested in knowing the accuracy with which we can predict or forecast the success of individuals on the job of machinist, knowing the scores they earn on a test of spatial visualization. If scores on the test are highly related to measures of success on the job of machinist, then knowing the score an individual earns on the test enables us to predict with reasonable accuracy how good a machinist he will turn out to be. We might also wish to know whether our predictions from scores on the test of spatial visualization are better or poorer than those we might make from scores on a test of finger dexterity. If scores on the test of spatial visualization are more highly related to measures of job success than are scores on the test of finger dexterity, then it is clear that if we use the first rather than the second test our predictions will be more accurate.

The second problem usually arises from theoretical considerations. For example, we might ask whether it is reasonable to postulate a general trait of manual dexterity. To answer this question we could administer to a group of individuals several different tests which by their very nature would seem to measure this trait. That is, all sets of operations seem to follow equally well from the definition of the trait. We might use tests which involve quickly and accurately placing small pegs into holes, twisting knobs to designated positions, packing blocks into a box, and twisting nuts onto bolts. If scores on all these tests are highly related so that the order of individuals on any one is very similar to the order on all the others, then it would appear that very nearly the same abilities and traits account for individual differences on all of them. We might label these hypothetical common abilities and traits manual dexterity. Suppose in addition we find that scores on these tests are completely unrelated to scores on other tests which by their very nature seem to measure quite different traits, such as tests of reasoning, spatial visualization, and mechanical information. We should feel more certain about the nature of our hypothesized trait of manual dexterity, because it is clear that our tests are measuring a restricted domain of abilities and not some general ability or completely dissimilar ability.

Both of these types of problems require knowledge about the extent of relationships among abilities. In the first case, descriptions of the degree of relationships among variables indicate the accuracy with which we can predict scores on one from scores on another. In the second case, descriptions of the degree of relationships among variables give us some notion of the extent to which scores on them are determined by the same factors, thus permitting us to draw inferences about the nature of the psychological traits which underlie individual differences.

It is therefore apparent that we need some way to describe the degree of relationship between variables. In this chapter we shall consider the theoretical and practical foundations for measuring degrees of relationship, and in the following chapter we shall develop the commonly used index of relationship, a statistic known as the Pearsonian coefficient of correlation.

On first consideration of the problem it might seem to be a fairly simple matter to develop an index or coefficient that gives a quantitative description of the degree of relationship between two variables, and in a certain sense this is true. Nevertheless, for such an index to give us the precision of description we frequently need, and especially to be of such a character as to permit us to draw the inferences we wish to draw, we shall find it necessary to take one or another of certain theoretical positions. These theoretical positions give more meaning to the coefficient of correlation but require the use of hypothetical models which some may be unwilling to accept, holding that these models do not coincide sufficiently with the characteristics of relationships as they actually exist in the real world.

TYPES OF RELATIONSHIP BETWEEN VARIABLES

In order to examine the nature of the relationships between two variables we can plot the scores of each person on those two variables in a chart called a scatter diagram. The scatter diagram is a bivariate or joint frequency distribution. It gives the distribution of scores on two variables simultaneously. Examples of scatter diagrams are given in Figs. 5-1 and 5-5. In these figures each point represents the two scores of an individual, one on variable X and the other on variable Y.

When we examine the ways in which the points arrange themselves in the diagrams shown in Figs. 5-1 and 5-5, we can see that there is a variety of different types of relationship that can hold between scores on two variables. The relationship may be linear or nonlinear; it may be high or low or to some intermediate degree; or it may be positive or negative.

LINEAR AND NONLINEAR CORRELATION

In a linear relationship the points in the scatter diagram tend to swarm around a straight line, whereas in a nonlinear relationship they tend to swarm around a curved line. By inspection it appears that a straight line best fits through the points in Fig. 5-1a and b. On the other hand, it is obvious that the best-fitting lines through the points in Fig. 5-1c and d are curved.

By and large the relationships found between scores yielded by measures of ability, personality, and performance are linear. Curvilinear relationships, while rare, are found between some psychological variables. For example, sometimes the relationship between measures of motivation and performance such as problem solving is curvilinear as is represented in Fig. 5-1c. Those individuals with low levels of motivation (X) tend to perform poorly (Y). As we move up to persons having higher and higher levels of motivation, we find a tendency for their performance to be better and better. However, the increase in performance is not proportional to the increase in motivation.

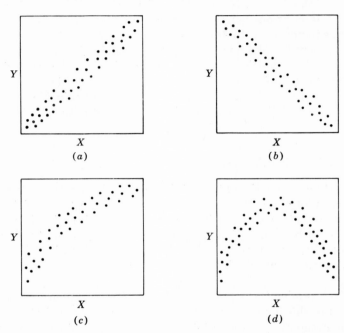

Figure 5-1 Examples of linear and nonlinear correlation. (a) Positive linear correlation; (b) negative linear correlation; (c) nonlinear correlation; (d) nonlinear correlation.

The curvilinear relationship shown in Fig. 5-1d is even less frequently encountered. It is sometimes found with industrial workers when the scores they earn on an intelligence test (X) are plotted against the length of time they remain on the job (Y). Those who earn either low or high scores on the test tend to stay on the job a shorter time than those who earn average scores.

Because linear correlation holds between scores yielded by the very large proportion of devices used in psychological measurement, we shall consider it in detail. While it cannot be denied that the relationships between some psychological variables are nonlinear, nevertheless with the tests commonly used in the measurement of psychological traits the relationships among their scores ordinarily are linear or very close to being linear.

Except in extraordinary circumstances, linear correlation holds between two variables when their scores are normally distributed. Many psychological traits when measured have distributions of scores not too dissimilar to a normal frequency distribution. Indeed, as we have seen, there may be sufficient reason to transform scores which are not normally distributed into other values which are. In most instances when scores are normalized their relationships will become linear.

If the relative magnitudes of the units along the scales are of no great significance but only the order of individuals is important, then it makes no difference whether we describe the degree of relationship between raw scores of X and Y or the degree of relationship between some function of the raw scores. Such a circumstance might occur if we believed that the units along our scales were unequal. By taking some function of the scores the units might still be unequal, but the scores would be linearly related. Thus, with the data shown in Fig. 5-1c, if the differences between successive values of X were made smaller and smaller, the points to the top and right in the diagram would be drawn closer to the left, whereas the positions of those at the left would not be greatly changed. Consequently, by this change in the magnitude of the units, all points would swarm around a straight line rather than a curved line. If we plot in the scatter diagram, say, the square root of the scores in X instead of the raw scores, the relationship between X and Y may be linear.

DEGREES OF CORRELATION

Some human characteristics are associated with each other to a very high degree, others to intermediate degrees, and still others are completely unrelated. Figure 5-5 illustrates relationships of different degrees. If we measured the length of the right and left arms of normal men we should find a very high degree of relationship between the two sets of measurements. The person with the longest right arm probably would have the longest left arm, the person with the second longest right arm would have the second longest left arm, and so on. The height and weight of men obviously are related, but the relationship between these two properties is far from perfect. By and large those men who are tall weigh more than those who are short, and conversely those who are heavy tend to be taller than those who are light in weight. But there are many exceptions to the general tendency so that we are not surprised by the appearance either of Mr. Stringbean who is very tall but weighs little or of Mr. Five-by-five who is short but weighs a great deal. Finally, if we examined the relationship between grades and the length of the left foot of women students in college we should probably find that on the average those who earn high grades have just the same size foot as those who earn poor grades, and conversely those with large feet earn just the same grades as those with small feet. There is, then, no relationship at all between these two variables.

When the relationship between scores on two tests is high, it means that individual differences in the two traits being measured are determined by very nearly the same factors and that scores on the one can be predicted very accurately from scores on the other. When the relationship is low, then it means that individual differences in the two traits are determined by quite different factors and that the prediction of scores on the one from scores on the other is very poor.

POSITIVE AND NEGATIVE CORRELATION

The relationship between scores on two variables may be either positive or negative. When a positive relationship exists between two variables, then high scores on one tend to be associated with high scores on the other and low scores on one with low scores on the other, as shown in Fig. 5-1a. With a negative relationship the reverse is true: high scores on one variable are associated with low scores on the other and low scores on one with high scores on the other as in Fig. 5-1b. The two relationships can be of the same degree but differ in their direction as do the relationships shown in Fig. 5-1a and b.

While negative relationships are found between psychological variables, such relationships to a high degree are seldom encountered. In many of the cases where a negative relationship between two variables is found, the direction of one or the other of the scales can be reversed without any loss in meaning. For example, scores on a test of "emotional instability" may be negatively correlated with scores on a test of "sociability." By the simple expedient of reversing the scoring of the first test we make it a measure of "emotional stability." In reversing the direction of the scale we do not change the degree of relationship between scores on the two tests but merely change the direction of the relationship from negative to positive.

THE ASSOCIATION BETWEEN VARIABLES IN TERMS OF THE VARIATION AMONG INDIVIDUALS

The scores we obtain from the application of a set of operations are the quantitative descriptions we have of the extent to which individuals possess or manifest some trait. When the scores yielded by two different sets of operations are related, it means that the two variables they measure have something in common. That is, differences among individuals in one variable are due to some extent to the same factors that determine differences among them in the other variable. We can first approach correlation, then, in terms of common variation.

VARIATION IN THE SCORES ON ONE VARIABLE IN RELATION TO SCORES ON THE OTHER VARIABLE

Figure 5-2 is a *bivariate distribution,* the joint frequency distribution of scores on two variables. This scatter diagram is represented with a series of columns for the various values of the X variable and a series of

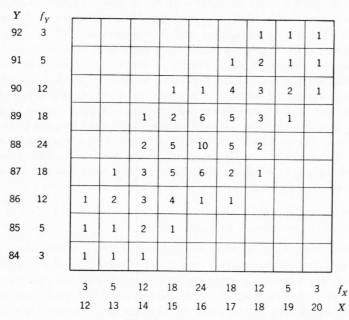

Y	f_Y									
92	3							1	1	1
91	5						1	2	1	1
90	12				1	1	4	3	2	1
89	18			1	2	6	5	3	1	
88	24			2	5	10	5	2		
87	18		1	3	5	6	2	1		
86	12	1	2	3	4	1	1			
85	5	1	1	2	1					
84	3	1	1	1						
	f_X	3	5	12	18	24	18	12	5	3
	X	12	13	14	15	16	17	18	19	20

Figure 5-2   The relationship between two variables.

rows for the various values of the Y variable. At the bottom of the diagram is given the frequency distribution of scores on X (fX), and to the left the frequency distribution of scores on Y (fY). On variable X three individuals earn a score of 12, five a score of 13, and twelve a score of 14; and on variable Y three earn a score of 84, five a score of 85, and twelve a score of 86. In a scatter diagram these distributions are termed the marginal distributions. In each of the cells in the scatter diagram are given the numbers of individuals earning a particular pair of scores. Thus two individuals earn a score of 14 on X and 85 on Y, and five individuals earn a score of 17 on X and 80 on Y.

If we take the cases that fall in any given column, that is, those individuals who have the same particular score on X, we see that they differ among themselves in their Y scores. Similarly, we find that the cases falling in any given row, that is, those individuals who have the same particular score on Y, differ among themselves in their X scores. As we have said, the scores yielded by a set of operations are the quantitative descriptions we have of the extent to which individuals possess or manifest some trait. Therefore we can say of the three cases with the X score of 20 that for them X is a constant and Y is a variable. All three individuals are the same in the degree to which they possess or manifest trait X but differ among themselves in the degree to which they possess or manifest trait Y. Similarly, we can say of the 12 cases with Y scores of 86 that for them Y is a constant and X is a variable. All 12 individuals are the same in the degree to which they possess or manifest trait Y but differ among themselves in the degree to which they possess or manifest trait X. By sorting individuals according to their X scores into columns, for those in any given column we are holding X constant and are permitting Y to vary; and by sorting them according to their Y scores into rows, for those in any given row we are holding Y constant and are permitting X to vary. Consequently, in each of the columns we have a distribution of scores on the Y variable with the effects of the X variable eliminated, and in each of the rows we have a distribution of the scores on the X variable with the effects of the Y variable eliminated.

THE EFFECTS OF HOLDING CONSTANT VARIATION IN ONE VARIABLE UPON THE EXTENT OF VARIATION IN THE OTHER

We have just seen that when we consider the individuals whose scores fall in any given column or row in a scatter diagram, we have a group of individuals for whom one property is a variable and the other is a constant. That is, in one property the individuals differ among themselves and in the other they are all the same. Let us now examine the extent of variation in one variable when variation in the other is held constant, in relation to the association between the two variables.

Figure 5-3 gives a scatter diagram which represents the association between the scores of 50 individuals on two variables X and Y. In this figure each pair of scores is represented by solid dots. For simplicity let us just consider variation in Y as a consequence of the relationship between X and Y. We shall therefore be dealing with the columns in the scatter diagram though we could just as well deal with the rows, thereby examining the variation in X as a consequence of the relationship between X and Y.

From an inspection of the scatter diagram in Fig. 5-3 we can see that scores on the two variables are positively related. Low scores on the one tend to be associated with low scores on the other, and high scores on the one tend to be associated with high scores on the other. The distribution of Y scores earned by the entire 50 cases is given in the marginal distribution to the right in column y. The mean of the raw scores on Y for the entire 50 cases is 20.0. The means of the Y scores of the individuals in

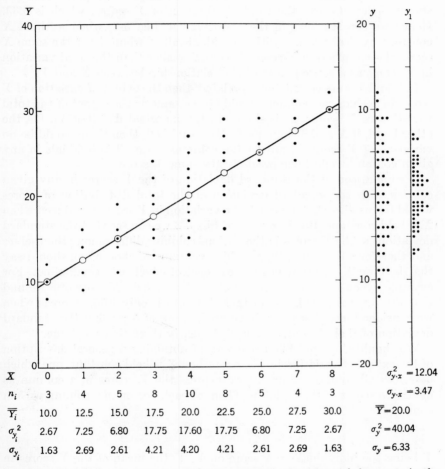

X	0	1	2	3	4	5	6	7	8	
n_i	3	4	5	8	10	8	5	4	3	$\sigma_{y \cdot x}^2 = 12.04$
$\overline{Y}_i$	10.0	12.5	15.0	17.5	20.0	22.5	25.0	27.5	30.0	$\sigma_{y \cdot x} = 3.47$
$\sigma_{y_i}^2$	2.67	7.25	6.80	17.75	17.60	17.75	6.80	7.25	2.67	$\overline{Y} = 20.0$
										$\sigma_y^2 = 40.04$
σ_{y_i}	1.63	2.69	2.61	4.21	4.20	4.21	2.61	2.69	1.63	$\sigma_y = 6.33$

Figure 5-3 An example of linear correlation wherein the means of the scores in the columns all fall precisely on the same straight line.

each column are given at the foot of the figure in row $\overline{Y}_i$ and are represented in the scatter diagram by circles.

If we take the cases in any column we have a distribution of Y scores when X is constant. This can be compared with the total distribution of Y scores for all individuals regardless of their X scores, as represented in the distribution to the right of the chart in column y. This comparison would tell us whether holding X constant has any effect upon the range of individual differences in Y. At the foot of Fig. 5-3 in row σ_{y_i} are given the standard deviations of the Y scores of the individuals in each column. These values range from 1.63 to 4.21, which may be compared with the standard deviation of the total distribution of Y scores, which is 6.33. Hence we can say that in the case given in Fig. 5-3, when we hold X constant by dealing only with individuals all of whom have the same X score, the variation in Y scores becomes smaller than the total variation in Y scores as a consequence of the relationship between X and Y.

If X and Y were completely unrelated, then the extent of variation of Y scores in each of the columns would be the same as the extent of the total variation of Y scores, as is shown in the marginal distribution. On the other hand, if X and Y were perfectly correlated, then there would be no variation of Y scores in any of the columns since all individuals in any given column would have precisely the same Y score.

A comparison of the standard deviation of the Y scores in any given column with the standard deviation of the total distribution of scores would tell us directly how much the variation in Y scores is reduced when X is held constant. But in row σ_{y_i} of Fig. 5-3 we can see that the standard deviations of the Y scores in the various columns differ among themselves and therefore, depending upon which column we choose, we should say that holding X constant has a great deal of effect or a small effect. For example, when we consider those cases who have an X score of 8 we find that the standard deviation of their Y scores is only 1.63, whereas when we consider those cases who have an X score of 5 we find the standard deviation of their Y scores to be 4.21, nearly three times as large.

We should therefore like some way of obtaining a general description of the extent of variation in Y scores when X is held constant, one which describes all columns. Suppose we express the Y scores in a column as deviation scores of that column. Then for each person in a column we can compute

$$y_i = Y - \bar{Y}_i$$

Y being the individual's raw score on Y, $\bar{Y}_i$ the mean of the Y scores in his column, and y_i his deviation score from the mean of the Y scores of individuals who have the same X score as he.

By transmuting the scores in any given column to deviation scores from its own mean, we do not change the characteristics of the distribution of scores in that column but only the numerical values of the scores. Hence for any column

$$\sigma_{Y_i}{}^2 = \sigma_{y_i}{}^2 \quad \text{and} \quad \sigma_{Y_i} = \sigma_{y_i}$$

and the distribution of y_i scores describes the extent of individual differences in that column just as well as does the distribution of Y scores. Inasmuch as these y_i scores are deviation scores, their mean, of course, is zero. The distribution of these y_i scores in any column gives us in deviation-score form the distribution of individuals on the Y variable with X constant. Now by the simple expedient of transforming all scores in every column to y_i scores, we have for each person a measure of his standing on the Y variable with X held constant. To the right in Fig. 5-3 in column y_i there have been assembled the y_i scores of all individuals regardless of their column. This can be considered as a summary distribution of scores in Y when X is held constant. The standard deviation of this distribution gives a summary description for the entire scatter diagram of the extent of variation in Y when X is held constant. In the case illustrated in Fig. 5-3 this standard deviation is 3.47 and is smaller than the standard deviation of the distribution of Y scores, which is 6.33. For purposes of comparison, in column y of Fig. 5-3 the distribution of scores in variable Y is expressed in terms of deviation- rather than raw-score form. Clearly, the extent of variation in y_i scores is less than that in y scores.

When one property, such as Y, is variable and another, such as X, is held constant in relation to it, the scores are sometimes symbolized as $Y \cdot X$. If scores on both variables are expressed in deviation- rather than raw-score form, then with y variable and x constant we have $y \cdot x$. We could if we wish use $y \cdot x$ rather than y_i. Hence we symbolize the standard deviation of the total distribution of y_i scores gathered from all the columns as $\sigma_{y \cdot x}$. This is termed the *partial standard deviation* since it describes the extent of variation in one variable with the effects of the other held constant or eliminated. Similarly, we should symbolize the standard deviation of the total distribution of x_i or $x \cdot y$ scores, the variation in the X scores of the rows with Y held constant, as $\sigma_{x \cdot y}$.

The variance of the total distribution of y_i or $y \cdot x$ scores, $\sigma_{y \cdot x}^2$, is nothing more nor less than the weighted mean of the variances σ_i^2 of the columns. This can be shown as follows:

$$\sigma_{y \cdot x}^2 = \sigma_{Y - \bar{Y}_i}^2$$

Since $Y - \bar{Y}_i = y_i$ we can write the variance as

$$\sigma_{y \cdot x}^2 = \frac{\Sigma y_i^2}{n}$$

Let there be k columns, that is, 1 to k values of X. We can then write the above as

$$\sigma_{y \cdot x}^2 = \frac{\Sigma y_i^2 + \cdots + \Sigma y_k^2}{n}$$

In the numerator of the above formula we have the sums of the y_i scores squared of all the columns added together. In any column

$$\sigma_{y_i}^2 = \frac{\Sigma y_i^2}{n_i}$$

and therefore

$$n_i \sigma_{y_i}^2 = \Sigma y_i^2$$

Hence

$$\sigma_{y \cdot x}^2 = \frac{n_i \sigma_{y_i}^2 + \cdots + n_k \sigma_{y_k}^2}{n} \tag{5-1}$$

which is a weighted mean. That is, in calculating the mean of the $\sigma_{y_i}^2$ values each variance is weighted or multiplied by the number of cases on which it is based.

For the relationship illustrated in Fig. 5-3 the partial variance of 12.04, which was computed directly from the distribution in column y_i to the right of the figure, could be computed as the weighted mean of the variances of the columns from Eq. (5-1) as follows:

$$\sigma_{y \cdot x}^2 = \frac{\begin{array}{c} 3(2.67) + 4(7.25) + 5(6.80) + 8(17.75) + 10(17.60) + 8(17.75) \\ + 5(6.80) + 4(7.25) + 3(2.67) \end{array}}{50}$$

$$= \frac{602.02}{50} = 12.04$$

Let us now look at another relationship, that between the pairs of scores of another 50 individuals, depicted in Fig. 5-4. Again we have a positive relationship between the two variables, since low scores on the one tend to be associated with low scores on the other and high scores on the one with high scores on the other. But whereas the points in the first scatter diagram tended to swarm around a straight line, in this case they tend to swarm around a curved line.

The distribution of the Y scores earned by the entire 50 cases represented in Fig. 5-4, given in the marginal distribution to the right in column y, has a mean of 17.0. The means of the Y scores of the individuals in each column are given at the foot of the figure in row $\bar{Y}_i$ and are represented in the scatter diagram by circles.

A comparison of the variation of the Y scores in any column with the total variation in Y as given in the distribution to the right in column y again tells us the effects of holding X constant upon the variation in Y. The standard deviations of the Y scores in each of the columns are given in row σ_{y_i} at the foot of Fig. 5-4, and range from 1.63 to 3.57. They are all smaller than the standard deviation of the total distribution of Y

scores, which is 9.60. Again we have a case wherein by holding X constant by dealing only with individuals all of whom have the same X score, the variation in Y scores becomes smaller than the total variation

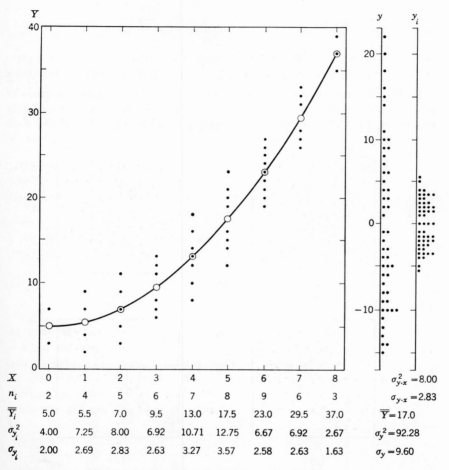

X	0	1	2	3	4	5	6	7	8	
n_i	2	4	5	6	7	8	9	6	3	$\sigma_{y\cdot x}^2 = 8.00$
$\overline{Y_i}$	5.0	5.5	7.0	9.5	13.0	17.5	23.0	29.5	37.0	$\sigma_{y\cdot x} = 2.83$
$\sigma_{y_i}^2$	4.00	7.25	8.00	6.92	10.71	12.75	6.67	6.92	2.67	$\overline{Y} = 17.0$
σ_{y_i}	2.00	2.69	2.83	2.63	3.27	3.57	2.58	2.63	1.63	$\sigma_y^2 = 92.28$
										$\sigma_y = 9.60$

Figure 5-4 An example of nonlinear correlation wherein the means of the scores in the columns all fall precisely on the same curved line.

in Y scores as a consequence of the relationship between X and Y. The partial standard deviation $\sigma_{y\cdot x}$, which gives a summary description for the whole scatter diagram of the variation in the columns, is 2.83, which is substantially smaller than the standard deviation of the total distribution of Y scores, which is 9.60. Again we can see that the partial variance

$\sigma^2_{y \cdot x}$ is the weighted mean of the variances of the individual columns:

$$\sigma^2_{y \cdot x} = \frac{\begin{aligned}2(4.00) + 4(7.25) + 5(8.00) + 6(6.92) + 7(10.00) + 8(12.75) \\ + 9(6.67) + 6(6.92) + 3(2.67)\end{aligned}}{50}$$

$$= \frac{400.08}{50} = 8.00$$

THE MAGNITUDE OF THE PARTIAL VARIATION IN ONE VARIABLE AS A CONSEQUENCE OF THE DEGREE OF RELATIONSHIP WITH THE OTHER VARIABLE

In Fig. 5-5 are four scatter diagrams illustrating different degrees of relationship. Figure 5-5a shows two variables which are completely unrelated, Fig. 5-5d two variables which are highly related, and Fig. 5-5b

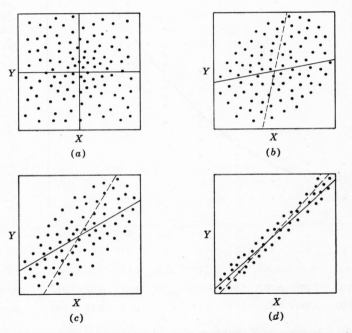

Figure 5-5 Examples of various degrees of relationship between two variables in relation to the slope of the regression line.

and c pairs of variables related to degrees intermediate between these two extremes. We can see in Fig. 5-5a that when there is no relationship at all between X and Y, Y scores for individuals all of whom have the same X score are the same as the total variation in Y scores. But as we go to higher and higher degrees of relationship as in Fig. 5-5b to d, relative to the total variation in Y scores the variation in Y scores for individuals all of whom have the same X score becomes smaller and smaller. The same state of affairs also holds if we consider the variation in the X scores of those individuals all of whom have the same Y score in comparison with the total variation in X scores.

Hence it is apparent that the higher the degree of relationship between two variables, the less the variation among the scores in the columns and in the rows. When there is no relationship at all between two variables, then the variation among the scores in any column or in any row is equal to the total variation. That is, when there is no relationship between the two variables,

$$\sigma_{y \cdot x} = \sigma_y \quad \text{and} \quad \sigma_{x \cdot y} = \sigma_x$$

or

$$\sigma_{y \cdot x}^2 = \sigma_y{}^2 \quad \text{and} \quad \sigma_{x \cdot y}^2 = \sigma_x{}^2$$

When the relationship between the two variables is perfect, then there is no variation at all among the scores in any column or in any row. That is, when the relationship is perfect,

$$\sigma_{y \cdot x} = 0 \quad \text{and} \quad \sigma_{x \cdot y} = 0$$

or

$$\sigma_{y \cdot x}^2 = 0 \quad \text{and} \quad \sigma_{x \cdot y}^2 = 0$$

ACCOUNTING FOR THE VARIATION AMONG INDIVIDUALS IN ONE VARIABLE AS A CONSEQUENCE OF THE RELATIONSHIP BETWEEN THAT VARIABLE AND ANOTHER VARIABLE

Whatever the factors are that produce the differences among individuals in a variable—be the factors innate or learned characteristics, abilities or personality traits—we can hold their observable effects constant by selecting individuals all of whom have the same score on that variable. When we eliminate the differences among individuals in their scores on a variable, then, we presume that the effects of the factors which cause the differences also are eliminated. If people were all the same in variable X, then the variation among them in variable Y would be described by $\sigma_{y \cdot x}$ rather than by σ_y. Similarly, if people were all the same in variable Y, then the variation among them in variable X would be described by $\sigma_{x \cdot y}$ rather than by σ_x.

Suppose that, having eliminated the differences among individuals in variable X, we also found that we had eliminated all the differences among them in variable Y. This would mean that the factors which produce differences among individuals in variable X are precisely and entirely the same factors which produce differences among them in variable Y. In this case, of course, the two variables would be perfectly correlated. On the other hand, suppose that, having eliminated all the differences among individuals in variable X, we found that the extent of the differences among them in variable Y was not changed at all. This would mean that the factors which produce differences among individuals in variable X are completely different from the factors which produce differences among them in variable Y. In this case the two variables would be completely uncorrelated.

The total variation in a variable, that is, the extent to which individuals differ among themselves in a variable, can be measured either by the variance or by the standard deviation of the total distribution of scores on that variable. The extent of variation, or the extent to which individuals differ among themselves in a variable when the factors that produce the differences among them in a second variable are held constant, is measured by the partial variance or the partial standard deviation of the first variable.

To summarize:

$\sigma_y{}^2$ = extent of total variation among individuals in Y

$\sigma_{y \cdot x}^2$ = extent of variation among individuals in Y remaining after variation among them in X has been eliminated, and factors that produce individual differences in X have been held constant; that is, $\sigma_{y \cdot x}^2$ is the variation in Y due to factors *other* than those that produce differences among individuals in X

Therefore we can say

$\sigma_y{}^2 - \sigma_{y \cdot x}^2$ = extent of variation among individuals in Y due to *same* factors that produce differences among them in X

Let us symbolize this variation as $\sigma_{y'}{}^2$ so that

$$\sigma_{y'}{}^2 = \sigma_y{}^2 - \sigma_{y \cdot x}^2 \tag{5-2}$$

Consequently,

$\dfrac{\sigma_{y'}{}^2}{\sigma_y{}^2}$ = proportion of total variation among individuals on variable Y that can be accounted for by same factors that produce differences among them in X when extent of variation is measured by variance of scores   (5-3)

If we prefer to measure the variation among individuals by means of the standard deviation of their scores rather than by the variance, as is the common practice, we write Eq. (5-3) as

$\dfrac{\sigma_{y'}}{\sigma_y}$ = proportion of total variation among individuals on variable Y that can be accounted for by same factors that produce differences among them in X when extent of variation is measured by standard deviation of scores   (5-4)

Substituting for $\sigma_{y'}$ from Eq. (5-2) in Eq. (5-4) gives

$$\frac{\sigma_{y'}}{\sigma_y} = \frac{\sqrt{\sigma_y{}^2 - \sigma_{y \cdot x}^2}}{\sigma_y}$$

$$= \sqrt{\frac{\sigma_y{}^2 - \sigma_{y \cdot x}^2}{\sigma_y{}^2}}$$

$$= \sqrt{\frac{\sigma_y{}^2}{\sigma_y{}^2} - \frac{\sigma_{y \cdot x}^2}{\sigma_y{}^2}}$$

$$= \sqrt{1 - \frac{\sigma_{y \cdot x}^2}{\sigma_y{}^2}} \tag{5-5}$$

By a similar development for variable X we could show

$$\frac{\sigma_{x'}}{\sigma_x} = \sqrt{1 - \frac{\sigma_{x \cdot y}^2}{\sigma_x{}^2}} \tag{5-6}$$

THE PROPORTION OF ACCOUNTABLE VARIATION AS AN INDEX OF THE DEGREE
OF RELATIONSHIP BETWEEN TWO VARIABLES

We have seen that the magnitudes of $\sigma_{y \cdot x}^2$ and of $\sigma_{x \cdot y}^2$ vary with the degree of relationship between X and Y. The higher is the relationship between the two variables the smaller are $\sigma_{y \cdot x}^2$ and $\sigma_{x \cdot y}^2$. We have also seen that when there is no relationship between X and Y,

$$\sigma_{y \cdot x}^2 = \sigma_y{}^2 \qquad \text{and} \qquad \sigma_{x \cdot y}^2 = \sigma_x{}^2$$

and when the relationship between X and Y is perfect,

$$\sigma_{y \cdot x}^2 = 0 \qquad \text{and} \qquad \sigma_{x \cdot y}^2 = 0$$

When there is no relationship between the two variables, then, the numerator of the second term in Eqs. (5-5) and (5-6) equals the denominator so that the term becomes 1 and the entire formula equals 0.00. When the relationship between the two variables is perfect, then the numerator of the second term in Eqs. (5-5) and (5-6) is zero so that the term becomes 1 and the entire formula equals 1.00. For degrees of relationship between these two extremes the formulae would give intermediate values. Therefore the *proportion of accountable variation*, $\sigma_{y'}/\sigma_y$ and $\sigma_{x'}/\sigma_x$, provides an index or coefficient indicative of the degree of relationship between two variables.

As an illustration we can apply Eq. (5-5) to the data in Fig. 5-3:

$$\frac{\sigma_{y'}}{\sigma_y} = \sqrt{1 - \frac{12.04}{40.04}} = \sqrt{1 - 0.30} = \sqrt{0.70} = 0.84$$

We cannot compute the relationship between the two variables from Eq. (5-6) because we did not go through the process of computing $\sigma_{x\cdot y}^2$ and σ_x^2. Had we computed these values then we also could have a statement of the relationship between X and Y by comparing the variation in X when Y is constant with the total variation in X.

THE PROPORTION OF ACCOUNTABLE VARIATION AS A GENERAL INDEX OF RELATIONSHIP FOR BOTH LINEAR AND NONLINEAR RELATIONSHIPS

We developed Eqs. (5-5) and (5-6) from accountable variation taking the variation in the columns or in the rows as the variation in the scores on one variable when variation in the scores on the other is held constant. In each column we expressed the scores as deviations from the mean of that column, or in each row we took the scores as deviations from the mean of that row. We then assembled all deviation scores from the columns into a single distribution to calculate $\sigma_{y\cdot x}$ or all the deviation scores from the rows into a single distribution to calculate $\sigma_{x\cdot y}$.

In developing Eqs. (5-5) and (5-6) we imposed no conditions with respect to the nature of the relationship and therefore they can be used regardless of whether the relationship is linear or nonlinear. Hence they are generalized formulae indicative of the degree of relationship between two variables. The name given to both these parallel formulae is the correlation ratio. The correlation ratio is symbolized as η (eta), so that we have

$$\eta_{yx} = \sqrt{1 - \frac{\sigma_{y\cdot x}^2}{\sigma_y^2}} \qquad (5\text{-}7)$$

$$\eta_{xy} = \sqrt{1 - \frac{\sigma_{x\cdot y}^2}{\sigma_x^2}} \qquad (5\text{-}8)$$

If we apply Eq. (5-7) to the data in Fig. 5-4, we find for these data, which are related in a curvilinear fashion, that

$$\frac{\sigma_{y'}}{\sigma_y} = \eta_{y\cdot x} = \sqrt{1 - \frac{8.00}{92.28}} = \sqrt{1 - 0.08} = \sqrt{0.92} = 0.96$$

HOMOSCEDASTICITY AS A MODEL IN CORRELATION

Common observation indicates that height and weight in human beings are positively correlated, though we recognize that the relationship is by no means perfect. Consequently if we take people of any given height we should expect, and indeed we should find, that the variation among them in weight is smaller than the variation in weight among all individuals regardless of height. By taking people all of whom are the same height we have eliminated the effects of whatever factors produce differences among them in height. Equations (5-5) and (5-6) permit us to calculate the extent to which variation among individuals in weight is reduced as a result of holding height constant.

We should expect the degree to which the variation among individuals in weight is reduced to be the same regardless of whether we hold height constant by considering only individuals who are 5.5 ft tall or only individuals who are 5.9 ft tall. That is, by taking individuals of any given height, regardless of what that particular height may be, we presume we are holding the same set of factors constant. But suppose we should find that for those individuals whose height is 5.5 ft the variation among them in weight is substantially smaller than it is for those individuals whose height is 5.9 ft. Then clearly a very complex situation holds with respect to the factors which determine height and weight. Indeed, these factors would seem to be related in a most intricate fashion. With people who are shorter there would seem to be a more intimate relationship between height and weight than there is with people who are taller. Whatever the factors that produce differences among individuals in height may be, these factors are of such a nature that when they produce individuals who are short they also produce individuals who are homogeneous in weight and when they produce individuals who are tall they also produce individuals who are quite heterogeneous in weight.

Let us look again at the examples of the relationships given in Figs. 5-3 and 5-4. In both these cases we can see that the extent of variation among individuals is not equal. Indeed, there appears to be a systematic relationship between the extent of variation among individuals in their Y scores and their X scores. Those individuals with either low or high X scores tend to differ less among themselves in their Y scores than those whose X scores have an intermediate value.

Complicated relationships such as these are very difficult to understand. If the extent of variation in the Y scores in all columns were precisely the same and the extent of variation in the X scores in all rows were precisely the same, then the situation would be far more comprehensible and interpretable. We can conceive of a set of factors—nutritional, genetic, or whatever—which determine height. To some extent these factors also determine weight. But when the effects of these factors that produce differences among individuals in height are held constant, then we expect the differences in weight among all individuals—regardless of their particular weight—to be reduced to the same extent.

When the standard deviations of the scores in all the columns are equal to each other and the standard deviations of the scores in all rows also are equal to each other, we say that the relationship is *homoscedastic*. Homoscedasticity is a state of affairs that is much more easily understood and explained than is heteroscedasticity and therefore a state of affairs we wish actually held. The facts of the matter are that in many cases the relationships between scores on psychological variables are very nearly homoscedastic. In many instances the variation among the standard deviations of the scores in the columns and the standard deviations of the scores in the rows appear to vary from one another in a completely unsystematic fashion and are very similar in magnitude. Because the number of cases in any given column or row ordinarily is small, it seems reasonable to explain the differences as being due to the random effects of sampling error. In the examples of relationships given in Figs. 5-3 and 5-4 it will be observed that there are very few cases having either high or low scores on variable X so that we cannot put very much dependence upon the extent of their variation in Y scores. Frequently as we increase the number of individuals whose scores enter into the relationship, the condition of homoscedasticity is more and more closely approximated, thus giving support to the notion that the differences among the columns and among the rows in their standard deviations are the result of sampling error.

Finally, with the exception of very rare circumstances when the scores on the two variables being related are normally distributed, homoscedasticity holds. In this case the distributions of the scores in the columns and in the rows also are very likely to be normally distributed. Hence if we can justify the normalizing of scores we are very likely to have a relationship that is homoscedastic.

As a consequence we might take homoscedasticity as a model. We should then be saying that the relationships between our variables are homoscedastic—or so nearly homoscedastic that the difference is quite unimportant. Now we can more easily comprehend formulae such as (5-5) and (5-6), and in effect we are saying that the determinants of behavior are simple. Furthermore, we do not have to regard the partial standard deviation as a summary statement or average description of the entire scatter diagram, but rather as a description of the extent of variation among individuals in one variable after the effects of the factors that produce individual differences in another are held constant and eliminated. Homoscedasticity implies simplicity of determination of behavior; and even though it may not be precisely correct, many are willing to accept it because it does seem to have some justification and at least is comprehensible.

Nevertheless, it cannot be denied that homoscedasticity does not hold for all relationships. Indeed, there are striking departures from it that cannot easily be explained away as resulting from sampling error or from scales with inadequate or unequal units. If we do not have a homoscedastic relationship or cannot justify acceptance of homoscedasticity as a model, then the partial standard deviation is merely a summary

statement of the distributions of scores in the columns and rows and
Eqs. (5-5) and (5-6) also are summary statements. We can draw very
few implications from the partial standard deviation and formulae
related to it, and we are admitting that the factors determining the relationship between two variables operate in a most complex manner.

THE ASSOCIATION BETWEEN VARIABLES IN TERMS OF THE NATURE OF THE RELATIONSHIP

In describing the nature of the relationships that hold between variables we said of some that the scores tend to swarm around a straight line
and of others that they tend to swarm around a curved line. Basic to the
theory of correlation and to the development of an index of the degree of
relationship is the matter of the nature of the association. In this section
we shall discuss the problem of describing a relationship by means of a
line running through the swarm of points.

DESCRIBING THE NATURE OF RELATIONSHIPS

If the relationship between two variables is positive, then low scores
on the one tend to be associated with low scores on the other and high
scores on the one tend to be associated with high scores on the other. If
the relationship is negative, then the trend is in the other direction, with
low scores on one variable tending to be associated with high scores on the
other. With positive relationships, then, as we proceed from low to high
scores on one variable we find higher and higher scores on the other, and
with negative relationships we find just the reverse.

Let us now examine the trend in the relationship shown in Fig. 5-3.
For simplicity we shall again deal only with the columns, though we could
just as well deal with the rows. In this figure each pair of scores is represented by a solid dot. We can see that scores on the two variables are
positively related. As we consider individuals who have higher and higher
X scores, we find that on the average they have higher and higher Y
scores. To show this we can calculate the mean of the Y scores for the
individuals in each column. The means are given at the foot of the scatter
diagram and are represented in the chart by circles. To show the trend
graphically, a line has been drawn through the means of the columns. A
line drawn through a scatter diagram to represent the trend of the
association is termed a *regression line*.

If we look at the regression line in Fig. 5-3 we can see that the trend of
the relationship between X and Y is quite regular. Indeed, the regression
line is a straight line and therefore we call the relationship a linear
relationship.

A line can be described by an equation. In the case of a straight line when the two variables are X and Y the equation is

$$Y = a_Y + b_{Y \cdot X} X$$

where a_Y and $b_{Y \cdot X}$ are constants, a_Y being the intercept, that value of Y when X is zero, and $b_{Y \cdot X}$ the slope of the line relative to the X axis of the chart, the number of units change in Y for each unit change in X. Knowing a_Y and $b_{Y \cdot X}$, if we enter any given value of X in the formula we can calculate a value of Y such that the pair of values X and Y describe a point falling on the line.

We can also write the equation for a straight line as

$$X = a_X + b_{X \cdot Y} Y$$

where a_X, the intercept, is the value of X when Y is zero, and $b_{X \cdot Y}$ is the slope of the line relative to the Y axis. Knowing a_X and $b_{X \cdot Y}$, if we enter any given value of Y in the formula we can calculate a value of X such that the pair of values X and Y describe a point falling on the line.

Let us look at the relationship represented in Fig. 5-3. It is apparent that this is a linear relationship since the points all swarm around a straight line. Furthermore, it can be seen that the means of the Y scores in the columns all fall precisely on the same straight line. From the equation for this straight line we can calculate the mean of the Y scores, $\bar{Y}_i$, falling in any given column X_i. We write the equation for this straight line as

$$\bar{Y}_i = a_Y + b_{Y \cdot X} X_i \qquad (5\text{-}9)$$

When the equation for a line is used to describe the trend of the relationship in a scatter diagram it is termed a *regression equation*, and in the case of a linear relationship the slope of the line, b, is termed a *regression coefficient*.

In the example of a linear relationship given in Fig. 5-3 it can be seen by inspection that

$$a_Y = 10 \qquad \text{and} \qquad b_{Y \cdot X} = 2.5$$

Therefore the regression equation in this instance is

$$\bar{Y}_i = 10 + 2.5 X_i$$

The five individuals who have an X score of 2 have Y scores of 12, 13, 14, 17, and 19. The mean of their Y scores is 15, or, by the regression equation,

$$\bar{Y}_i = 10 + (2.5)(2) = 15$$

If we were concerned with the regression line drawn through the means of the X scores in the rows, these means also falling precisely on a straight line, the regression equation would be

$$\bar{X}_i = a_X + b_{X \cdot Y} Y_i \tag{5-10}$$

A comparison of Eqs. (5-9) and (5-10) indicates that these two equations describe different lines since their intercepts a_Y and a_X and their slopes $b_{Y \cdot X}$ and $b_{X \cdot Y}$ are not necessarily the same. Consequently in every scatter diagram we have two regression lines, one which cuts through the columns and around which the Y scores in the columns cluster and one which cuts through the rows and around which the X scores in the rows cluster.

When a positive relationship exists between two variables, as in Fig. 5-1a, then the regression coefficient b is positive, indicating for every unit increase in X the number of units of increase in Y. When the relationship is negative as in Fig. 5-1b, then the regression coefficient is negative, indicating for every unit increase in X the number of units of decrease in Y.

Now let us look at the relationship shown in Fig. 5-4. Again we can see by inspection that the relationship is positive. On the average, low X scores are associated with low Y scores and high X scores are associated with high Y scores. Furthermore, if we examine the regression line which is drawn through the means of the columns we see that, as in the previous example, the trend of the association is quite regular. However, in this case the trend does not follow a straight line but rather a curved one, and therefore we call the relationship a curvilinear or nonlinear relationship. As in the previous example, we can set up an equation which describes the regression line and therefore the nature of the relationship between scores on the two variables. There are, of course, a wide variety of different curved lines and an equal number of equations to describe them. The equation for the particular curve shown in Fig. 5-4 is

$$\bar{Y}_i = a_Y + b_{Y \cdot X} X_i^2$$

where $a_Y = 5$ and $b_{Y \cdot X} = 0.5$. The five individuals who have an X score of 2 have Y scores of 4, 5, 6, 9, and 11. The mean of their Y scores is 7, or, by the regression equation,

$$\bar{Y}_i = 5 + (0.5)(4) = 7$$

The regression line in this example is a very simple curve and consequently the regression equation also is very simple. With other curvilinear relationships the regression equation may involve more than just two constants and more functions than just a single square, and the function may be of a more complex nature. Whether the regression line is straight or curved, the nature of the relationship can be described by an equation.

With cases such as the two we have just described, not only is the nature of the relationship simple but also we can give some reasonable explanation of the relationship. For example, in the first case, which is a linear relationship, suppose that scores on an intelligence test are the X variable and grades earned in school are the Y variable. We recognize that school grades depend upon the operation of a number of factors such as reading ability and interest in academic work, and that intelligence is only one of them. Therefore we do not expect a perfect relationship between intelligence and school grades. Nevertheless, as we consider individuals of greater and greater degrees of intelligence we do expect them to earn better and better grades, with equal increases in intelligence on the average to be associated with equal increases in grades.

In the second case, which is a curvilinear relationship, suppose that athletic prowess of high school boys is the X variable and the number of other children in school knowing a boy is the Y variable. Again we have a reasonable explanation of the basis of the relationship. We do, of course, recognize the fact that the number of children knowing a given boy is a function of a variety of factors and that athletic prowess is only one of them. Yet we expect that on the average the more a boy participates in school athletics and the more proficiency he displays in school sports, the larger is the number of other children who know him. Furthermore, we might also expect those children who manifest very high levels of athletic proficiency to be known by a disproportionately greater number of children because they have a disproportionately greater opportunity to be seen in action. Therefore a curvilinear relationship might well be anticipated.

THE REGRESSION COEFFICIENT AS AN INDEX OF THE DEGREE OF LINEAR RELATIONSHIP

As we have seen, linear correlation is of great importance for problems in psychological measurement. We wish therefore to have some index or coefficient which indicates the degree of relationship between scores on two variables when the relationship between those variables is linear. In Eqs. (5-7) and (5-8) we developed indices which permit us to describe quantitatively the degree of relationship between two variables. However, these formulae are general ones, and we wish now to consider the quantitative description of relationships that are of a linear sort.

Figure 5-5 shows four different degrees of relationship between variables. In Fig. 5-5a the two variables are completely unrelated, and in Fig. 5-5d they are very closely related. Figure 5-5b and c represent intermediate degrees of relationship. In each of the four diagrams in Fig. 5-5 the two regression lines have been drawn. The solid lines represent the straight lines drawn through the means of the Y scores in the columns, and the dotted lines the straight lines drawn through the X scores of the rows. By inspection we can see that as we proceed from Fig. 5-5a through 5-5b and c to 5-5d, we have higher and higher degrees of relationship between pairs of variables. In our earlier discussion we saw from these diagrams that the higher the degree of relationship between two variables, the smaller the variation among the scores in the columns and in the rows. Now we can also see from these diagrams that the higher the degree of relationship between two variables, the steeper the regression line. The solid lines which are drawn through the means of the columns are referred to their base line X, the abscissa; and the dotted lines are drawn through the means of the rows and are referred to their base line Y, the ordinate.

The slope of the regression line, then, reflects the degree of relationship that holds between two variables; that is, the steeper the line, the higher the degree of relationship. In our development of Eqs. (5-9) and (5-10), the regression equations, we saw that the regression coefficient b describes the degree of slope of the regression line, the trend of the association between the two variables. The regression coefficient, then, gives a measure of the degree to which two variables are related. The larger the magnitude of the regression coefficient, the higher the degree of relationship. In addition, the regression coefficient indicates the direction of the relationship. When the relationship is positive the regression coefficient is positive, and when the relationship is negative the regression coefficient is negative. In view of the value of the regression coefficient as a measure of relationship, we must develop a formula which will permit easy calculation of this constant.

THE EQUIVALENCE OF THE MEANS IN THE REGRESSION EQUATIONS

Before we begin our development let us determine the value of $\bar{Y}_i$, the mean of the Y scores in a column, when X in the regression equation is taken as the mean of all of the X scores, $\bar{X}$. Let there be k values of X, that is, k columns in the scatter diagram. There are, then, k different values of X that can be placed in the regression equation (5-9), and k values of $\bar{Y}_i$ will be obtained. The regression equation (5-9) is

$$\bar{Y}_i = a_Y + b_{Y \cdot X} X_i$$

This is the equation for the mean of the Y scores in any single column i. Now let us multiply both sides of the equation by n_i, the number of cases in that column:

$$n_i \bar{Y}_i = n_i a_Y + n_i b_{Y \cdot X} X_i$$

But $\bar{Y}_i = \Sigma Y_i / n_i$, or $n_i \bar{Y}_i = \Sigma Y_i$. Furthermore, since the number of times a constant is summed to itself is equal to that number times the constant, we can write $\Sigma X_i = n_i X_i$. Hence

$$\Sigma Y_i = n_i a_Y + b_{Y \cdot X} \Sigma X_i$$

This is the equation for any one column. The other columns in the scatter diagram have similar equations. Let us now add together the equations for all columns, that is, column 1 plus column 2, etc., to column k:

$$\Sigma Y_1 = n_1 a_Y + b_{Y \cdot X} \Sigma X_1$$
$$\Sigma Y_2 = n_2 a_Y + b_{Y \cdot X} \Sigma X_2$$
$$\cdot \cdot \cdot \cdot \cdot \cdot \cdot \cdot \cdot \cdot \cdot \cdot$$
$$\underline{\Sigma Y_k = n_k a_Y + b_{Y \cdot X} \Sigma X_k}$$
$$\Sigma Y_1 + \cdots + \Sigma Y_k = n_1 a_Y + \cdots + n_k a_Y + b_{Y \cdot X} \Sigma X_1 + \cdots$$
$$+ b_{Y \cdot X} \Sigma X_k$$

But the sum of the Y scores in the entire scatter diagram, ΣY, is equal to the sum of the sums of the Y scores in all the columns, that is,

$$\Sigma Y = \Sigma Y_1 + \cdots + \Sigma Y_k$$

Therefore

$$\Sigma Y = n_1 a_Y + \cdots + n_k a_Y + b_{Y \cdot X} \Sigma X_1 + \cdots + b_{Y \cdot X} \Sigma X_k$$
$$= a_Y(n_1 + \cdots + n_k) + b_{Y \cdot X}(\Sigma X_1 + \cdots + \Sigma X_k)$$

The total number of cases in the entire scatter diagram is equal to the sum of the numbers of cases in all the columns. That is,

$$n = n_1 + \cdots + n_k$$

and the sum of all the X scores in the entire scatter diagram, ΣX, is equal to the sum of the sums of all the X scores of all the columns. That is,

$$\Sigma X = \Sigma X_1 + \cdots + \Sigma X_k$$

Therefore

$$\Sigma Y = a_Y n + b_{Y \cdot X} \Sigma X$$

Dividing both sides of the equation by n, the total number of cases, we have

$$\frac{\Sigma Y}{n} = \frac{a_Y n}{n} + b_{Y \cdot X} \frac{\Sigma X}{n}$$
$$\bar{Y} = a_Y + b_{Y \cdot X} \bar{X} \qquad (5\text{-}11)$$

$\bar{Y}$, of course, is the mean of all the Y scores in the scatter diagram, and $\bar{X}$ the mean of all the X scores. By a similar derivation we could show

$$\bar{X} = a_X + b_{X \cdot Y} \bar{Y} \qquad (5\text{-}12)$$

Therefore if we place $\bar{X}$, the mean of X, in the one regression equation and solve it, the result will be $\bar{Y}$, the mean value of Y; if we place $\bar{Y}$, the mean value of Y, in the other regression equation and solve it, the result will be $\bar{X}$, the mean value of X. Thus if in our scatter diagram we plot a point for $\bar{Y}_i$ for that value of X which equals the mean of all the X scores and also plot another point for $\bar{X}_i$ for that value of Y which equals the mean of the Y scores, the two points will fall exactly at the same place. Since one of these is a point on one regression line and the other a point on the other regression line, we can see that the regression lines have the property that they intersect or cross each other at the means of the two distributions, $\bar{X}$ and $\bar{Y}$.

THE REGRESSION EQUATION IN DEVIATION-SCORE FORM

So far we have been considering only raw scores. If now we deal with deviation scores, we write the regression equation from Eq. (5-9) as

$$\bar{y}_i = a_y + b_{y \cdot x} x_i$$

These deviation scores are the deviations from the means of the entire distributions. Consequently $\bar{y}_i$ refers to those scores, expressed as deviations from the mean of the entire Y distribution, which fall in column i.

From Eqs. (5-11) and (5-12) we know that the regression lines cross at the point representing the means of the distributions. Since with deviation scores the means are zero [Eq. (3-5)], the intercept a necessarily is zero. That is, when x_i is zero, $\bar{y}_i$ is zero; and when y_i is zero, $\bar{x}_i$ is zero. We can therefore write the two regression equations in deviation-score form as

$$\bar{y}_i = b_{y \cdot x} x_i \tag{5-13}$$
$$\bar{x}_i = b_{x \cdot y} y_i \tag{5-14}$$

Let us now derive a formula that will permit us to compute the regression coefficients from deviation scores. For any value of x, that is, for any column x_i,

$$\bar{y}_i = \frac{\Sigma y_i}{n_i} \quad \text{or} \quad n_i \bar{y}_i = \Sigma y_i$$

Substituting for $\bar{y}_i$ from Eq. (5-13), we have

$$n_i b_{y \cdot x} x_i = \Sigma y_i$$

Let us now multiply both sides of the equation by x_i, remembering that x is a constant for this column since all individuals falling in it have the same x score:

$$n_i b_{y \cdot x} x_i{}^2 = x_i \Sigma y_i$$

But a constant times the sum of a variable is equal to the sum of the constant times the variable. In other words, $x_i \Sigma y_i = \Sigma x_i y_i$. Therefore

$$n_i b_{y \cdot x} x_i{}^2 = \Sigma x_i y_i$$

Now let us sum these equations for the entire scatter diagram, letting there be 1 to k columns or values of x:

$$n_1 b_{y \cdot x} x_1{}^2 + \cdots + n_k b_{y \cdot x} x_k{}^2 = \Sigma x_1 y_1 + \cdots + \Sigma x_k y_k$$

The sum of the sums of the columns equals the sum of the entire scatter diagram.   Hence

$$\Sigma x_1 y_1 + \cdots + \Sigma x_k y_k = \Sigma xy$$

Therefore

$$n_1 b_{y \cdot x} x_1{}^2 + \cdots + n_k b_{y \cdot x} x_k{}^2 = \Sigma xy$$
$$b_{y \cdot x}(n_1 x_1{}^2 + \cdots + n_k x_k{}^2) = \Sigma xy$$

In the above equation, n_1 to n_k are the frequencies with which each of the various values of x occurs. Therefore the terms in the parentheses represent a frequency distribution with each value of x squared. So we could write

$$n_1 x_1{}^2 + \cdots + n_k x_k{}^2 = f_1 x_1{}^2 + \cdots + f_k x_k{}^2 = \Sigma f x^2 = \Sigma x^2$$

Hence

$$b_{y \cdot x} \Sigma x^2 = \Sigma xy$$

Dividing both sides of the equation by the total number of cases, n, we have

$$b_{y \cdot x} \frac{\Sigma x^2}{n} = \frac{\Sigma xy}{n}$$
$$b_{y \cdot x} \sigma_x{}^2 = \frac{\Sigma xy}{n}$$
$$b_{y \cdot x} = \frac{\Sigma xy}{n \sigma_x{}^2} \tag{5-15}$$

By a similar derivation it can be shown that

$$b_{x \cdot y} = \frac{\Sigma xy}{n \sigma_y{}^2} \tag{5-16}$$

The only difference between Eqs. (5-15) and (5-16) is in the variance term in the denominator. Therefore unless the variances of the scores on the two variables are equal, that is, $\sigma_x{}^2 = \sigma_y{}^2$, the two regression coefficients necessarily differ in magnitude. In most instances where either raw or deviation scores are used, the variances of the two distributions will not be equal. If, however, standard scores are used, then the two regression coefficients will necessarily be equal since the variances of both distributions will have the value of 1.00.

MODELS OF CORRELATION BASED ON REGRESSION LINES OF GIVEN SHAPES

Now let us look at the scatter diagram in Fig. 5-6. When we connect the means of the Y scores in the successive columns with a line (the solid line), it is quite a jagged affair and constitutes a very complex curve indeed. The equation for this curve would be extremely complicated. Yet as we look at the means of the columns it appears that they fluctuate in a random fashion around a straight line (the dotted line), and therefore we might be inclined to term the relationship linear.

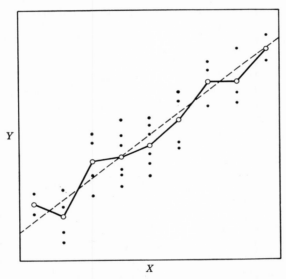

Figure 5-6   An example of a relationship termed linear even though the means of the scores in the columns do not all fall precisely on the same straight line.

What would be our reaction to the statement that the dots in Fig. 5-6 do not "swarm around" a straight line? Undoubtedly we should first point out that altogether there are only 34 cases and that with such a small total number we should not feel secure in making any definite statements about the means of the columns, each of which is based on very few cases. Furthermore, we should say that if the nature of the relationship between the two variables is as complicated a curve as is actually represented by the line drawn through the means of the columns, we should be positing a most complex association between the two variables. We should be saying, from left to right in Fig. 5-6, that as X increases, Y first decreases, then markedly increases, and then decreases more gradually.

Suppose that variable X is an intelligence test and variable Y is grades earned in school. Then we should be maintaining that children with very low intelligence do poorly in school but that those who are a little brighter do even less well, those still brighter do considerably better, and so on. This description of the relationship makes neither good common sense nor good psychological sense.

A much simpler hypothesis, and undoubtedly a more reasonable one, is that the relationship between X and Y is linear but because there are so few cases in our particular group, the means of the columns depart from a straight line just because of sampling error. In effect we are saying that if we did not have just 34 cases but perhaps 34,000 cases, the means of the columns would fall on a straight line. In actual practice, with a situation such as that in Fig. 5-6 where the means of the columns (and of the rows) appear to fluctuate in a random fashion around a straight line, as we increase the number of cases the means of the columns are very likely to come closer and closer to a straight line. But the fact remains that with the limited number of cases ordinarily available to us, seldom do all the means fall exactly on the same straight line. As a matter of fact, even with as many as 34 million cases the means of the columns probably would not fall on the same straight line, though the discrepancies are likely to be ever so small and perhaps would be discernible only in the fourth or fifth decimal place.

Let us now consider the example given in Fig. 5-7. Again we see that a line drawn through the means of the columns (the solid line) is a jagged thing and forms an extremely complicated curve. Such a complex relationship would be difficult to represent by an equation and almost impossible to explain in terms of a functional relationship. If variable X is the athletic prowess of high school boys and Y the number of other children knowing each boy, taking a line running through the means of the columns in Fig. 5-7 as the relationship between these two variables would lead to very curious conclusions. We should have to say that very unathletic boys are not well known, those a bit more athletically inclined are even less well known, those still more athletic are known considerably better, and those still more athletic are again less well known.

But as in the example shown in Fig. 5-6, we see that the means of the columns appear to fluctuate around a regular line, in this case a smoother and simpler curve than that drawn through the means of the columns. Again we are likely to find that as we increase the numbers of cases the means of the columns will more and more closely approach a smooth and simple curve. Therefore undoubtedly we should be willing to hypothesize that the simple curve as represented by the dotted line in the figure, or one very similar to it, would hold if we increased the number of cases.

Only rarely is it found that the means of the columns and the means of the rows fall precisely on the same straight lines or on smooth and simple curves. Yet ordinarily, as we have just seen, we are unwilling to accept as a description of the relationship between the two variables the complex curve which in fact passes through these means. We look for simplicity and regularity in nature partly because it seems more reasonable to us to conceive of a world which is simple and regular, and partly because as yet we do not have the mental power or the intellectual tools to deal with complexity and irregularity.

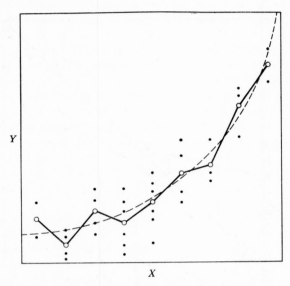

Figure 5-7 An example of a relationship termed curvilinear with a simple curved relationship even though the means of the scores in the columns do not all fall precisely on the same simple curve.

Consequently, when we deal with the relationship between scores on two variables we adopt a straight line or some simple curve as a model and use it to describe the nature of the relationship. The equations for the regression lines that we adopt for a particular set of data, then, do not in fact perfectly describe the association between the two variables as we observe it from the scores earned by a particular sample of individuals. The lines do describe the general trend, and it is our hypothesis that they give a better description. We hypothesize that the straight lines or simple curves we adopt are the best approximations we can get to the regression lines we should find characterizing the relationship between two variables if, instead of our limited sample of individuals, we had an infinitely large number who are of the same general sort as those in our particular sample.

THE BEST-FITTING STRAIGHT LINE IN A LEAST-SQUARES SENSE AS A
MODEL OF LINEAR CORRELATION

Let us now see whether we can derive the regression coefficient without
reference to the means of the columns and rows. That is, let us see whether
we can derive it on the basis of straight lines (the regression lines) that
give the best fit to all the points in the scatter diagram. We shall be considering all the individual points in the scatter diagram, each of which

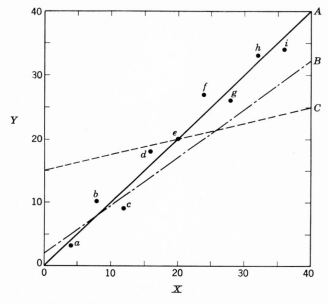

Figure 5-8   Three different straight lines drawn through a set of points.

represents a pair of scores, and not just the means as we did in our
previous derivation.

Figure 5-8 shows the scatter diagram of the relationship between two
variables for nine cases. Obviously we can run an infinite number of
different straight lines through this set of points, but which of these lines
shall we consider to give the best fit? In common parlance we say that
the best-fitting straight line runs through the "middle" of the points.
However, this is a bit vague and we need a more precise statement of
what constitutes the best-fitting straight line. We might say that the
straight line which best fits the points is one where the differences
between the points and the line are at a minimum. That is, if we calculated the difference between each point in a column (or row) and the

point where the straight line passes through it, the mean of these deviations would be smaller than the mean of the deviations from any other
line.

By inspection it is apparent that line A in Fig. 5-8 gives the best fit to
the nine points, line B the second best fit, and line C the poorest fit.
Indeed, line C hardly represents the points at all. Table 5-1 gives the
deviations of the nine points from the three lines. In the table we see that
the means of the deviations from lines A and C are equal, both being
zero, and are smaller than the mean of the deviations from line B, which

TABLE 5-1.   Illustration of the Deviations from Three Straight
Lines and the Squares of Their Deviations

Point	Deviations from line:			Square of the deviations from line:		
	A	B	C	A	B	C
a	−1	−2	−13	1	4	169
b	+2	+2	− 6	4	4	36
c	−3	−2	− 9	9	4	81
d	+2	+4	− 1	4	16	1
e	0	−3	0	0	9	0
f	+3	+7	+ 6	9	49	36
g	−2	+3	+ 4	4	9	16
h	+1	+7	+ 9	1	49	81
i	−2	+5	+10	4	25	100
Sum	0	21	0	36	169	520
Mean	0.00	2.33	0.00	4.00	18.77	57.78

is 2.33. It is therefore clear that the mean of the absolute deviations does
not distinguish between straight lines in terms of the adequacy with
which they fit a set of points.

However, the mean of the squares of the deviations does give an index
of fit which is more descriptive of the degree to which the different lines
fit a set of points. It will be observed in Table 5-1 that the mean of the
squares of the deviations is least for line A, the best-fitting line, and is
greatest for line C, the poorest-fitting line. For this reason, and for other
mathematical considerations, the best-fitting line is taken as that line
from which the mean of the squared deviations is at a minimum.

Let us now develop the equation for the straight line which in a least-
squares sense gives us the best fit through the points in a scatter diagram.
That is, we wish to discover the equation for the straight line from which

the mean of the squares of the deviations is at a minimum.* As we have seen, there are two regression lines in a scatter diagram, one cutting through the columns and the other cutting through the rows. Let us first consider the best-fitting line cutting through the columns.

For convenience in derivation let us take the scores on both variables as deviation scores. We saw in Eq. (5-13) that under these circumstances the intercept a is zero and that the formula for a straight line is

$$\bar{y} = b_{y \cdot x} x_i$$

We are not now saying that the straight line necessarily passes through the means of the columns, so let us write the equation as

$$y' = b_{y \cdot x} x_i \qquad (5\text{-}17)$$

where y' merely refers to that point in column x_i through which the straight line passes.

The question now is, what is the straight line described by $b_{y \cdot x}$ from which the mean of the squared deviations is at a minimum. There are a variety of values we could take as a first estimate of $b_{y \cdot x}$, but let us take

$$b_{y \cdot x} = \frac{\Sigma xy}{n\sigma_x{}^2}$$

Again note that we are not saying that the line described by the foregoing value of $b_{y \cdot x}$ passes through the means of the columns. All we are saying is that it is a value we can calculate from the scores on the two variables, a value we can use as our first estimate of the slope of the best-fitting line in a least-squares sense.

Previously we used the symbol y_i to represent the deviation of an individual's score from $\bar{y}_i$, the mean of his column. Let us now use the symbol v to represent the deviation of an individual's score from the y' of his column when the slope of the line, $b_{y \cdot x}$, is $\Sigma xy/n\sigma_x{}^2$. Then

$$v = y - y'$$

Substituting for y' from Eq. (5-17), we have

$$v = y - b_{y \cdot x} x_i \qquad (5\text{-}18)$$

Squaring both sides of the equation gives

$$v^2 = y^2 - 2b_{y \cdot x} x_i y + b_{y \cdot x}^2 x_i{}^2$$

---

* We shall employ a very roundabout procedure using only simple algebra to develop the equation for the best-fitting straight line. By means of the calculus the same proof could be made in very few steps.

This is the square of the deviation score of any individual from y' in the column in which his x score falls when $b_{y\cdot x} = \Sigma xy/n\sigma_x^2$.

Now let us sum the squared deviations for all individuals in all columns:

$$\Sigma v^2 = \Sigma y^2 - 2b_{y\cdot x}\Sigma xy + b_{y\cdot x}^2\Sigma x^2$$

Dividing both sides of the equation by n, the total number of cases, gives

$$\frac{\Sigma v^2}{n} = \frac{\Sigma y^2}{n} - 2b_{y\cdot x}\frac{\Sigma xy}{n} + b_{y\cdot x}^2\frac{\Sigma x^2}{n}$$

Remembering we are taking $b_{y\cdot x}$ as $\Sigma xy/n\sigma_x^2$, then $\Sigma xy/n = b_{y\cdot x}\sigma_x^2$:

$$\frac{\Sigma v^2}{n} = \sigma_x^2 - 2b_{y\cdot x}b_{y\cdot x}\sigma_x^2 + b_{y\cdot x}^2\sigma_x^2$$

$$= \sigma_y^2 - b_{y\cdot x}^2\sigma_x^2 \tag{5-19}$$

This is the mean of the squares of the deviations from a line when its slope is taken as

$$b_{y\cdot x} = \frac{\Sigma xy}{n\sigma_x^2}$$

If we can show that the mean of the squares of the deviations from a straight line with any other slope, say $\Sigma xy/n\sigma_x^2 + A$ or, more simply, $b_{y\cdot x} + A$, is greater than this, we shall have proved that the regression line as given by Eq. (5-9) and its equivalents is the straight line from which the squares of the deviations are at a minimum.

Let us symbolize a deviation from a line with a slope other than $b_{y\cdot x} = \Sigma xy/n\sigma_x^2$ as d. Then, parallel to Eq. (5-18), we should write this deviation as

$$d = y - (b_{y\cdot x}x_i + A)$$
$$= y - b_{y\cdot x}x_i - A$$

Squaring both sides of the equation gives

$$d^2 = y^2 - 2b_{y\cdot x}x_iy + b_{y\cdot x}^2x_i^2 - 2Ay + 2Ab_{y\cdot x}x_i + A^2$$

This is the square of the deviation score of any individual from the y' of the column in which his x score falls when the slope of the line which describes y' is some value other than $b_{y\cdot x}$, namely, $b_{y\cdot x} + A$. Summing the deviation scores for all individuals in all columns gives

$$\Sigma d^2 = \Sigma y^2 - 2b_{y\cdot x}\Sigma xy + b_{y\cdot x}^2\Sigma x^2 - 2A\Sigma y + 2Ab_{y\cdot x}\Sigma x + \Sigma A^2$$

Dividing both sides of the equation by n, the total number of cases, we get

$$\frac{\Sigma d^2}{n} = \frac{\Sigma y^2}{n} - 2b_{y\cdot x}\frac{\Sigma xy}{n} + b_{y\cdot x}^2\frac{\Sigma x^2}{n} - 2A\frac{\Sigma y}{n} + 2Ab_{y\cdot x}\frac{\Sigma x}{n} + \frac{\Sigma A^2}{n}$$

Since the mean of the deviation scores is zero, the terms involving $\Sigma x/n$ and $\Sigma y/n$ are zero and drop out. The sum of the constant A^2 divided by the number of cases is equal to the constant. That is, $\Sigma A^2/n = A^2$. Finally, we can substitute $b_{y \cdot x}\sigma_x^2$ for $\Sigma xy/n$. Hence

$$
\begin{aligned}
\frac{\Sigma d^2}{n} &= \sigma_y^2 - 2b_{y \cdot x}b_{y \cdot x}\sigma_x^2 + b_{y \cdot x}^2\sigma_x^2 + A^2 \\
&= \sigma_y^2 - b_{y \cdot x}^2\sigma_x^2 + A^2
\end{aligned}
\tag{5-20}
$$

Let us now compare Eq. (5-19) with Eq. (5-20):

$$
\frac{\Sigma v^2}{n} = \sigma_y^2 - b_{y \cdot x}^2\sigma_x^2
$$

$$
\frac{\Sigma d^2}{n} = \sigma_y^2 - b_{y \cdot x}^2\sigma_x^2 + A^2
$$

It is clear from the above equations that $\Sigma v^2/n$ is smaller than $\Sigma d^2/n$. In other words, we have proved that the regression line as given by Eq. (5-9) and its equivalents is that straight line which in a scatter diagram is the line of best fit in a least-squares sense. The mean of the squares of the deviations from it is less than the mean of the squares of the deviations from any other straight line that might be drawn through the scatter diagram. The same reasoning, of course, would hold for the line drawn through the rows.

We can therefore take the regression coefficient either way we may wish. We can, as in our original derivation, impose the condition that the means of the rows and of the columns fall precisely on straight lines; or, as in our second development, we can impose no conditions at all except that we are fitting a straight line in a least-squares sense. With the first derivation we define the regression coefficient as the slope of the regression line when the means of the scores in both the columns and rows fall precisely on straight lines. With the second development we define the regression coefficient as the slope of the regression line when the regression lines are the best-fitting straight lines in a least-squares sense. It should be obvious that the regression lines obtained by our first development also are best-fitting straight lines since we saw that the mean of a distribution—for example, the mean of the distribution of scores in a column or in a row of a scatter diagram—is the point of least squares [Eq. (3-6)].

THE RELATIONSHIP BETWEEN ACCOUNTABLE VARIATION AND THE REGRESSION COEFFICIENT

In Eq. (5-5) we developed a formula which indicates the proportion of variation among individuals in one variable that is accounted for by variation among them in another variable. We also saw that the proportion of accountable variation provides an index of the extent to which two variables are correlated. The greater the proportion of variation in one variable that can be accounted for by the same factors that produce variation in the other, the higher the two variables are related. In Eqs. (5-15) and (5-16) we developed formulae for the regression coefficient, which describes the slope of the regression line. We also saw that the regression coefficient provides an index of the extent to which two variables are correlated. Let us now consider the relationship between the proportion of accountable variation and the regression coefficient.

THE RELATIONSHIP BETWEEN THE PROPORTION OF ACCOUNTABLE VARIATION AND THE REGRESSION COEFFICIENT

The accountable variance as given by Eq. (5-2) is

$$\sigma_{y'}{}^2 = \sigma_y{}^2 - \sigma_{y \cdot x}^2$$

It will be recalled that in developing this formula, in each column we dealt with the deviations of the scores from the means of the columns. Solving for $\sigma_{y \cdot x}^2$, we have

$$\sigma_{y \cdot x}^2 = \sigma_y{}^2 - \sigma_{y'}{}^2 \tag{5-21}$$

In Eq. (5-19) we developed the formula which gives us the mean of the squares of the deviations from the regression line. These deviations we symbolized as v. Let us presuppose the condition under which we first developed the regression equations (5-9) and (5-10), namely, the condition that the regression line is a straight line passing directly through the means of the columns. The deviations from the regression line, v, then are in fact the deviations from the means of the columns and therefore $v = y_i$. Since the partial variance is the mean of the squares of the deviations from the means of the columns, we can write for the case where the regression line passes through the means of the columns

$$\frac{\Sigma v^2}{n} = \frac{\Sigma (y_i - \bar{y}_i)^2}{n} = \sigma_{y \cdot x}^2$$

Equation (5-19) then is

$$\frac{\Sigma v^2}{n} = \sigma_{y \cdot x}^2 = \sigma_y{}^2 - b_{y \cdot x}^2 \sigma^2$$

Substituting for $\sigma_{y \cdot x}^2$ in the above in Eq. (5-21), we have

$$\sigma_y{}^2 - b_{y \cdot x}^2 \sigma_x{}^2 = \sigma_y{}^2 - \sigma_{y'}{}^2$$
$$\sigma_{y'}{}^2 = b_{y \cdot x}^2 \sigma_x{}^2$$
$$\sigma_{y'} = b_{y \cdot x} \sigma_x \tag{5-22}$$

Similarly, we could show

$$\sigma_{x'} = b_{y \cdot x} \sigma_y \tag{5-23}$$

Hence, given the condition that the regression lines pass directly through the means of the columns and rows, we could calculate from the regression coefficient the extent of variation in one variable that is due to the same factors which produce differences among them in another.

We also said that both the proportion of accountable variation ($\sigma_{y'}/\sigma_y$ and $\sigma_{x'}/\sigma_x$) and the regression coefficient ($b_{y \cdot x}$ and $b_{x \cdot y}$) are indices of the degree of correlation between variables. If we divide Eq. (5-22) by σ_y and Eq. (5-23) by σ_y, we can see the relationship between these two indices:

$$\frac{\sigma_{y'}}{\sigma_y} = b_{y \cdot x} \frac{\sigma_x}{\sigma_y} \tag{5-24}$$

$$\frac{\sigma_{x'}}{\sigma_x} = b_{x \cdot y} \frac{\sigma_y}{\sigma_x} \tag{5-25}$$

With given values of σ_x and σ_y, then, as the proportion of accountable variation increases so does the magnitude of the regression coefficient. However, it is also apparent that $\sigma_{y'}/\sigma_y$ does not equal $b_{y \cdot x}$, nor does $\sigma_{x'}/\sigma_x$ equal $b_{x \cdot y}$. Hence when we calculate these two values for a given set of data they give us different quantitative descriptions of the degree of relationship. We shall deal with this matter later.

HOLDING CONSTANT VARIATION IN A VARIABLE BY USE OF THE REGRESSION LINE

In our original development we held constant variation among individuals in one variable by subtracting from each person's score in the second variable the mean of the scores in the second variable of those individuals who have the same score as he in the first variable ($y_i - \bar{y}_i$). We saw that if we are dealing with a circumstance such as that shown in Figs. 5-6 and 5-7 where lines drawn through the means of the columns are very irregular, if we accept those lines we are presuming a very complex functional relationship between the two variables. Since such complex relationships are very difficult to understand and to explain, and the number of cases in a given set of data is limited so that we do not entirely trust the particular complex relationship that exists among them, we may prefer to assume that a much simpler functional relationship exists. When the means of the columns and of the rows appear to fluctuate in a random fashion around straight lines, we may prefer to use the best-fitting straight lines as describing the relationship. We take these straight lines, then, as a description of the functional relationship between variables and ignore the actual means of the columns and rows. Consequently we do not use $y_i - \bar{y}_i$ as a means for holding x constant; instead, we use v, the deviation from the regression line. In a similar fashion, if we feel that a simple curve rather than a complex one as in Fig. 5-7 gives a more reasonable description of the functional relationship, then again we deal with variations from the simple curve rather than from the means of the columns as a procedure for holding x constant.

If we accept the best-fitting straight line as the description of the functional relationship between two variables, then in this sense we can reconcile $\Sigma v^2/n$ as having the same meaning as $\sigma_{y \cdot x}^2$, the partial variance. From this point of view we can accept Eqs. (5-24) and (5-25) without presuming that in our data the means of the columns and rows fall precisely on straight lines or that to hold a variable constant we must calculate the deviations from the means of the columns or the rows.

Summary

When the scores on two variables are related, it means that differences among individuals on one are to some degree due to the same factors that produce differences among them on the other. Furthermore, it means that scores on one can be predicted on a better-than-chance basis from scores on the other. Since the relationships between variables have these important implications, it is desirable to have some index or coefficient which describes the degree of relationship between two variables. Inasmuch as linear relationships are so characteristically found between scores on psychological traits, we wish to develop a coefficient of linear correlation.

The bivariate distribution, or scatter diagram, of the scores on two variables places individuals in columns in terms of their scores on variable X, and in rows in terms of their scores on variable Y. Therefore, for individuals in any column, X is a constant and Y a variable; and for individuals in any row, Y is a constant and X a variable. If one property is held constant, a comparison of the extent of variation among individuals in the other with the total variation among individuals permits an estimation of the degree to which the same factors produce differences among individuals in both. This value, the proportion of accountable variation, varies with the degree of relationship between the two variables and hence can be used as an index of relationship.

If the extent of variation in Y scores with X constant differs from column to column, or the variation in X scores with Y constant varies from row to row, the interpretation of the effects of common factors is difficult. With this heteroscedasticity the proportion of accountable variation is only an average statement. Therefore it may be desirable to adopt homoscedasticity, equal variation in all columns and equal variation in all rows, as a model. In such a case, the average variation in the columns is used as a description of the variation in all columns, and the average variation in the rows as a description of the variation in all rows. Homoscedasticity holds when scores on both variables are normally distributed.

Linear relationship can be defined as that situation wherein the means of the Y scores in the columns all fall on a straight line, and the means of the X scores in the rows also fall on a straight line. These two lines are termed regression lines, and each is described by the regression equation. The slope of a regression line is described by the regression coefficient, one of the terms in the regression equation. Inasmuch as the magnitude of the regression coefficient varies with the degree of relationship between two variables, it, too, can be used as an index of association. It has the desirable feature of indicating whether the relationship is positive or negative.

Seldom, if ever, do the means of the columns and the means of the rows fall precisely on straight lines. However, they often appear to be random fluctuations from such lines. Therefore, linear correlation is commonly adopted as a model. In such a case the best-fitting straight line in a least-squares sense is taken to describe the relationship. It just so happens that the slope of this best-fitting straight line is given by the regression coefficient. Whether or not the means of the columns and rows fall precisely on straight lines, the regression coefficient is still an index of the degree of relationship between two variables.

Selected Readings

Binder, A.: Considerations of the place of assumptions in correlation analysis, *Am. Psychologist,* **14** :504–510, 1959.

Ezekiel, M.: "Methods of Correlation Analysis," Wiley, 1941.

Fisher, R. A.: "Statistical Methods for Research Workers," Oliver & Boyd, 1946.

Nygaard, P. H.: A percentage equivalent for the coefficient of correlation, *J. Educational Psychol.,* **17** :86–97, 1926.

Pearson, K.: Notes on the history of correlation, *Biometrika,* **13** :24–25, 1920–21.

Tryon, R. C.: The interpretation of the coefficient of correlation, *Psychological Rev.,* **36** :419–445, 1929.

Yule, G. U., and M. G. Kendall: "Theory of Statistics," Griffin, 1940.

chapter 6   The Measure-

ment of Linear Correlation

Our task is to develop an index or coefficient that describes the degree of relationship existing between two variables when the relationship is taken to be linear. The index should be of such a nature that when there is little or no relationship between the two variables its value is small and when the relationship is high its value is large. When the relationship is positive the sign of the index should be positive, and when the relationship is negative the sign of the index should be negative. Finally, an index of relationship for a given set of data should be given as a single number summarizing and describing all aspects of the relationship.

    In Chap. 5 we introduced some concepts basic to the understanding of the theory of linear correlation. We saw how both the proportion of accountable variation and the regression coefficient provide indices of the degree of relationship between two variables. In this chapter we shall examine the adequacy of these two values as indices of correlation in light of the above criteria for an acceptable index of relationship. They will be found wanting in certain respects, but we shall be able to develop from them another index, the Pearsonian coefficient of correlation, which is much more satisfactory. We shall critically evaluate this coefficient and then we shall consider it in relation to models of correlation. Finally, we

141

shall describe ways for measuring relationships when one or both variables are dichotomous.

ACCOUNTABLE VARIATION AND THE REGRESSION COEFFICIENT AS INDICES OF CORRELATION

In Chap. 5 we saw that the accountable variation among individuals as measured by $\sigma_{y'}/\sigma_y$ and $\sigma_{x'}/\sigma_x$ varies with the degree of relationship existing between two variables. The higher the degree of relationship, the higher are the values $\sigma_{y'}/\sigma_y$ and $\sigma_{x'}/\sigma_x$. In addition we saw that the regression coefficient b measuring the slope of the regression line also varies with the degree of relationship between two variables. The higher the degree of relationship, the higher is the value b, indicating steeper and steeper regression lines. Let us now see how well $\sigma_{y'}/\sigma_y$, $\sigma_{x'}/\sigma_x$, and b serve as indices of relationship.

THE PROPORTION OF ACCOUNTABLE VARIATION AS AN INDEX OF RELATIONSHIP

We have seen that when the relationship between two variables is low the value of the proportion of accountable variation, $\sigma_{y'}/\sigma_y$ and $\sigma_{x'}/\sigma_x$, is low and when the relationship is high the value of the proportion of accountable variation is large. When there is no relationship at all between two variables, the variation among individuals in the columns and rows of a scatter diagram is equal to the total variation. That is, the partial variance is equal to the total variance:

$$\sigma_{y \cdot x}^2 = \sigma_y{}^2 \quad \text{and} \quad \sigma_{x \cdot y}^2 = \sigma_x{}^2$$

Equations (5-5) and (5-6) give the proportion of accountable variation in terms of the partial and total variances:

$$\frac{\sigma_{y'}}{\sigma_y} = \sqrt{1 - \frac{\sigma_{y \cdot x}^2}{\sigma_y{}^2}} \tag{5-5}$$

$$\frac{\sigma_{x'}}{\sigma_x} = \sqrt{1 - \frac{\sigma_{x \cdot y}^2}{\sigma_x{}^2}} \tag{5-6}$$

When the partial variation equals the total variation, then the numerator of the second term to the right in the equations equals the denominator so that it becomes 1 and the entire expression under the square-root sign becomes equal to zero. Hence the lowest value that $\sigma_{y'}/\sigma_y$ and $\sigma_{x'}/\sigma_x$ can take is zero, and this occurs when there is no relationship at all between the two variables.

When the two variables are perfectly correlated, then there is no variation at all among the individuals either in the columns or in the rows. In this case the partial variance is zero so that the fraction becomes zero and the entire expression under the square-root sign becomes 1. Hence the highest value that $\sigma_{y'}/\sigma_y$ and $\sigma_{x'}/\sigma_x$ can take is unity, and this occurs when the relationship between the two variables is perfect. This is a most desirable characteristic for an index of relationship to have. It permits easy comparisons among relationships in terms of their degree.

However, as an index of relationship the proportion of accountable variation has the undesirable feature of not indicating the direction of the relationship. From Eqs. (5-5) and (5-6) it can be seen that $\sigma_{y'}/\sigma_y$ and $\sigma_{x'}/\sigma_x$ are always positive. Furthermore, for any given relationship there may be two different values of accountable variation, one for $\sigma_{y'}/\sigma_y$ and the other for $\sigma_{x'}/\sigma_x$.

THE REGRESSION COEFFICIENT AS AN INDEX OF RELATIONSHIP

In our earlier discussion of linear correlation we saw that the closer the association between two variables, the steeper is the slope of the regression line. Since the slope of the regression line is described by the regression coefficient, we can say that the higher the degree of relationship between scores on two variables, the higher is the value of the regression coefficient. The regression coefficient, therefore, can be used as an index of the degree of relationship between two variables.

When two variables are completely unrelated, the means of the scores in all the columns are equal to each other and so are the means of the rows. Consequently the regression lines are parallel to the base lines and, having no slope, the regression coefficients that describe them are zero. Hence when $b = 0$ the two variables are uncorrelated. In this way b has a most desirable feature as an index of relationship. However, when b is determined from raw or deviation scores it does not have a single maximum value, and in this way it is deficient. It will be recalled that b describes the number of units of change in one variable that is associated with one unit of increase in the other. This number may be very small or it may be very large, but it has no absolute ceiling for all bivariate distributions. The largest value it could have for any given set of data would be the difference between the lowest and highest scores earned, and this range, of course, differs with different sets of data.

A second desirable feature of the regression coefficient as an index of linear correlation is that it indicates the direction of the relationship. When the relationship is positive, then b is positive, indicating that an increase in one variable is associated with an increase in the other. When the relationship is negative, then b is negative, indicating that an increase in one variable is associated with a decrease in the other.

However, the regression coefficient has two important shortcomings. First of all, as we have seen in Eqs. (5-15) and (5-16), for any bivariate distribution of raw or deviation scores there are two regression coefficients, and ordinarily they are different in magnitude. Hence the regression coefficient does not give a single unique description of the relationship. But, more important, the magnitude of the regression coefficient is a function of the nature of the units in which the scale is expressed. Let us look at the scatter diagram shown in Fig. 6-1. Here we see illustrated a hypothetical relationship between intelligence as measured by mental age and reading proficiency as measured by grade level achieved. If we express mental age in units of years, then the regression coefficient is

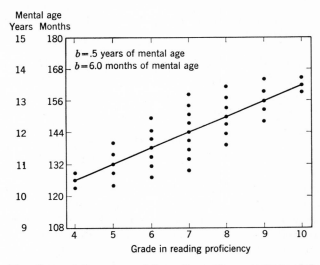

Figure 6-1   The effects of the nature of the units on the magnitude of the regression coefficient.

+.5, and if we express it in units of months then it is +6.0. For one and the same relationship, then, we can have different values of b depending upon the nature of the units in which we happen to express our variables. In the case just given it really makes no difference whether we express mental age in years or in months, since all we wish to know is the relationship between intelligence and reading ability.

A COEFFICIENT OF LINEAR CORRELATION

We have seen the need in psychological measurement for an index which describes the degree of relationship between variables which are associated in a linear fashion. We have also set forth the characteristics that such an index should possess if it is to be useful. Finally, we have considered two possible indices, the proportion of accountable variation and the regression coefficient, and we have seen that they are not altogether satisfactory. We shall now develop the commonly used index of linear relationship, the *Pearsonian coefficient of correlation,* named after Karl Pearson, the famous English biometrician who first developed it. Depending on how we view this coefficient, it may or may not possess the features we wish in an index of relationship. We can best begin our development of the Pearsonian coefficient from the regression coefficient, and then we shall be able to relate it to accountable variation.

THE PEARSONIAN COEFFICIENT OF CORRELATION

We saw that one important shortcoming of the regression coefficient lies in the fact that while its magnitude does vary with the degree of relationship that exists between the two variables, it also varies with the nature of the units in which those variables are expressed. Consequently we might have two relationships which are of precisely the same degree, yet the regression coefficient of one might be quite different in magnitude from the regression coefficient of the other.

If scores on all variables were expressed in terms of the same units, this problem would be resolved. In Chaps. 3 and 4 we dealt with the problem of making scores on different variables comparable. We said that if scores are referenced to the total distribution in which they occur, then in one sense scores in one variable can be considered comparable to scores in another. One way of doing this is by means of standard scores. A given standard score in two variables has the same meaning in the sense that it refers to an individual who stands the same distance from the mean in terms of standard-score units. If we are willing to accept standard scores on different variables as being expressed in the same units, then the problem of units in connection with the regression coefficient is solved. If we transmute scores on all variables to standard scores when we speak of a change in one variable being associated with a certain number of units of change in another variable, as we do with the regression coefficient, then we are doing so in terms of standard deviation units.

Let us therefore specify the use of standard scores when we compute our index of correlation, the regression coefficient. To differentiate the circumstance when standard scores are used in the computation of the regression coefficient rather than raw or deviation scores, the symbol r is used instead of b. Since r is so commonly used as an index of relationship, it is termed a coefficient of correlation, the Pearsonian coefficient of correlation.

Let us begin our derivation of r with the formula for the regression coefficient given as Eq. (5-15):

$$b_{y \cdot x} = \frac{\Sigma xy}{n\sigma_x^2} \qquad (5\text{-}15)$$

In standard scores this formula is

$$b_{z_y \cdot z_x} = r_{y \cdot x} = \frac{\Sigma z_x z_y}{n \sigma_{z_x}^2}$$

Since the variance of standard scores, $\sigma_{z_x}^2$, is 1.00,

$$r_{y \cdot x} = \frac{\Sigma z_x z_y}{n} \tag{6-1}$$

The formula for the other regression coefficient is

$$b_{x \cdot y} = \frac{\Sigma xy}{n \sigma_y^2}$$

In standard scores this would be

$$r_{x \cdot y} = \frac{\Sigma z_x z_y}{n} \tag{6-2}$$

The terms to the right in Eqs. (6-1) and (6-2) are precisely the same. Hence we can say that $r_{y \cdot x} = r_{x \cdot y}$. Since the Pearsonian coefficient of correlation is the regression coefficient when scores on both variables are expressed as standard scores, we can say that when standard scores are related the two regression lines have exactly the same slope. Hence with standard scores the two regression coefficients have precisely the same value and are commonly symbolized as r_{xy}. We can also see from Eqs. (6-1) and (6-2) that the Pearsonian coefficient of correlation also is a mean, being the mean of the cross products of standard scores.

Ordinarily the formula for the Pearsonian coefficient is given in terms of deviation rather than standard scores. Since $z_x = x/\sigma_x$ and $z_y = y/\sigma_y$,

$$\begin{aligned} r_{xy} &= \frac{\Sigma(x/\sigma_x)(y/\sigma_y)}{n} \\ &= \frac{(1/\sigma_x \sigma_y)\Sigma xy}{n} \\ &= \frac{\Sigma xy}{n \sigma_x \sigma_y} \end{aligned} \tag{6-3}$$

MAXIMUM AND MINIMUM VALUES OF THE PEARSONIAN COEFFICIENT OF CORRELATION

Let us now see what the minimum and maximum values of the Pearsonian coefficient of correlation are. That is, when we apply Eq. (6-3) or its equivalents to a set of data and perform the indicated computations, what are the smallest and largest values we could possibly obtain?

When there is no relationship at all between two variables, the two regression lines are parallel to their base lines. The lines, then, have the slope of .00; hence the value of the coefficient of correlation r is .00. This, of course, is a minimum value. If we are dealing with the special case where the means of the scores in the columns and rows fall exactly on straight lines, then when the two variables are completely uncorrelated the means of the scores in all the columns are equal to each other and are equal to the mean of the total distribution of Y scores. Similarly, the means of the scores in all the rows are equal to each other and are equal to the mean of the X scores.

When the correlation between two variables is perfect, then by definition each person's standard score on one variable is exactly equal to his standard score on the other variable. That is, $z_x = z_y$. Therefore, from Eq. (6-1),

$$r_{xy} = \frac{\Sigma z_x z_y}{n} = \frac{\Sigma z^2}{n}$$

But this is the variance of standard scores, which is 1.00 [Eq. (4-3)]. Therefore the highest value that r can attain is 1.00, which represents a perfect correlation.

THE EFFECTS OF THE SHAPES OF THE DISTRIBUTIONS OF SCORES ON THE MAXIMUM VALUE OF r

Up to now in our development of the Pearsonian coefficient of correlation we have not mentioned the shapes of the distributions of scores in the two variables, and we have imposed no conditions whatsoever concerning their nature. But let us see what effects they might have upon the maximum value that r can take.

In Fig. 6-2a we have two distributions of scores, both of which are skewed, and skewed in opposite directions. Suppose we deliberately try to place the scores of the eight individuals in the scatter diagram so that the highest possible relationship holds. If we are completely successful we shall have all individuals placed in the cells in the diagonal running from the upper right-hand corner of the diagram to the lower left-hand corner. But because of the nature of the two distributions of scores this is impossible. The best we can do is represented in Fig. 6-2a. This is the highest possible relationship that can exist between scores on these two particular variables for these particular eight cases. When we compute the Pearsonian coefficient by means of Eq. (6-3) we find it to be only .91.

Similarly, in Fig. 6-2b we have two variables whose distributions of scores differ in degree of kurtosis. In this diagram also the cases are placed as nearly as possible to fall in the diagonal of cells running from the upper right-hand to the lower left-hand corner. The highest possible value for the Pearsonian coefficient in this instance is only .92.

Therefore we can see from these examples that when the distributions of scores on the two variables differ in shape, the maximum value for r is less than 1.00. The maximum value varies with the nature of the two distributions and is lower the more the two distributions differ in skewness and kurtosis. However, we can see in Fig. 6-2c and d that it is not the shapes of the distributions of scores as such that limit the maximum value of r but only the differences in shape. In these two diagrams we have distributions that in one case are highly skewed and in the other are highly

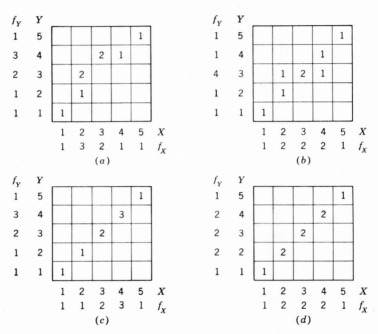

Figure 6-2   Examples of the effects of the nature of the distributions of scores on the maximum value of r. (a) Two distributions skewed in opposite directions, r = .91; (b) one platykurtic and one leptokurtic distribution, r = .92; (c) two distributions skewed in the same direction, r = 1.00; and (d) two distributions with the same degree of kurtosis, r = 1.00.

platykurtic; yet because in both variables the distributions are of the same shape, all individuals can be placed in the diagonal cells, resulting in maximum coefficients of 1.00.

SOLUTIONS TO THE PROBLEM OF THE MAXIMUM VALUE OF THE
PEARSONIAN COEFFICIENT

We have just seen that unless the distributions of scores on both variables being related have exactly the same skewness and kurtosis (that is, the same shape), it is impossible for the Pearsonian coefficient computed from their scores ever to have a value as high as 1.00. Therefore if we wish to define the Pearsonian coefficient as always having a maximum possible value of 1.00, we shall have to specify that it is to be applied only in those instances where the shapes of the distributions of scores on both variables being related are precisely the same. However, seldom if ever do two distributions of scores have precisely the same shape. Hence this specification would so limit the instances where the Pearsonian coefficient could be used that it would be valueless.

There are three solutions to this problem. First of all, we can face the fact that the relationship between two variables cannot be perfect and accept the situation as it is. It is apparent from the arrangements of scores in the scatter diagrams of Fig. 6-2a and b that with the particular individuals involved neither relationship is perfect. On the basis of this first point of view we should say that the fact that they are the highest possible relationships which could occur under the circumstances has no significance at all. It cannot be denied that neither relationship is perfect, and that is just the nature of the case. However, it should be clear that if we adopt this point of view we are in effect saying that the particular operations by means of which we measure individuals on the two variables define the nature of those variables. There may be no reason other than one's personal inclination for not adopting this position. Nevertheless, there are those who wish to divorce particular operations from the definition of the variable. As we have seen, we may wish to consider a particular set of operations merely as one of perhaps several different and equally good ways for measuring a particular variable. If we are unwilling to agree to a proposition such as "Intelligence is defined as that which is measured by test X," then we cannot accept this first point of view.

As a second solution to the problem of the maximum value of the Pearsonian coefficient we could take the position that the normal frequency distribution is indeed the "true" distribution of scores on all variables. In Chap. 4 we considered the various arguments on this matter. If we were willing to accept this point of view, we could justify transmuting scores into other values which are normally distributed. Then all frequency distributions would have exactly the same shape, and the maximum possible value of r for all relationships would in fact be 1.00. However, this is quite an extreme position to take, and for many there is insufficient theoretical or empirical basis to justify making such an assumption about the manner in which individuals differ among themselves on all variables.

Finally, we might solve the problem of the maximum value of r by taking the normal frequency distribution as a model. We do not have to adopt the extreme position given above: that scores always are normally distributed but only the large proportion of frequency distributions are so nearly similar to a normal distribution that a normal distribution gives quite a good representation of them. This point of view is something like the one we adopt with respect to the shape of the world. We say that the world is spherical in shape even though the obvious irregularities on its surface, the mountains and valleys, prove it is not. Nevertheless, for most practical purposes we can ignore the differences between the true shape of the world and that of our model. So while actual distributions of scores are not precisely normal, we might say that we consider them as being so without any great loss or without introducing any great degree of inaccuracy of description. Indeed, in most instances if we compute the Pearsonian coefficient between raw scores and then transmute the scores to other values which do distribute in a normal fashion, we shall find that the Pearsonian coefficient for the normalized scores ordinarily will be greater, but not more than about .02 to .05. Furthermore, even with distributions of scores such as those in Fig. 6-2a and b, which differ markedly from a normal distribution, the maximum value of r is not greatly below 1.00. Finally, since only in very rare instances are relationships between psychological variables anywhere near perfect, the fact that the maximum value of 1.00 cannot be attained might be considered purely an academic problem. Yet as with all imperfect models the instances of great deviation from them are troublesome. It is of little help to assure the mountain climber that conceptually he is walking along a plain. Nor does it help when one is seeking to relate ratings highly negatively skewed through the leniency error with positively skewed scores on a test which is too difficult for the individuals being tested.

THE REGRESSION EQUATION EXPRESSED IN TERMS OF THE PEARSONIAN COEFFICIENT OF CORRELATION

We have shown in Eq. (5-13)

$$\bar{y}_i = b_{y \cdot x} x_i$$

This is the regression equation in deviation-score form. When standard scores are used, this equation is written as

$$\bar{z}_{y_i} = r_{xy} z_{x_i} \tag{6-4}$$

and similarly

$$\bar{z}_{x_i} = r_{xy} z_{y_i} \tag{6-5}$$

Very seldom are two variables perfectly related. Consequently the coefficient of correlation between two variables ordinarily is less than 1.00. If we examine Eqs. (6-4) and (6-5) we can see the origin of the term "regression," which we have used so often in our discussion of correlation. If we take any value for r_{xy} that is less than 1.00 and insert any value for z_{x_i} in Eq. (6-4), we shall find that $\bar{z}_{y_i}$ will be smaller than z_{x_i}, that is, closer to the mean. Hence we have a "regression" toward the mean. The same situation, of course, would hold for $\bar{z}_{x_i}$ and z_{y_i} in Eq. (6-5).

Since $z = x/\sigma$, we can write Eq. (6-4) as

$$\frac{\bar{y}_i}{\sigma_y} = r_{xy} \frac{x_i}{\sigma_x}$$

Therefore

$$\bar{y}_i = r_{xy} \frac{\sigma_y}{\sigma_x} x_i \tag{6-6}$$

and

$$\bar{x}_i = r_{xy} \frac{\sigma_x}{\sigma_y} y_i \tag{6-7}$$

Equations (6-6) and (6-7) are the regression equations in deviation-score form utilizing r instead of b.

Since $y = Y - \bar{Y}$ and $x = X - \bar{X}$, we can write Eq. (6-6) as

$$\bar{Y}_i - \bar{Y} = r_{xy} \frac{\sigma_y}{\sigma_x} (X_i - \bar{X})$$

Rearranging terms gives

$$\bar{Y}_i = r_{xy} \frac{\sigma_y}{\sigma_x} (X_i - \bar{X}) + \bar{Y} \tag{6-8}$$

Similarly,

$$\bar{X}_i = r_{xy} \frac{\sigma_x}{\sigma_y} (Y_i - \bar{Y}) + \bar{X} \tag{6-9}$$

Equations (6-8) and (6-9) are raw-score forms of the regression equations.

INTERPRETATIONS OF THE PEARSONIAN COEFFICIENT AS
DESCRIBING THE REGRESSION LINE

There are two reasons that the regression line is important to us. First of all, it is useful when we wish to predict scores on one variable from scores on another. Secondly, it provides a description of the nature of the functional relationship between two variables. In Chap. 5 we saw that with linear relationships the slope of the regression line is given by the regression coefficient. Since the Pearsonian coefficient is derived from the regression coefficient and, indeed, is no more nor less than one form of it, it too describes the regression line. Let us therefore examine specifically the kinds of descriptions this coefficient can be interpreted as giving of the regression line.

Suppose we know nothing about a person except that he took a particular test, test Y. Let us say that we wish to know his score on it. What would be our best guess or prediction? Since the person's score might be anywhere in the total distribution of Y scores we might say that any Y score picked at random is just as good a guess as any other Y score. However, this is not true because obviously we should like to select a score that is least likely to be in error, that is, a score of such a value that the difference between it and the Y score the individual actually earned is at a minimum. It will be recalled that in Chap. 3 we saw that the mean of a distribution of scores is that score in the distribution from which the squared deviations or differences are at a minimum [Eq. (3-7)]. Therefore if we choose the mean of the Y scores as our best prediction of the Y score of our individual, the predicted score is that score which in the long run is least likely to be in error.

But suppose we know something else about the individual, say his score on test X. Now what would be our best prediction of his Y score? Let us presume that scores on the two tests are positively related in a linear fashion. Again our best guess would be the mean, though in this case the mean of the Y scores of those individuals who earned the same score as he did on test X. Therefore, if the regression line goes through the means of the columns, or the means of the rows if we are predicting X from Y, we can use the regression equation to obtain the best prediction of the individual's Y score from the only other information we have about him, his score on test X. Consequently, the regression equation is of utmost importance for predicting an individual's score on one variable from his score on another.

Suppose we have the following data on two tests:

$$\bar{X} = 10 \qquad \sigma_x = 2 \qquad \bar{Y} = 100 \qquad \sigma_y = 20 \qquad r_{xy} = .50$$

Let us now predict the score on test Y of an individual whose X score is 12, and therefore whose x score is $+2$ and whose z_x score is $+1$. We apply Eqs. (6-8), (6-6), and (6-4) as follows:

$$\bar{Y}_i = (.50)^{2}\!\%_2(12 - 10) + 100 = 110 \qquad (6\text{-}8)$$
$$\bar{y}_i = (.50)^{2}\!\%_2(2) = 10 \qquad (6\text{-}6)$$
$$\bar{z}_{y_i} = (.50)(1) = .5 \qquad (6\text{-}4)$$

In Eqs. (6-4) and (6-5) we saw that the Pearsonian coefficient describes the regression line when scores on both variables are expressed in standard-score form. Now let us see how this coefficient can be interpreted.

When we first developed the regression equation we dealt only with that circumstance wherein the means of the columns and of the rows fall precisely on straight lines. If we accept this circumstance, then the Pearsonian coefficient is very valuable in terms of the interpretations that can be made directly from it. It precisely describes the functional relationship between two variables, and from it we can directly obtain the best possible prediction of scores in one variable from scores in the other. However, as we saw, seldom if ever do we actually find the means of the columns or of the rows falling precisely on the same straight line. Therefore, valuable as this would make the Pearsonian coefficient in terms of the information it gives us directly, the circumstances in which it could be applied would be so limited that it would be useless.

Taking linear correlation to refer to the general tendency of the points in the bivariate distribution to "swarm" around a straight line, we showed that in a least-squares sense the regression equation describes the straight line that best fits the "swarm" of points. We might, then, define the Pearsonian coefficient as the slope of the regression line when scores on both variables are expressed as standard scores and the regression line is the best-fitting line in a least-squares sense. Now of what conceivable value would such a line in and of itself be to us? To be sure, it does describe the general tendency of the "swarm" of points, but that is all it does for us. It does not tell us about the characteristics of the functional relationship, nor does it permit us to make the type of predictions we want from scores on one variable to scores on the other.

Finally, we might adopt linear correlation as a model, taking the best-fitting straight line in a least-squares sense as defining our model. With standard scores this is given, of course, by the Pearsonian coefficient. As a representation of the functional relationship between the two variables the regression equation then represents our *theory* of how the two variables are related. In prediction we use the regression equation to obtain estimates of the means of the scores in the columns and rows. Therefore we use estimates in making our predictions. These estimates have some value, since an estimate is better than no information at all. In a somewhat similar fashion, for practical purposes of navigation we may adopt the theory that the world is flat. If we are concerned only with a small portion of the earth's surface, say the eastern Mediterranean Sea, we pass a plane through the earth's surface, projecting the features on the surface of the sphere to the plane.

By using a theoretical model whose characteristics are quite similar to but perhaps not precisely the same as those of the facts of the matter, we have a good representation of those facts and we can make good predictions about them. Obviously our model is better the more congruent its characteristics are with those of the facts. Hence the model of a flat world is quite satisfactory if we are concerned only with the eastern Mediterranean Sea but is of considerably less value if we are concerned with the entire Pacific Ocean. Similarly, our model of linear correlation is quite good if the means of the columns and of the rows fluctuate in a random fashion around a straight line and their deviations from it are small. Such a model is of substantially less value if the fluctuations of the means from the regression line are great or if, instead of swarming around a straight line, the points tend to swarm around a line with substantial curvature.

Indeed, we may have more faith in the model of linear correlation than in the characteristics of a particular set of data. Let us say that in the bivariate distribution of the scores of a particular sample of individuals, the means of the columns and of the rows do not fall on straight lines but rather fluctuate randomly around straight lines. We should probably hypothesize that with other samples we should have the same state of affairs but with the particular fluctuations of the means of the columns and rows varying from sample to sample. Hence we should conclude that if we had the entire population rather than just a sample, the means of the columns and of the rows would fall precisely on straight lines. We take the best-fitting straight lines in a least-squares sense in our original sample as the best estimate of the regression line in the population. Consequently we should believe that with other samples, prediction from the straight line of best fit will be more accurate than predictions from the means of the columns or of the rows of our original sample.

VARIATION FROM THE REGRESSION LINE—THE STANDARD ERROR OF ESTIMATE OR PREDICTION

We have seen that when we restrict linear correlation to those situations where the means of the columns and of the rows fall on straight lines, the regression equation gives us the best prediction of an individual's score on one variable from his score on the other. That is, the best prediction of an individual's y score from his x score is $\bar{y}_i$, and the best prediction of his x score from his y score is $\bar{x}_i$. We should also like to know the magnitude of the error of our prediction. The error of prediction for any given individual is

$$y - \bar{y}_i$$

That is, the difference between an individual's actual y score and the score we predict for him, $\bar{y}_i$, is our error. A distribution of these errors for all individuals would give a good index of how far off we are in predicting y from x. The wider the distribution the larger are our errors, and the smaller the distribution the smaller are our errors. Since the standard deviation is a measure of how spread out a distribution is, we can use it as an index of the extent of our errors of prediction. This value, $\sigma_{y-\bar{y}}$, we discussed in Chap. 5, and we saw that it can be symbolized as $\sigma_{y \cdot x}$. This is the partial standard deviation and refers to the variation in y when x is constant. Similarly, $\sigma_{x \cdot y}$ would describe the distribution of our errors in predicting x scores from y scores.

But we have already developed the formula for the standard deviation of these errors in prediction in another connection. We symbolized these differences as

$$v = y - \bar{y}_i$$

and developed the formula for the mean of the squares of these deviations, which is the variance or the square of the standard deviation when we are dealing with deviations from the regression line, as in Eq. (5-19):

$$\frac{\Sigma v^2}{n} = \sigma_y{}^2 - b^2_{y\cdot x}\sigma_x{}^2$$

In Eq. (5-15) we have

$$b_{y\cdot x} = \frac{\Sigma xy}{n\sigma_x{}^2}$$

Substituting for $b_{y\cdot x}$ from Eq. (5-15) in Eq. (5-19), we have

$$\frac{\Sigma v^2}{n} = \sigma_y{}^2 - \left(\frac{\Sigma xy}{n}\right)^2 \frac{\sigma_x{}^2}{\sigma_x{}^4}$$

From Eq. (6-3) we know that $\Sigma xy/n = \sigma_x\sigma_y r_{xy}$. Hence

$$\frac{\Sigma v^2}{n} = \sigma_y{}^2 - \frac{\sigma_x{}^2\sigma_y{}^2 r_{xy}{}^2\sigma_x{}^2}{\sigma_x{}^4}$$

$$= \sigma_y{}^2 - \sigma_y{}^2 r_{xy}{}^2$$

$$= \sigma_y{}^2(1 - r_{xy}{}^2) \qquad (6\text{-}10)$$

This, then, is the variance of the distribution of errors in predicting y from x which we symbolized as $\sigma_{y\cdot x}$. Therefore we can write Eq. (6-10) as

$$\sigma^2_{y\cdot x} = \sigma_y{}^2(1 - r_{xy}{}^2) \qquad (6\text{-}11)$$

and

$$\sigma^2_{x\cdot y} = \sigma_x{}^2(1 - r_{xy}{}^2) \qquad (6\text{-}12)$$

From these two equations we can write

$$\sigma_{y\cdot x} = \sigma_y \sqrt{1 - r_{xy}{}^2} \qquad (6\text{-}13)$$

and

$$\sigma_{x\cdot y} = \sigma_x \sqrt{1 - r_{xy}{}^2} \qquad (6\text{-}14)$$

Equations (6-13) and (6-14) are called the *standard error of estimate* or the *standard error of prediction*, because they describe the extent of error in predicting scores on one variable from scores on the other. Since we are dealing with deviations from values which fall on the regression lines, the means of the columns and of the rows or our estimates of them [Eqs. (6-13) and (6-14)] also describe the extent to which individual points in the scatter diagram vary from the regression line.

If we are dealing with standard scores, then $\sigma_y = \sigma_x = 1$; hence Eqs. (6-13) and (6-14) become

$$\sigma_{z_y\cdot z_x} = \sqrt{1 - r_{xy}{}^2} \qquad (6\text{-}15)$$

and

$$\sigma_{z_x\cdot z_y} = \sqrt{1 - r_{xy}{}^2} \qquad (6\text{-}16)$$

It will be observed that the terms to the right in Eqs. (6-15) and (6-16) are the same. Therefore $\sigma_{z_y \cdot z_x} = \sigma_{z_x \cdot z_y}$. Consequently, when individual differences in the two variables being related are given in standard-score form, the extent of variation in the columns is exactly the same as the extent of variation in the rows. The relationship between the standard error of estimate and the Pearsonian coefficient of correlation is shown in Fig. 6-3. The higher the relationship between the two variables, the more accurately scores on one are predicted from scores on the other. Furthermore, equal increases in the magnitude of the coefficient are associated with disproportionately greater and greater decreases in the error of prediction.

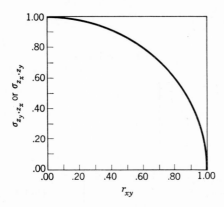

Figure 6-3 The relationship between the extent of variation around the regression line and the coefficient of correlation.

INTERPRETATIONS OF THE STANDARD ERROR OF ESTIMATE— THE MODEL OF NORMAL LINEAR CORRELATION

In linear correlation we make predictions of scores on one variable from scores on the other by means of the regression line. This is true whether we deal only with those situations wherein the means of the columns and of the rows all fall precisely on the same straight lines which are the regression lines or whether the regression lines are taken as the best-fitting straight lines in a least-squares sense. The deviations from the regression line are our errors in prediction; and the standard deviation of these deviations—the standard error of estimate or prediction, $\sigma_{y \cdot x}$ and $\sigma_{x \cdot y}$—describes the extent of our errors of prediction. Now, how shall we regard the standard error of estimate? The problems of interpretation revolve around homoscedasticity and normality of the distribution of the deviations from the regression line.

We might say that we shall consider linear correlation as referring only to that circumstance wherein homoscedasticity holds. That is, we shall compute the Pearsonian coefficient only when the standard deviations of the distributions of the scores in the various columns are all equal to each other and when the standard deviations of the scores in the various rows are equal to each other. As we have seen, under these circumstances the error of prediction is precisely the same for all values on the predictor variable. The error in predicting y from low values of x would be precisely the same as the error of predicting y from high values of x. The difficulty with adopting homoscedasticity as a necessary condition is that it seldom if ever occurs. As a consequence, this condition would be too restrictive so that the Pearsonian coefficient would be of little value to us.

A second alternative is not to require homoscedasticity. In this case, as we saw, the standard error of estimate or prediction then gives us an average of the errors of prediction. However, with any average, important differences may be obscured, and it may well be that the bivariate distribution is fan-shaped or shaped like a spindle or a dumbbell so that at one level of scores on the predictor variable the error of prediction is considerably greater than it is at other levels.

As is the case with all standard deviations, the standard error of estimate or prediction is most interpretable when the distribution of scores from which it is calculated is a normal frequency distribution. If the distributions of scores in the columns and rows are normal, then we can set limits within which an individual's predicted score will fall with a given probability. For example, in a normal frequency distribution 84 per cent of the cases fall between plus and minus one standard deviation of the mean. Therefore if on the basis of the regression equation we predict an individual's score as 50, the standard error of estimate being 5, we can say that the chances are 84 in 100 that the individual's score will be between 45 and 55. Hence if the distribution of scores in the columns and in the rows are normal, the standard error of estimate has considerable meaning. If the scores in the total distributions of the two variables are normal, then with linear correlation the scores in the columns and in the rows will be normally distributed, and, in addition, the columns and rows will be homoscedastic. Therefore we might specify that the scores in the marginal distributions of the scatter diagram must form normal frequency distributions. However, we know that distributions of scores are seldom if ever precisely normal. Only if we can justify transmuting the scores on our variables to other values which are precisely normally distributed would this stipulation not be too restrictive.

If we adopt the position that there is to be no restriction on the shapes of the marginal distributions, and hence on the shapes of the distributions of scores in the columns and rows, the Pearsonian coefficient can be widely applied. But as we have just noted, the standard error of estimate then is difficult to interpret.

Finally, we might adopt what is termed *normal linear correlation* as a model. In normal linear correlation the distributions of scores in the two marginal distributions and the distributions of scores in each of the columns and rows also are normal and, in addition, homoscedastic. Furthermore, in this model the means of the columns and of the rows all fall precisely on the same straight lines. In this model are included all the models we referred to in our earlier discussions. As we have seen, the model is taken as a representation of the facts. There is no implication that the characteristics of the model exactly represent the characteristics of the facts, but only that the two sets of characteristics are quite similar. Suppose that with a particular bivariate distribution we find that the marginal distributions of scores have shapes not too unlike a normal frequency distribution. In addition, suppose that the means of the columns and of the rows seem to fluctuate in a random fashion around the regression lines and do not depart too much from them, the regression lines being the best-fitting lines in a least-squares sense. Then in this case the model of normal correlation would be a useful model. We can attribute differences between our model and the actual facts to the random effects of sampling, or we can say that the model is sufficiently close to the facts to be considered as an acceptable description of them. Adopting the model, we can then calculate the Pearsonian coefficient by means of Eq. (6-3) or its equivalents, using it as a description of the extent to which our two variables are related. We use Eq. (6-4) and its equivalents as the regression equation and make predictions by means of it, and we use Eq. (6-13) and its equivalents as the standard error of estimate to describe the extent of error in making predictions from any value of our predictor variable. Whenever we use a model, however, we should always bear in mind that the model is only a representation of the facts and not necessarily a precise description of them.

THE PEARSONIAN COEFFICIENT AND ACCOUNTABLE VARIATION

Let us return to Eq. (6-11):

$$\sigma_{y \cdot x}^2 = \sigma_y{}^2(1 - r_{xy}{}^2)$$

Rearranging terms, we have

$$\frac{\sigma_{y \cdot x}^2}{\sigma_y{}^2} = 1 - r_{xy}{}^2$$

$$r_{xy}{}^2 = 1 - \frac{\sigma_{y \cdot x}^2}{\sigma_y{}^2}$$

$$= \frac{\sigma_y{}^2}{\sigma_y{}^2} - \frac{\sigma_{y \cdot x}^2}{\sigma_y{}^2}$$

$$= \frac{\sigma_y{}^2 - \sigma_{y \cdot x}^2}{\sigma_y{}^2}$$

From Eq. (5-2) we know that $\sigma_y{}^2 - \sigma_{y \cdot x}^2$, which we have symbolized as $\sigma_{y'}{}^2$, is an accountable variance. Therefore

$$r_{xy}{}^2 = \frac{\sigma_{y'}{}^2}{\sigma_y{}^2}$$

or

$$r_{xy} = \frac{\sigma_{y'}}{\sigma_y} \tag{6-17}$$

Similarly,

$$r_{xy} = \frac{\sigma_{x'}}{\sigma_x} \tag{6-18}$$

Therefore we can say that the Pearsonian coefficient directly gives us the proportion of accountable variation. Since the terms to the left in Eqs. (6-17) and (6-18) are the same, obviously both equations have the same value. Now depending upon how we interpret the Pearsonian coefficient and the standard error of estimate, we should, of course, give various interpretations to Eqs. (6-17) and (6-18). Clearly, these formulae are most meaningful with normal linear correlation. In particular, as the means of the columns and of the rows depart from the regression lines and as the distributions of scores in the columns and rows depart from homoscedasticity, Eqs. (6-17) and (6-18) become less and less adequate as descriptions of the proportion of accountable variation.

COMPUTATION OF THE PEARSONIAN COEFFICIENT OF CORRELATION

It is not very convenient to compute the Pearsonian coefficient either from Eq. (6-1) or from Eq. (6-3) since they involve standard and deviation scores. Therefore let us develop a formula that will permit computation of the Pearsonian coefficient of correlation directly from raw scores. Since $x = X - \bar{X}$ and $y = Y - \bar{Y}$, we can write Eq. (6-3) as

$$
\begin{aligned}
r_{xy} &= \frac{\Sigma xy}{n\sigma_x\sigma_y} = \frac{\Sigma(X - \bar{X})(Y - \bar{Y})}{n\sigma_x\sigma_y} \\
&= \frac{\Sigma(XY - \bar{Y}X - \bar{X}Y + \bar{X}\bar{Y})}{n\sigma_x\sigma_y} \\
&= \frac{\Sigma XY/n - \bar{Y}(\Sigma X/n) - \bar{X}(\Sigma Y/n) + \Sigma\bar{X}\bar{Y}/n}{\sigma_x\sigma_y} \\
&= \frac{\Sigma XY/n - \bar{Y}\bar{X} - \bar{X}\bar{Y} + \bar{X}\bar{Y}}{\sigma_x\sigma_y} \\
&= \frac{\Sigma XY/n - \bar{X}\bar{Y}}{\sigma_x\sigma_y} \tag{6-19}
\end{aligned}
$$

Equations (6-1), (6-3), and (6-19) are all mathematically equivalent and hence yield the same value for r when computed from the same set of data. This is illustrated in Table 6-1.

CORRELATION WITH DICHOTOMOUS VARIABLES

Usually we think of psychological tests as providing a range of scores so that individuals are distributed along a wide variety of quantitative descriptions which are ordered along a continuous scale. However, quite often in psychological measurement we deal with measuring instruments

Table 6-1.   Illustration of the Computation of the Pearsonian Coefficient of Correlation by Three Different Mathematically Equivalent Formulae

Individuals	X	Y	X^2	Y^2	XY	x	y	xy	z_x	z_y	$z_x z_y$
a	16	7	256	49	112	+ .5	+1	+ .5	+ .21	+ .69	+ .14
b	14	5	196	25	70	-1.5	-1	+ 1.5	- .64	- .69	+ .44
c	12	3	144	9	36	-3.5	-3	+10.5	-1.48	-2.07	+ 3.06
d	16	6	256	36	96	+ .5	0	.0	+ .21	.00	.00
e	15	5	225	25	75	- .5	-1	+ .5	- .21	- .69	+ .14
f	18	8	324	64	144	+2.5	+2	+ 5.0	+1.06	+1.38	+ 1.46
g	14	6	196	36	84	-1.5	0	.0	- .64	.00	.00
h	20	8	400	64	160	+4.5	+2	+ 9.0	+1.91	+1.38	+ 2.64
i	13	4	169	16	52	-2.5	-2	+ 5.0	-1.06	-1.38	+ 1.46
j	15	6	225	36	90	- .5	0	.0	- .21	.00	.00
k	16	7	256	49	112	+ .5	+1	+ .5	+ .21	+ .69	+ .14
l	17	6	289	36	102	+1.5	0	.0	+ .64	.00	.00
m	15	5	225	25	75	- .5	-1	+ .5	- .21	- .69	+ .14
n	19	9	361	81	171	+3.5	+3	+10.5	+1.48	+2.07	+ 3.06
o	15	6	225	36	90	- .5	0	.0	- .21	.00	.00
p	13	5	169	25	65	-2.5	-1	+ 2.5	-1.06	- .69	+ .73
q	18	7	324	49	126	+2.5	+1	+ 2.5	+1.06	+ .69	+ .73
r	16	6	256	36	96	+ .5	0	.0	+ .21	.00	.00
s	11	4	121	16	44	-4.5	-2	+ 9.0	-1.91	-1.38	+ 2.64
t	17	7	289	49	119	+1.5	+1	+ 1.5	+ .64	+ .69	+ .44
20	310	120	4,906	762	1,919			+59.0			+17.22

$\bar{X} = {}^{310}\!/_{20} = 15.50$

$\bar{Y} = {}^{120}\!/_{20} = 6.00$

$$\sigma_x = \sqrt{\frac{4,906}{20} - \left(\frac{310}{20}\right)^2} = \sqrt{245.80 - (15.50)^2} = \sqrt{245.80 - 240.25}$$

$$= \sqrt{5.55} = 2.36$$

$$\sigma_y = \sqrt{{}^{762}\!/_{20} - ({}^{120}\!/_{20})^2} = \sqrt{38.10 - (6.00)^2} = \sqrt{38.10 - 36.00}$$

$$= \sqrt{2.10} = 1.45$$

Computation of r by Eq. (6-3):

$$r_{xy} = \frac{\Sigma xy}{n\sigma_x\sigma_y} = \frac{59.0}{(20)(2.36)(1.45)} = .86$$

Computation of r by Eq. (6-1):

$$r_{xy} = \frac{\Sigma z_x z_y}{n} = \frac{17.22}{20} = .86$$

Computation of r by Eq. (6-19):

$$r_{xy} = \frac{\Sigma XY/n - \bar{X}\bar{Y}}{\sigma_x\sigma_y} = \frac{1,919/20 - (15.50)(6.00)}{(2.36)(1.45)} = .86$$

which separate people into categories that are only two in number. The items in an objective test usually are of this kind, the individual's responses being classified as being incorrect or correct. With opinion and personality inventories the responses may be limited to two alternatives such as "yes" or "no," or "like" or "dislike." With certain rating devices only two steps of response are permitted. Thus with adjective checklists the individual is either checked or not checked as being "cheerful," "shy," etc. Finally, we may have items involving the choice between two qualitatively different alternatives. Thus in an interest inventory the individual may be asked questions such as whether the occupation of "clerk" or of "mechanic" more interests him, and in a personality inventory he may be asked questions such as whether the trait of "cheerfulness" or "industriousness" better describes him.

CORRELATION WITH DISCONTINUOUS DICHOTOMOUS VARIABLES

Let us now turn to the problem of correlation involving discontinuous dichotomous variables. With these variables there are only two possible scores, 0 and 1. In developing the Pearsonian coefficient we did not stipulate that the variables being related were multistep variables, but only that the quantitative descriptions vary from low amounts of the traits being measured to higher amounts. Dichotomous scales are only a special case of multistep scales, and therefore there is no reason why we cannot directly apply the Pearsonian coefficient to them. However, since we are dealing with individual differences in only two stages rather than in many, we shall derive formulae which are mathematically equivalent to the Pearsonian coefficient but easier to calculate for this special case. When we are dealing with dichotomous variables which are qualitative in nature, we can arbitrarily assign the values of 0 and 1 to the two categories.

There are two types of correlation we need to consider. In one we are concerned with the relationship between a discontinuous dichotomous variable and a continuous or multistep one, and in the other we consider the correlation between two dichotomous variables. The coefficient for the first type of relationship is termed the *point biserial coefficient* and is symbolized as r_{pbis}. The coefficient of correlation for the second type of a relationship is termed the *phi coefficient* and is symbolized as ϕ.

Equation (6-19) for the Pearsonian coefficient of correlation is

$$r_{xy} = \frac{\Sigma XY/n - \bar{X}\bar{Y}}{\sigma_x \sigma_y}$$

Let us say that X is the dichotomous variable and Y is the continuous variable. Then from Eqs. (3-17) and (3-19) we can make appropriate substitutions in Eq. (6-19) for $\bar{X}$ and σ_x. Now recall that there are only two possible scores in variable X, namely, 0 and 1. Therefore the numerator of the first term in the numerator of Eq. (6-19), ΣXY, is the sum of the Y scores times the X scores of those cases whose X score is 0 plus the sum of the Y scores of those cases whose X score is 1. That is,

$$r_{pbis} = \frac{(\Sigma X_0 Y_0 + \Sigma X_1 Y_1)/n - p_x \bar{Y}}{\sigma_y \sqrt{p_x q_x}}$$

Y scores have been symbolized as Y_0 and Y_1 to indicate that they are the Y scores of those cases whose X score is 0 and those whose X score is 1, respectively. Since $X_0 = 0$, the first term in the numerator, $\Sigma X_0 Y_0$, is zero and drops out. Furthermore, $X_1 = 1$ and therefore the second term in the numerator, $\Sigma X_1 Y_1$, is $\Sigma 1 Y_1$ or simply ΣY_1. Hence

$$r_{pbis} = \frac{\Sigma Y_1/n - p_x \bar{Y}}{\sigma_y \sqrt{p_x q_x}}$$

Since the sum of a set of scores is equal to the mean times the number of cases, $\Sigma Y_1 = n_1 \bar{Y}_1$. Consequently

$$r_{pbis} = \frac{n_1 \bar{Y}_1/n - p_x \bar{Y}}{\sigma_y \sqrt{p_x q_x}}$$

Since $n_1/n = p_x$,

$$r_{pbis} = \frac{p_x \bar{Y}_1 - p_x \bar{Y}}{\sigma_y \sqrt{p_x q_x}}$$

$$= \frac{p_x(\bar{Y}_1 - \bar{Y})}{\sigma_y \sqrt{p_x q_x}}$$

Dividing the numerator and denominator by $\sqrt{p_x}$ gives

$$r_{pbis} = \frac{\sqrt{p_x}\,(\bar{Y}_1 - \bar{Y})}{\sigma_y \sqrt{q_x}}$$

$$= \frac{\bar{Y}_1 - \bar{Y}}{\sigma_y} \sqrt{\frac{p_x}{q_x}} \qquad (6\text{-}20)$$

Equation (6-20) is quite simple and easy to compute. But since sometimes we are dealing with a large number of dichotomous variables, for example, the many items of a test, the computations become laborious. Hence Eq. (6-19) has been plotted in Fig. 6-4, which permits the quick estimation of the point biserial coefficient when $(\bar{Y}_1 - \bar{Y})/\sigma_y$ and p_x are known. For example, if the difference between the means divided by the standard deviation is .35 and p is .25, the biserial coefficient is .20; and if the first value is .50 and the second is .45, the coefficient is .45.

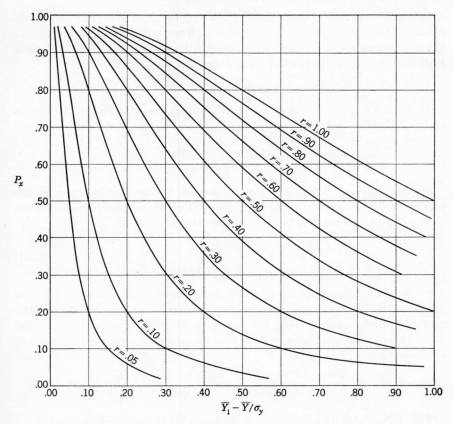

Figure 6-4   Chart for estimating the point biserial coefficient of correlation.

Now let us turn to the relationship between two discontinuous dichoto-mous variables. In deriving the coefficient of correlation between two such variables we can again begin with Eq. (6-19):

$$r_{xy} = \frac{\Sigma XY/n - \bar{X}\bar{Y}}{\sigma_x \sigma_y}$$

In this case there are only two degrees of X and of Y, namely, 0 and 1. Hence all the possible cross products are $X_0 Y_0$, $X_0 Y_1$, $X_1 Y_0$, and $X_1 Y_1$. The sum of the cross products, then, is

$$\Sigma XY = n_{x_0 y_0} X_0 Y_0 + n_{x_0 y_1} X_0 Y_1 + n_{x_1 y_0} X_1 Y_0 + n_{x_1 y_1} X_1 Y_1$$

where the subscripts of n indicate the particular combination of scores obtained by those n individuals. Thus $n_{x_0 y_0}$ is the number of individuals obtaining scores of 0 in both X and Y. Whenever X or Y is zero, the whole term in which it occurs becomes zero and drops out. Hence the first three terms are zero and drop out, and only the last term, $n_{x_1y_1}X_1Y_1$, remains. But since in this term both X and Y are 1,

$$n_{x_1y_1}X_1Y_1 = n_{x_1y_1}$$

Hence $\Sigma XY = n_{x_1y_1}$. Substituting this in Eq. (6-19) and for the means and standard deviations from Eqs. (3-17) and (3-19), we have

$$\phi = \frac{n_{x_1y_1}/n - p_xp_y}{\sqrt{p_xq_xp_yq_y}}$$

Symbolizing $n_{x_1y_1}/n$ as p_c, the proportion of cases who score in the higher category of both variables, that is, those cases who in common are in the higher category of both variables, we have

$$\phi = \frac{p_c - p_xp_y}{\sqrt{p_xq_xp_yq_y}} \tag{6-21}$$

Suppose that the proportion of individuals falling in the top category of X, p_x, is .30; the proportion in the top category of Y, p_y, is .60; and the proportion who score in the top category on both variables, p_c, is .25. Then the relationship between the two variables as measured by the phi coefficient is

$$\phi = \frac{.25 - (.30)(.60)}{\sqrt{(.30)(.70)(.60)(.40)}} = \frac{.25 - .18}{\sqrt{.0504}} = \frac{.07}{.2245} = .31$$

UPPER LIMITS OF THE VALUES OF COEFFICIENTS OF CORRELATION COMPUTED FROM DISCONTINUOUS DICHOTOMOUS VARIABLES

As is the case with the Pearsonian coefficient, the highest value that the point biserial and the phi coefficients can reach is a function of the distribution of cases in the two variables being related. Let us take a simple case involving nine persons who are divided on two discontinuous dichotomous variables as follows:

X	n	Y	n
1	5	1	3
0	4	0	6

If the correlation between X and Y were perfect, then all individuals would have either the score of 1 or the score of 0 on both variables. However, in the above example this manifestly is impossible. Five persons make a score of 1 on X, but only three do so on Y. So at the best there can be only three cases earning scores of 1 on both variables. Similarly, there are six cases who earn a score of 0 on Y and only four who earn a score of 0 on X. So at the best only four cases can have scores of 0 on both variables. Therefore it is impossible for all cases to have the same scores on both variables. Consequently, with such distributions of X and Y a phi coefficient of +1.00 can never be obtained. Only if the proportions falling in the top categories on both variables are precisely the same is it possible to obtain a coefficient of +1.00. However, under such circumstances it would be impossible to obtain a perfect negative coefficient of −1.00. If p_x is precisely equal to q_y, then it is possible to obtain a perfect negative coefficient but not a perfect positive coefficient. Only when

$$p_x = q_x = p_y = q_y = .50$$

is it possible to obtain a perfect positive and a perfect negative coefficient. The greater the dissimilarity between p_x and p_y, the lower is the upper limit of phi.

By a similar effect there are upper limits to the point biserial coefficient of correlation.   Consider the following example:

X	n	Y	n
1	5	4	1
0	4	3	2
		2	3
		1	2
		0	1

If the relationship between X and Y were perfect, then the five individuals earning the score of 1 on variable X would also earn the highest scores on variable Y and the four individuals earning the score of 0 on X would all earn the lowest scores on Y. But in the foregoing example it can be seen that the Y scores of the five cases with the score of 1 on X would have to overlap with the Y scores of the four cases who have the score of 0 on X. Hence the maximum value that the point biserial coefficient of correlation could have with these particular distributions is less than 1.00.

CORRELATION WITH DICHOTOMOUS VARIABLES BASED UPON
CONTINUOUS VARIABLES

When we have a dichotomous variable that is formed from a continuous variable arbitrarily divided into two parts, or is assumed to be so, we must make some assumption about the nature of the distribution of scores on the continuous variable in order to compute a coefficient of correlation. Since we know nothing about the distribution of scores on the continuous variable which is dichotomized—otherwise we should have the multistep scores on the continuous variable—the most convenient assumption is that it is normal. Again formulae for the correlation of such variables can be derived which are the mathematical equivalents of the Pearsonian coefficient. However, these formulae involve the characteristics of the normal frequency distribution and are too complex to

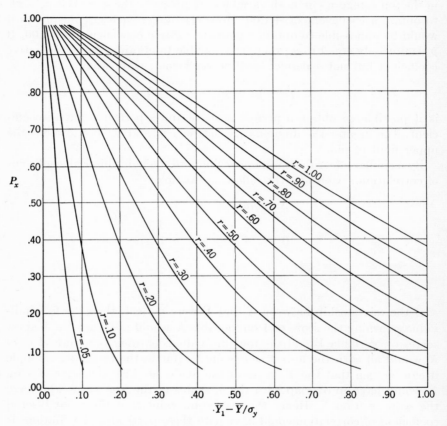

Figure 6-5   Chart for estimating the biserial coefficient of correlation.

develop here. It is to be noted that because of the assumption of normality, and indeed because of the prior assumption that the variable is a continuous one, these formulae largely are used only in connection with theoretical problems. For the practical problems of psychological measurement the formulae for correlation involving discontinuous dichotomous variables are more pertinent.

Again we have two types of correlation, one involving a dichotomous and a continuous variable and the other involving two dichotomous variables. For the first type of correlation the coefficient is termed the *biserial coefficient* and for the second it is termed the *tetrachoric coefficient*.

The formula for the biserial coefficient of correlation is

$$r_{bis} = \frac{\bar{Y}_1 - \bar{Y}}{\sigma_y} \frac{p_x}{o} \tag{6-22}$$

where p_x is the proportion of individuals falling in the upper category of variable X the dichotomized variable, $\bar{Y}_1$ is their mean score on the continuous variable Y, $\bar{Y}$ and σ_y are the mean and standard deviation of the scores of all cases on Y, and o is the ordinate of the normal distribution curve at the point above which p_x cases fall.

Equation (6-22) can readily be plotted in the form of a chart which permits the estimation of the biserial coefficient. Such a chart is presented in Fig. 6-5. The values we need in order to estimate the biserial coefficient are p_x and $(\bar{Y}_1 - \bar{Y})/\sigma_y$. Reading from Fig. 6-5 we can see that if the first value is .35 and the latter is .10 the biserial coefficient is .10, and if the first value is .15 and the second is .70 then the biserial coefficient is about .45.

The formula for the tetrachoric coefficient of correlation is a very complex one and will not be given here. Several sets of diagrams have been developed for use in estimating the tetrachoric coefficient.* A convenient table which permits reasonably accurate estimates of the tetrachoric coefficient is given as Table 6-2.† To estimate the coefficient we need merely to know (a) the number of cases who are in the high category on both variables, (b) the number who are high on variable Y and low on variable X, (c) the number who are low on Y and high on X, and (d) the number who are low on both variables. We then compute the ratio ad/bc, enter Table 6-2 with the resulting value, and find our estimate of the tetrachoric coefficient. Suppose we have the following bivariate distribution of scores on two dichotomous variables:

	X	
Y	Low	High
High........	21	13
Low........	35	5

* L. Chesire, M. Saffir, and L. L. Thurstone, "Computing Diagrams for the Tetrachoric Correlation Coefficient," University of Chicago Book Store, 1938.

† For a detailed notion of the amount of error involved in these estimates see M. D. Davidoff, Note on "A table for the rapid determination of the tetrachoric correlation coefficient," *Psychometrika*, **19**:163–164, 1954.

TABLE 6-2.　Table for Estimating the Tetrachoric Coefficient of Correlation*

r_{tet}	ad/bc	r_{tet}	ad/bc	r_{tet}	ad/bc
.00	0–1.00	.34	2.42–2.48	.68	7.76–8.11
.01	1.01–1.03	.35	2.49–2.55	.69	8.12–8.49
.02	1.04–1.06	.36	2.56–2.63	.70	8.50–8.90
.03	1.07–1.08	.37	2.64–2.71	.71	8.91–9.35
.04	1.09–1.11	.38	2.72–2.79	.72	9.36–9.82
.05	1.12–1.14	.39	2.80–2.87	.73	9.83–10.33
.06	1.15–1.17	.40	2.88–2.96	.74	10.34–10.90
.07	1.18–1.20	.41	2.97–3.05	.75	10.91–11.51
.08	1.21–1.23	.42	3.06–3.14	.76	11.52–12.16
.09	1.24–1.27	.43	3.15–3.24	.77	12.17–12.89
.10	1.28–1.30	.44	3.25–3.34	.78	12.90–13.70
.11	1.31–1.33	.45	3.35–3.45	.79	13.71–14.58
.12	1.34–1.37	.46	3.46–3.56	.80	14.59–15.57
.13	1.38–1.40	.47	3.57–3.68	.81	15.58–16.65
.14	1.41–1.44	.48	3.69–3.80	.82	16.66–17.88
.15	1.45–1.48	.49	3.81–3.92	.83	17.89–19.28
.16	1.49–1.52	.50	3.93–4.06	.84	19.29–20.65
.17	1.53–1.56	.51	4.07–4.20	.85	20.66–22.68
.18	1.57–1.60	.52	4.21–4.34	.86	22.69–24.76
.19	1.61–1.64	.53	4.35–4.49	.87	24.77–27.22
.20	1.65–1.69	.54	4.50–4.66	.88	27.23–30.09
.21	1.70–1.73	.55	4.67–4.82	.89	30.10–33.60
.22	1.74–1.78	.56	4.83–4.99	.90	33.61–37.79
.23	1.79–1.83	.57	5.00–5.18	.91	37.80–43.06
.24	1.84–1.88	.58	5.19–5.38	.92	43.07–49.83
.25	1.89–1.93	.59	5.39–5.59	.93	49.84–58.79
.26	1.94–1.98	.60	5.60–5.80	.94	58.80–70.95
.27	1.99–2.04	.61	5.81–6.03	.95	70.96–89.01
.28	2.05–2.10	.62	6.04–6.28	.96	89.02–117.54
.29	2.11–2.15	.63	6.29–6.54	.97	117.55–169.67
.30	2.16–2.22	.64	6.55–6.81	.98	169.68–293.12
.31	2.23–2.28	.65	6.82–7.10	.99	293.13–923.97
.32	2.29–2.34	.66	7.11–7.42	1.00	923.98
.33	2.35–2.41	.67	7.43–7.75		

a = number of cases high on both variables
b = number of cases high on y and low on x
c = number of cases low on y and high on x
d = number of cases low on both variables

* M. D. Davidoff and H. W. Goheen, A table for the rapid determination of the tetrachoric correlation coefficient, *Psychometrika*, **18**:115–121, 1953.

Then $a = 13$, $b = 21$, $c = 5$, and $d = 35$. To estimate the tetrachoric coefficient we calculate

$$\frac{(13)(35)}{(21)(5)} = \frac{455}{105} = 4.31$$

Entering Table 6-2 with the value 4.31, we find that our estimate of the tetrachoric coefficient r_{tet} is .52. In the event that the numerator (ad) is smaller than the denominator (bc), the two are interchanged and the value bc/ad is computed. This is a negative correlation. We again enter the table with our number and find the estimate of the tetrachoric coefficient, but we place a minus sign before it to indicate that the relationship is negative.

When the marginal distributions of both variables are 0.5 and 0.5, that is, when 0.5 of the cases fall in one category of each dichotomous variable and 0.5 fall in the other, the estimates of the tetrachoric coefficient from Table 6-2 are accurate within two decimal places. As the marginal distributions differ from the proportions 0.5 and 0.5, the estimates of the tetrachoric coefficient are less and less accurate. But even with marginal distributions of 0.3 and 0.7 on both variables the error is no larger than about 0.02, and with greater departures in the marginal distributions from 0.5 and 0.5 the error seldom is greater than about 0.05. Consequently the estimates of the tetrachoric coefficient given by Table 6-2 are sufficiently accurate for almost all practical purposes. When the proportions of cases in the two categories of the dichotomous variables are quite different, as with 0.05 of the cases falling in one category and 0.95 in the other, the tetrachoric coefficient is quite undependable as an index and should not be used.

When we use the tetrachoric coefficient of correlation we are in effect normalizing the scores on both variables being related. That is, we are taking both distributions to have the same shape. As a consequence the maximum value of the tetrachoric coefficient is always unity, a circumstance that is seldom true with the phi coefficient. When two dichotomous variables are being related, the value of the phi coefficient is always equal to or lower than the value of the tetrachoric coefficient.

For example, suppose we have the following bivariate distributions with two dichotomous variables:

	X	
Y	Low	High
High........	2	10
Low........	4	4

The phi coefficient is

$$\phi = \frac{.50 - (.70)(.60)}{\sqrt{(.70)(.30)(.60)(.40)}} = \frac{.08}{\sqrt{.0504}} = \frac{.08}{.2245} = .36$$

For the tetrachoric coefficient we should have

$$\frac{(10)(4)}{(2)(4)} = 5.00$$

and, from Table 6-2,

$$r_{tet} = .57$$

Summary

Although the proportion of accountable variation and the regression coefficient can be used as indices of the degree of relationship between two variables, they both have serious shortcomings when used in this way. For any given relationship both of them have two values and hence give two different descriptions of the degree of relationship. The proportion of accountable variation does not tell whether the relationship is positive or negative, and the regression coefficient is dependent upon the nature of the units of measurement.

This last shortcoming of the regression coefficient can be overcome if scores on all variables are expressed as standard scores. When the regression coefficient is computed by using standard scores, its two values for any given relationship are equal, and so it gives a single description of the degree of relationship. The regression coefficient in this form is termed the Pearsonian coefficient of correlation. The basic formula for the Pearsonian coefficient is the sum of the cross products of the standard scores on the two variables divided by the number of cases.

When the relationship between two variables is perfect, the Pearsonian coefficient has its maximum value of 1.00; and when no relationship at all exists between two variables, the coefficient has its minimum value of .00. However, the coefficient can only achieve the value of 1.00 when scores on both variables being related have precisely the same shape. But even with frequency distributions quite different in shape, the maximum value of the Pearsonian coefficient is quite high. This and other problems are resolved if the model of normal linear correlation is adopted. When scores are normally distributed, it can be expected that the means of the columns and rows will fall precisely on the regression lines, and the relationship will be homoscedastic, with the distributions of scores in each column and row also being normal.

In linear correlation, when the means of the columns and the means of the rows fall precisely on the regression lines, the Pearsonian coefficient (being the regression coefficient) describes those means. Furthermore, the Pearsonian coefficient exactly equals the proportion of accountable variation. However, when the means of the columns and rows do not fall on straight lines, the regression line is the line of best fit and is interpreted either as giving estimates of the means or as describing the linear model which is imposed. When the regression line is the line of best fit, variation from it in any column or row is different from variation from the mean of that column or row.

While the Pearsonian coefficient was derived in terms of multistep or continuous variables, it can also be applied to dichotomous variables. Dichotomous variables are of two sorts, those which are two-step discontinuous variables and those which are multistep or continuous variables which have been dichotomized.

With discontinuous dichotomous variables the Pearsonian coefficient can be directly applied. However, for convenience in computation, formulae somewhat different from, though mathematically equal to, the basic formula for the Pearsonian coefficient are used. When scores on two discontinuous dichotomous variables are being related, the coefficient is termed phi; and when scores on a discontinuous dichotomous variable are being related to those on either a multistep or a continuous variable, the coefficient is termed the point biserial.

With multistep or continuous variables which are dichotomized it must be assumed that the dichotomized variables are normally distributed. The coefficient of correlation between two such dichotomized variables is termed the tetrachoric, and the coefficient of correlation between such a dichotomized variable and a multistep or continuous variable is termed the biserial. The biserial coefficient is readily computed from a formula, but the formula for the tetrachoric coefficient is too complex and so the value is estimated from a table. Because the tetrachoric and biserial coefficients are based upon normal distributions of scores, their values ordinarily are higher than those of the phi and point biserial coefficients.

Selected Readings

Chesire, L., M. Saffir, and L. L. Thurstone: "Computing Diagrams for the Tetrachoric Correlation Coefficient," University of Chicago Book Store, 1938.

Dunlap, J. W.: Note on computation of biserial correlations in item evaluation, *Psychometrika*, **1**:51–60, 1936.

Guilford, J. P., and N. C. Perry: Estimation of other coefficients of correlation from the phi coefficient, *Psychometrika*, **16**:335–346, 1951.

Hayes, S. P.: Diagrams for computing tetrachoric coefficients of correlation from percentage differences, *Psychometrika*, **11**:163–172, 1946.

Jaspen, N.: Serial correlation, *Psychometrika*, **11**:23–30, 1946.

Symonds, P. M.: Variations of the product moment (Pearsonian) coefficient of correlation, *J. Educational Psychol.*, **17**:458–469, 1926.

Yule, G. U.: On the methods of measuring the association between two attributes, *J. Roy. Statist. Soc.*, **75**:576–642, 1912.

chapter 7 The Combination of Component Variables into a Composite Variable

Many of the scores which result from our operations of measurement are composites made up of the sum or average of the scores on a series of component variables. Perhaps the most familiar composite in psychological measurement is the score an individual is assigned on most achievement, aptitude, and personality tests. Ordinarily such tests are composed of a series of items each of which is scored 1 when the answer is correct and 0 when it is wrong. An individuals' score on the test is the sum of the scores he earns on the individual items. The items, then, are the components forming the composite, which is the total test. Many tests are made up of several subtests, and the individual's score is the total of his scores on all the component subtests. Here the subtests are the components and the total test the composite. Similarly, in many rating procedures each person is rated on a series of different scales, and his final score is the sum or average of the ratings he is assigned on the various scales. The individual rating scales are the components, and the sum or average of the ratings on them is the composite variable.

There are many situations in which we wish to combine scores on two or more variables into a single composite score. An individual's scores on several tests might be combined in order to obtain a picture of the general level of his abilities or traits in a particular area. Sometimes by combining the scores earned by an individual on several applications of the same test a more accurate or representative measure of the trait is obtained. In some instances we can obtain a better prediction of scores on one variable from a composite of scores on a series of predictor tests than we can from scores on any one of the predictor tests.

Let us consider some examples. A general measure of arithmetic ability would be given by the combination of scores on four tests one of which is composed of addition items, a second of subtraction items, a third of multiplication items, and a fourth of division items. In a like manner an overall index of the job proficiency of salesmen could be obtained from a composite made up of their total volume of sales, the number of new accounts they develop, and the number of repeat sales they make to the same customers.

Sometimes several measurements are taken on an individual with the same measuring instrument in order to obtain a more accurate or representative description of him. Thus when we measure reaction time it is common practice to take a number of determinations of speed of response and to average them. Similarly, if we are measuring some trait such as sociability by the rating method, we may combine the ratings assigned by different raters to each person. By this means we hope to obtain a more reliable index of the trait than is provided by the ratings assigned by a single rater.

Many of the types of behavior we wish to predict, such as academic performance or occupational success, are quite complex. Therefore a single test which measures only a restricted scope of traits will not give good predictions by itself. Hence we are likely to use a composite of a number of tests each measuring somewhat different traits so as to obtain better predictions of the complex variable.

Composite variables, then, are so common in psychological measurement that we need to examine their nature and characteristics. In this chapter we shall relate the mean and variance of composite scores to the means and variances of scores on the components that go to make them up. Since components often are expressed in very different kinds of units we shall consider the matter of making them comparable. We shall examine the correlation of composites with other single variables and with other composites, and we shall compare summed composite scores with average composite scores.

THE NATURE OF COMPOSITES

The type of composite with which we are concerned here is a simple additive composite, one in which the individual's scores on all components merely are added together to obtain a total or composite score. The formula for an individual's composite of raw scores is

$$X_c = X_1 + \cdots + X_k \qquad (7\text{-}1)$$

where c refers to the composite score and k is the number of variables entering into the composite. Suppose a composite is formed by four tests. An individual who earns scores of 11, 14, 21, and 12, respectively, on the component tests would have a composite score of 58.

For a composite of deviation scores Eq. (7-1) becomes

$$x_c = x_1 + \cdots + x_k \qquad (7\text{-}2)$$

and for standard scores

$$z_c = z_1 + \cdots + z_k \qquad (7\text{-}3)$$

THE MEAN OF COMPOSITE SCORES

From Eq. (7-1) the mean of composite scores can be written as

$$
\begin{aligned}
\bar{X}_c = \bar{X}_{X_1 + \cdots + X_k} &= \frac{\Sigma(X_1 + \cdots + X_k)}{n} \\
&= \frac{\Sigma X_1}{n} + \cdots + \frac{\Sigma X_k}{n} \\
&= \bar{X}_1 + \cdots + \bar{X}_k
\end{aligned}
\qquad (7\text{-}4)
$$

Equation (7-4) shows that the mean of composite scores is equal simply to the sum of the means of the individual components. If the means of the three component variables that form a composite are 42, 78, and 31, then the mean of the composite scores is 151.

From Eq. (7-4) it is apparent that if the scores on the component variables are in deviation- or standard-score form the mean of the composite scores must necessarily be zero since the mean of each of the component variables is zero.

THE VARIANCE AND STANDARD DEVIATION OF COMPOSITE SCORES

Using Eq. (7-2) as a basis, we can write the formula for the variance of composite scores as

$$\sigma_c{}^2 = \sigma^2_{x_1 + \cdots + x_k} = \frac{\Sigma(x_1 + \cdots + x_k)^2}{n} \qquad (7\text{-}5)$$

When we square the polynomial in the numerator we multiply each term by itself and with every other term as in Table 7-1. As can be seen in this table, when we square the polynomial there are k terms involving x^2, one for each of the 1 to k component variables. In addition

TABLE 7-1.   The Square of the Polynomial $(x_1 + \cdots + x_k)$

	x_1	x_2	$\cdots$	x_{k-1}	x_k
x_1	$x_1{}^2$	x_1x_2	$\cdots$	x_1x_{k-1}	x_1x_k
x_2	x_1x_2	$x_2{}^2$	$\cdots$	x_2x_{k-1}	x_2x_k
$\cdots$	$\cdots$	$\cdots$	$\cdots$	$\cdots$	$\cdots$
			$\cdots$		
			$\cdots$		
			$\cdots$		
x_{k-1}	x_1x_{k-1}	x_2x_{k-1}	$\cdots$	$x^2{}_{k-1}$	x_kx_{k-1}
x_k	x_1x_k	x_2x_k	$\cdots$	x_kx_{k-1}	$x_k{}^2$

there are $k(k-1)$ terms involving the product of the scores on two components. However, each of these cross-product terms appears twice in the table, once above the diagonal running from $x_1{}^2$ to $x_k{}^2$ and once below it. Hence in the table there are $[k(k-1)]/2$ terms of $2x_ix_{i'}$, where i and i' are any two components. Therefore we can write Eq. (7-5) as

$$\sigma_c{}^2 = \frac{\Sigma(x_1{}^2 + \cdots + x_k{}^2 + 2x_1x_2 + \cdots + 2x_{k-1}x_k)}{n}$$

$$= \frac{\Sigma x_1{}^2}{n} + \cdots + \frac{\Sigma x_k{}^2}{n} + 2\frac{\Sigma x_1x_2}{n} + \cdots + 2\frac{\Sigma x_{k-1}x_k}{n}$$

Since $\Sigma x^2/n = \sigma_x{}^2$, and $\Sigma x_ix_{i'}/n\sigma_i\sigma_{i'} = r_{ii'}$, so that $\Sigma x_ix_{i'}/n = \sigma_i\sigma_{i'}r_{ii'}$,

$$\sigma_c{}^2 = \sigma_1{}^2 + \cdots + \sigma_k{}^2 + 2\sigma_1\sigma_2r_{12} + \cdots + 2\sigma_{k-1}\sigma_kr_{(k-1)k} \quad (7\text{-}6)$$

The standard deviation of composite scores is

$$\sigma_c = \sqrt{\sigma_1{}^2 + \cdots + \sigma_k{}^2 + 2\sigma_1\sigma_2r_{12} + \cdots + 2\sigma_{k-1}\sigma_kr_{(k-1)k}} \quad (7\text{-}7)$$

Examples of the computation of the variance of composite scores from the variances, standard deviations, and intercorrelations among the component variables from Eq. (7-6) are given in Tables 7-2 and 7-3. The component variables in the illustration given in Table 7-2 are multistep variables and in Table 7-3 they are dichotomous variables, such as the items of a test each of which is scored 1 when the item is answered correctly and 0 when it is answered incorrectly. Ordinarily, of course, a test contains many items, but for simplicity of illustration the test in Table 7-3 is composed of only four items. Since each item is a discontinuous dichotomous variable, the coefficients of correlation among them are phi coefficients. It can be seen from Table 7-3 that the variance of

TABLE 7-2.   Illustration of the Computation of the Variance of Composite Scores from the Intercorrelations among the Components and Their Standard Deviations

		Components				
	1	2	3	4	σ	σ^2
1		.20	.40	.00	5	25
2			.30	.10	3	9
3				.50	6	36
4					4	16

$$\sigma_c^2 = 25 + 9 + 36 + 16 + 2(5)(3)(.20) + 2(5)(6)(.40) + 2(5)(4)(.00)$$
$$+ 2(3)(6)(.30) + 2(3)(4)(.10) + 2(6)(4)(.50)$$
$$= 153.2$$

TABLE 7-3.   Illustration of the Computation of the Variance of Composite Scores from the Intercorrelations among the Components and Their Standard Deviations with Dichotomous Items as the Component Variables

Persons	Items				$\Sigma i = X_c$
	1	2	3	4	
a	1	0	1	0	2
b	0	1	0	0	1
c	1	0	1	1	3
d	0	0	0	0	0
e	0	1	0	1	2
f	1	1	1	1	4
g	1	0	0	1	2
h	0	1	1	1	3
i	0	0	1	0	1
j	0	1	1	0	2
$\bar{X}_i = p$	.4	.5	.6	.5	$20 = \Sigma X_c$
					$\bar{X}_c = 2$
					$\sigma_c^2 = 1.2$

	Items				$\sigma_i = \sqrt{pq}$	$\sigma_i^2 = pq$
	1	2	3	4		
1		−.408	.250	.408	.49	.24
2			.000	.200	.50	.25
3				.000	.49	.24
4					.50	.25

$$\sigma_c^2 .24 + .25 + .24 + .25 + 2(.49)(.50)(-.408) + 2(.49)(.49)(.250)$$
$$+ 2(.49)(.50)(.408) + 2(.50)(.49)(.000) + 2(.50)(.50)(.200) + 2(.49)(.50)(.000)$$
$$= 1.2$$

total composite scores is precisely the same whether it is computed directly from the composite scores or from Eq. (7-6) from the variances, standard deviations, and intercorrelations among the component items.

Equation (7-6) also can be expressed in terms of the mean of the variances and of the covariances. By the covariance is meant the product of the standard deviations and the coefficient of correlation between two variables, $\sigma_i\sigma_{i'}r_{ii'}$. From Eq. (6-3), the formula for the Pearsonian coefficient of correlation, we can write the covariance as

$$\sigma_i\sigma_{i'}r_{ii'} = \frac{\Sigma x_i x_{i'}}{n}$$

The mean of a set of values is their sum divided by the number of values. Therefore the sum of a set of values is equal to the number of values times their mean. If we look at Eq. (7-6) we can see that in the first part we have the sum of the variances, which are k in number, and in the second part of the formula we have the covariances, which are $k(k - 1)$ in number. We can therefore write Eq. (7-6) as

$$\sigma_c{}^2 = k\overline{\sigma_i{}^2} + k(k - 1)\overline{\sigma_i\sigma_{i'}r_{ii'}} \tag{7-8}$$

where $\overline{\sigma_i{}^2}$ is the mean of the variances of the k variables, $r_{ii'}$ is the correlation between any pair of components, and $\overline{\sigma_i\sigma_{i'}r_{ii'}}$ is the mean of the $k(k - 1)$ covariance terms. Equation (7-8) has very little utility as a computational formula since seldom do we know the averages required by it. However, as we shall see later, it is of considerable value in deriving other formulae.

COMPOSITES FORMED OF COMPONENTS EXPRESSED IN STANDARD OR STANDARDIZED SCORES

In some instances the components that enter into a composite are so very nearly the same in character that the question of their comparability does not arise. An example is the composite formed by the sum of the ratings assigned by several raters to each member of a group of individuals when all raters use the same scale. But in other instances the components are quite different in nature. As an overall index of aggressiveness in nursery school children a composite might be formed of the number of times a child strikes other children, the number of toys he destroys, and the decibels of loudness of his screams of rage. If we merely sum the raw scores on the three variables for each child, we certainly have a very queer composite.

In the case of ratings we might say that since all raters use the same rating method all the ratings are comparable. Hence a simple sum or average of the components would be considered acceptable. However, in the composite of aggressiveness we are adding together such different things as the numbers of punches, toys, and decibels. This does not seem quite right.

To deal with this problem we must return to our earlier discussion of standardizing scores. In that discussion we considered various ways of rendering scores on different variables comparable. We saw that the use of standard scores, or of the several allied varieties of standardized scores, is a convenient way of accomplishing this. We express the scores on each variable in terms of the distribution of scores earned by the entire group. Scores on each variable, then, have the same meaning in terms of referencing the scores to those of the entire group. Thus by expressing each of the component variables in standard or standardized scores, the scores earned by each person on them can more reasonably be summed into a composite.

Let us now consider the variance of composite scores when the scores on each variable are transmuted into standard or standardized scores. If the scores are transmuted in this manner, then all standard deviations are equal. Since in Eq. (7-6) there are k variance terms and $k(k-1)$ covariance terms, when all standard deviations are equal this formula is written as

$$\sigma_c^2 = k\sigma_i^2 + 2\sigma_i^2 r_{12} + \cdots + 2\sigma_i^2 r_{(k-1)k}$$
$$= \sigma_i^2(k + 2r_{12} + \cdots + 2r_{(k-1)k}) \qquad (7\text{-}9)$$

or, parallel with Eq. (7-8),

$$\sigma_c^2 = \sigma_i^2[k + k(k-1)\overline{r_{ii'}}] \qquad (7\text{-}10)$$

Under these conditions the standard deviation of composite scores is

$$\sigma_c = \sigma_i \sqrt{k + 2r_{12} + \cdots + 2r_{(k-1)k}} = \sigma_i \sqrt{k + k(k-1)\overline{r_{ii'}}} \qquad (7\text{-}11)$$

If scores on all components are expressed as standard scores, then the standard deviation of the components is 1.00, so that Eqs. (7-9) to (7-11) become

$$\sigma_{c_z}^2 = k + 2r_{12} + \cdots + 2r_{(k-1)k} = k + k(k-1)\overline{r_{ii'}} \qquad (7\text{-}12)$$
$$\sigma_{c_z} = \sqrt{k + 2r_{12} + \cdots + 2r_{(k-1)k}} = \sqrt{k + k(k-1)\overline{r_{ii'}}} \qquad (7\text{-}13)$$

THE STANDARD DEVIATION OF COMPOSITE SCORES IN RELATION TO THE NUMBER OF COMPONENTS AND THEIR INTERCORRELATIONS

Sometimes the measuring device we use does not give us a sufficient range of scores for our purposes, and in order to increase the range we may add more components. For example, suppose we have a test consisting of 20 items and the range of individual differences is only 10 points.

This may not give us enough differentiation among individuals, enough different classes of persons, so we may double the number of items, expecting thereby to increase the range of scores from 10 to 20 points.

If we propose to increase the number of components in a composite, presumably the added components will be similar to the original ones in having the same average variance and average intercorrelations. Granting this we can turn to Eq. (7-13) to discover what effect the addition of components has on the standard deviation of composite

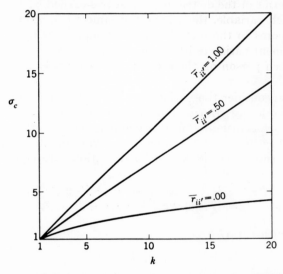

Figure 7-1 The standard deviation of composite scores (σ_c), in relation to the number of components in the composite (k), and the average of their intercorrelations ($\bar{r}_{ii'}$).

scores. This formula shows that the intercorrelation among the components is a critical factor. Equation (7-13) is plotted in Fig. 7-1 for three values of $\bar{r}_{ii'}$, the average of the intercorrelations among the components. From this figure we can derive the following principles:

1. As the number of components in the composite increases, the standard deviation of composite scores increases.
2. The higher the level of the intercorrelations among the components, the greater the effect upon the standard deviation of composite scores of increasing the number of components.

The intercorrelations among the components which form a composite seldom if ever will be of the order of 1.00. Indeed, if the components were perfectly correlated with each other, one of them alone would be as good as any number of them, and by adding together a number of them nothing new would be added in terms of traits measured. Therefore for all practical purposes we can say that if we increase the number of components by a given amount the increase in the range of scores will be less than that amount, and ordinarily will be substantially less.

THE CORRELATION BETWEEN SCORES ON A COMPOSITE VARIABLE AND SCORES ON ANOTHER VARIABLE

In a variety of circumstances we are interested in the relationship between scores on a composite variable and those on another variable which we shall term an outside variable. For example, we might have several different measures of the academic success of students, such as grades earned in different courses, which we have pooled together in order to obtain an overall index of academic success. If we are interested in the relationship between academic success and some other variable, say intelligence, then we should obtain the coefficient of correlation between the composite scores on academic success and the scores on an intelligence test.

As another example, we might be interested in predicting scores on some variable, for instance, measures of performance on a job. We might believe that a better prediction would be obtained from a composite of predictor tests than from any single test. A single test may measure only one aspect of the behavior we are trying to predict, whereas a combination of tests each measuring somewhat different traits may be expected to give better prediction. Again we should be concerned with the relationship between scores on a composite variable and scores on an outside variable.

THE CORRELATION BETWEEN COMPOSITE SCORES AND SCORES ON AN OUTSIDE VARIABLE

The formula for the correlation between scores on a composite variable and scores on an outside variable can be derived from Eq. (6-3) as follows. The composite variable c is comprised of 1 to k components, and the outside variable is symbolized as 0:

$$
\begin{aligned}
r_{x_0 c} = r_{x_0(x_1 + \cdots + x_k)} &= \frac{\Sigma x_0(x_1 + \cdots + x_k)}{n\sigma_0\sigma_c} \\
&= \frac{\Sigma(x_0 x_1 + \cdots + x_0 x_k)}{n\sigma_0\sigma_c} \\
&= \frac{\Sigma x_0 x_1 + \cdots + \Sigma x_0 x_k}{n\sigma_0\sigma_c} \\
&= \frac{\Sigma x_0 x_1/n + \cdots + \Sigma x_0 x_k/n}{\sigma_0\sigma_c}
\end{aligned}
$$

Remembering that the sum of the cross products of deviation scores divided by the number of cases is equal to the product of the standard deviations of the two variables and the coefficient of correlation between them, their covariance, we have

$$r_{z_0c} = \frac{\sigma_0\sigma_1r_{01} + \cdots + \sigma_0\sigma_kr_{0k}}{\sigma_0\sigma_c}$$

$$= \frac{\sigma_0(\sigma_1r_{01} + \cdots + \sigma_kr_{0k})}{\sigma_0\sigma_c}$$

$$= \frac{\sigma_1r_{01} + \cdots + \sigma_kr_{0k}}{\sigma_c} \tag{7-14}$$

If all the component variables are expressed in standard-score form, then the values for the standard deviations in the numerator all become 1.00, and in the denominator we can substitute for the standard deviation of composite scores from Eq. (7-13). This gives us

$$r_{z_0c_z} = r_{z_0(z_1+\cdots+z_k)} = \frac{r_{01} + \cdots + r_{0k}}{\sqrt{k + k(k-1)\overline{r_{ii'}}}} \tag{7-15}$$

where $\overline{r_{ii'}}$ represents the average of the coefficients of correlation among the component variables. In the numerator we have a set of values for which we can substitute their mean times the number of values:

$$r_{z_0c_z} = \frac{k\overline{r_{0i}}}{\sqrt{k + k(k-1)\overline{r_{ii'}}}}$$

where $\overline{r_{0i}}$ represents the average of the coefficients of correlation between the outside variable and all the component variables. If we divide the numerator and denominator by k we have

$$r_{z_0c_z} = \frac{\overline{r_{0i}}}{(1/k)\sqrt{k + k(k-1)\overline{r_{ii'}}}}$$

$$= \frac{\overline{r_{0i}}}{\sqrt{k/k^2 + [k(k-1)]/k^2\overline{r_{ii'}}}}$$

$$= \frac{\overline{r_{0i}}}{\sqrt{1/k + (k-1)/k\overline{r_{ii'}}}} \tag{7-16}$$

If the composite is formed of a very large number of components, say that k is an infinitely large number, then $1/k$ very closely approximates zero and $(k-1)/k$ very closely approximates 1.00. Then, symbolizing composite scores as c_{z_∞} to indicate that the composite is formed of an infinitely large number of components, we can write Eq. (7-16) as

$$r_{z_0 c_{z, \infty}} = \frac{\overline{r_{0i}}}{\sqrt{\overline{r_{ii'}}}} \qquad (7\text{-}17)$$

The practicalities of testing situations limit the length of the tests and the number of measurements we can use. Sometimes the amount of time available for testing is the limiting factor. If we are measuring the school achievement of graduating high school seniors, we might like to have a test of several hundred items in order to give full coverage of all subjects, but in an hour examination perhaps all we can use is a test of 100 items. In other situations it is physically or administratively impossible to obtain all the measurements we wish. Thus when friendliness is measured by ratings we might like to have the subjects rated by a very large number of acquaintances, but perhaps we can obtain only three such raters.

Equation (7-17) permits us to estimate the correlation between an outside variable and a composite variable, as the sum of the scores on the 100 items of the achievement or the average of the three ratings, when the composite is formed of an infinitely large number of components of the same nature, that is, having the same average correlations as that of the components we actually use. For example, suppose we wish to predict college grades from the high school achievement test. If $\overline{r_{0i}} = .50$ and $\overline{r_{ii'}} = .81$, Eq. (7-16) tells us that a 100-item test with these characteristics predicts college grades with a correlation of .555, and Eq. (7-17) tells us that even if we had an infinitely large number of such items the correlation would be only .556. Hence it would not be worthwhile to increase the length of the test. Suppose we wish to examine the relationship between friendliness and scores on a "sociability" inventory and $\overline{r_{0i}} = .20$ and $\overline{r_{ii'}} = .25$. Equation (7-16) tells us that ratings with these characteristics made by three individuals are correlated with inventory scores only .284, and Eq. (7-17) tells us that inventory scores would be correlated .500 with ratings if an infinitely large number of such raters could be used.

Equation (7-16) shows that the correlation between scores on a composite variable and an outside variable is a function of the number of component variables in the composite and the magnitude of the intercorrelations among them, together with the magnitude of the correlations between the components and the outside variable. Entering the three illustrative values of .20, .50, and .80 for $\overline{r_{ii'}}$ and for $\overline{r_{0i}}$ in Eq. (7-16) together with a number of values of k, the formula was solved for $r_{z_0 c_z}$ and the values were plotted in Fig. 7-2. From this figure the following principles can be derived:

1. The higher are the correlations between the components and the outside variable, the higher is the correlation between the composite and the outside variable.
2. The lower are the intercorrelations among the components, the higher is the correlation between the composite and the outside variable.
3. As the number of components in the composite increases (assuming the additional components are the same as the original components in terms of their average correlations with the other components and with the outside variable), the correlation between the composite and the outside variable increases.

We have seen that two general purposes for forming a composite are to obtain a better, more precise, or more representative measure of the variable in which we are interested and to obtain a better device for predicting another variable. These two purposes are likely to lead us to

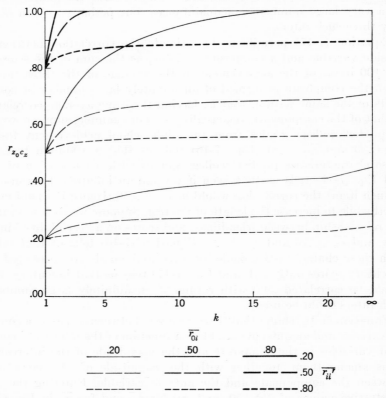

Figure 7-2   The effects on the correlation between scores on an outside variable and scores on a composite variable ($r_{z_0 c_z}$) of the number of components (k), the intercorrelations among the components ($\overline{r_{ii'}}$), and the correlations between the components and the outside variable ($\overline{r_{0i}}$).

form composites made up of components which have quite different levels of intercorrelation.

If we form a composite in order to obtain a better, more precise, or more representative measure of the variable in which we are interested, it is probable that the component variables we select will tend to measure the same kinds of traits and hence have relatively high intercorrelations. For example, if we were making up a test of arithmetic ability we should include items involving computations but not items involving memory span for numbers, knowledge of algebraic formulae, or interest in mathematics. The correlations among the scores people earn on computational items undoubtedly would be higher on the average than the correlations among the scores they earn on items involving memory span for numbers, knowledge of algebraic formulae, or interest in mathematics.

Similarly, if we were developing an index of the job proficiency of department heads in a business organization, such as the supervisors of persons in lower positions, we might include rating scales designed to measure the extent to which they communicate with their subordinates, clarify duties and standards of work, and administer discipline fairly. However, we should not include rating scales intended to measure effectiveness in planning new activities, promotability, and developing budgets, since these characteristics have nothing to do with the trait of supervisory ability. Again it is likely that scores on these first three scales would be more closely correlated with each other than scores on all six scales, since the former pertain to one domain of behavior whereas the latter pertain to quite different aspects of behavior.

The point is that when we form a composite of this sort, the very process we use—the definition of the variable we follow in selecting components—ordinarily will result in the selection of component variables which on the average will bear at least moderately substantial relationships with each other. Furthermore, it is highly probable that the components in the composite will be more highly related to each other than they are to any outside variable. That is, ordinarily

$$\overline{r_{ii'}} > \overline{r_{0i}}$$

The situation, then, is that represented in Fig. 7-2 by the solid and dashed lines but not by the dotted line. Specifically, the cases illustrated in the figure are:

$\overline{r_{ii'}}$	$\overline{r_{0i}}$
.80	.50
.80	.10
.50	.10

Referring to Fig. 7-2, we can see that while increasing the number of components does increase the correlation between composite scores and scores on the outside variable, the increase is not very great. Indeed, increasing the number of components by more than about five times produces little or no increase in the correlation.

When we develop a composite which we intend to use as a basis for predicting another or outside variable, it is likely that the components we select to form the composite will have relatively low intercorrelations. When we seek to predict some variable from several other variables, we try to select predictor variables which measure different aspects of the outside variable.

For example, suppose we wish to develop a battery of tests to predict success in a mechanics training course. On the basis of our analysis of the content and nature of the course we might decide that there are four general aspects which should be measured, namely, ability to learn, ability to understand written material, capacity to perceive the shapes and forms of objects, and manual dexterity. We might propose using an intelligence test to measure learning ability and a reading test to measure ability to understand written material. However, the intelligence test as well as the reading test involves reading and understanding what is read. Therefore we should probably not include the latter in our battery. Because performance on both tests depends heavily on verbal ability it is not surprising to find that their scores are highly correlated. Consequently, in our process of selecting tests we should deliberately exclude a test whose scores are highly correlated with those of another test already included.

To measure the capacity to perceive the shapes and forms of objects we might use a paper-and-pencil test wherein the individual makes judgments about the similarity and differences among two-dimensional geometric figures, or a performance test wherein spatial ability is measured by the speed and accuracy with which the individual places solid figures of different shapes in appropriately shaped holes in a board. It is likely that we should select the second type of test rather than the first, because the first involves reading instructions printed on the test and we already have measured verbal ability. Scores on a paper-and-pencil spatial ability test are more highly correlated with an intelligence test than are scores on a performance spatial ability test. Hence again we deliberately select a component for the composite on the basis of the fact that its correlations with other components are low.

Manual dexterity ordinarily is measured by means of a test involving speed and accuracy of placing pegs in holes in a board. However, this ability is measured to a substantial degree by the test we have selected to measure spatial ability, so we should not include a pegboard test. Again a variable which is correlated to a high degree with some other component in the composite is excluded.

Therefore when we form a composite with which we intend to predict some outside variable, we seek components that are relatively independent of each other. Naturally we also seek variables as components which also are highly correlated with the outside variable we wish to predict. The situation we try to achieve, then, is one wherein

$$\overline{r_{ii'}} < \overline{r_{0i}}$$

This situation is represented by the dotted and dashed lines in Fig. 7-2 but not by the solid lines. Specifically, the cases illustrated in the figure are:

$\overline{r_{ii'}}$	$\overline{r_{0i}}$
.50	.80
.10	.80
.10	.50

Referring to Fig. 7-2, we can see that increasing the number of components substantially increases the correlation between composite scores and scores on the outside variable. However, with the types of tests ordinarily usable in a practical predictive situation—as in the example given above for the mechanics training course—it is not easy to find many tests which bear low correlations with other tests and at the same time are highly correlated with the outside variable, the one to be predicted. Indeed, in most cases the fact will be that at the best $\overline{r_{0i}}$ is equal to but not higher than $\overline{r_{ii'}}$. The curves in Fig. 7-2 then rise more rapidly as the number of components increases than is likely to be the case in practice.

THE CORRELATION BETWEEN A COMPONENT AND A COMPOSITE WHEN THE COMPONENT IS A PART OF THE COMPOSITE

We have been considering the correlation between scores on a single variable and a composite variable when the single variable is outside of the composite. Sometimes we are interested in the correlation between scores on a single and a composite variable when the single variable is a member of the composite. The composite consists of 1 to k components, and we wish to obtain the coefficient of correlation between scores on one of these components, say component 1, and the total composite of scores. This correlation is

$$
\begin{aligned}
r_{1c} = r_{x_1(x_1 + \cdots + x_k)} &= \frac{\Sigma x_1(x_1 + \cdots + x_k)}{n\sigma_1\sigma_c} \\
&= \frac{\Sigma x_1/n + \Sigma x_1 x_2/n + \cdots + \Sigma x_1 x_k/n}{\sigma_1\sigma_c} \\
&= \frac{\sigma_1{}^2 + \sigma_1\sigma_2 r_{12} + \cdots + \sigma_1\sigma_k r_{1k}}{\sigma_1\sigma_c}
\end{aligned}
\tag{7-18}
$$

In the numerator we have the sum of the covariances between 1 and each of the other $k - 1$ components. Remembering that the sum of a set of values is equal to their mean times the number of values, we can write Eq. (7-18) as

$$r_{1c} = \frac{\sigma_1{}^2 + (k - 1)\overline{\sigma_1\sigma_i r_{1i}}}{\sigma_1\sigma_c} \qquad (7\text{-}19)$$

where $\overline{\sigma_1\sigma_i r_{1i}}$ represents the mean of the covariances of component 1 with all the other components.

If all the components are expressed in standard-score form, then the standard deviations in the numerator of Eq. (7-19) become 1.00 and we can substitute for the standard deviation of composite scores from Eq. (7-12). We then have

$$r_{z_1 c_z} = \frac{1 + (k - 1)\overline{r_{1i}}}{\sqrt{k + k(k - 1)\overline{r_{ii'}}}} \qquad (7\text{-}20)$$

Let us consider for a moment the meaning of $\overline{r_{ii'}}$ in Eq. (7-20). This term is the average of the coefficients of correlation among all the components in the composite. If this value is high, then we can say that the composite is homogeneous in the sense that the components tend to measure the same traits to a high degree; and if the value is low, then the composite is heterogeneous since the components measure few if any traits in common. Obviously $\overline{r_{ii'}}$ is equal to the average of the coefficients of each of the components with all others. That is,

$$\overline{r_{ii'}} = \frac{r_{1i} + \cdots + r_{ki}}{k} \qquad (7\text{-}21)$$

DEVELOPING HOMOGENEOUS COMPOSITES ON THE BASIS OF THE MAGNITUDE OF THE CORRELATION BETWEEN COMPONENT AND COMPOSITE VARIABLES

Equation (7-21) shows that if we wish to increase the homogeneity of a composite we should eliminate those component variables which on the average have the lowest correlations with the other components. Under ordinary circumstances it is too laborious to compute all the intercorrelations among the components in a composite so that for each component we can compute $\overline{r_{1i}}$. For example, if we had a test consisting of 50 items and we wished to eliminate those having the lowest correlations with other items and thereby develop a more homogeneous test, we should have to compute 1,225 intercorrelations—a most forbidding task.

However, Eq. (7-20) shows us that a coefficient of correlation between a component and the total composite is related to the average of the coefficients between the component and the other components. To show this effect, Eq. (7-20) is plotted in Fig. 7-3. From this figure we can derive the following principles:

1. The average of the coefficients of correlation between a component and the other components of a composite is directly proportional to the correlation between the component and the total composite.
2. The coefficient of correlation between a component and the total composite is higher than the average of the coefficients of correlation between the component and the other components. (This is because the component itself is included in the total composite.) This effect is lesser the higher is the average correlation (homogeneity) among the components.
3. The number of components has relatively little effect upon the proportional relationship between the correlation between a component and the total composite and the average of the correlations between the component and the other components.

An example of how eliminating those components with the lowest correlation with the total composite scores results in increasing the homogeneity of the composite $(\overline{r_{ii'}})$ is shown in Table 7-4. Recall that

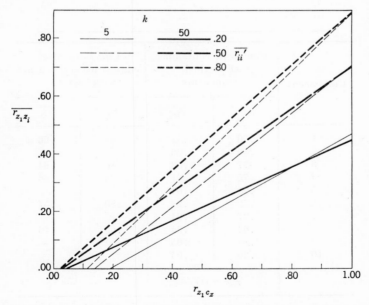

Figure 7-3   The average of the coefficients of correlation between one component of a composite and the other components $(r_{z_1 z_i})$ in relation to the coefficient of correlation between that component and total composite scores $(r_{z_1 c_z})$, the average of the intercorrelations among the components $(\overline{r_{ii'}})$, and the number of components (k).

under ordinary circumstances we do not know either the intercorrelations among the components or the average of the correlations between each component and the remainder of the components $(\overline{r_{1i}})$. These values are given in Table 7-4 to make the matter more comprehensible. In the

TABLE 7-4.   Illustration of Increasing the Homogeneity among Component Variables through Elimination of Components with Lowest Correlation with Total Composite Scores

Intercorrelations among the components $(r_{ii'})$									
	1	2	3	4	5	6	7	8	9	10
1	.07	.75	.77	.04	.59	.01	.51	.07	.02
2		.03	.05	.03	.10	.05	.07	.09	.03
3			.72	.02	.64	.08	.43	.10	.09
4				.06	.65	.00	.48	.00	.06
5					.08	.01	.09	.07	.00
6						.02	.40	.03	.01
7							.06	.04	.10
8								.04	.08
9									.05
10									

Component	Composite containing all original components		Composite after eliminating components with lowest r_{1c}	
	r_{1c}	$\overline{r_{1i}}$	r_{1c}	$\overline{r_{1i}}$
1	.76	.31	.88	.66
2	.30	.06		
3	.77	.32	.86	.64
4	.75	.31	.88	.66
5	.28	.04		
6	.70	.28	.80	.57
7	.27	.04		
8	.63	.24	.69	.46
9	.30	.05		
10	.29	.05		
	$\sigma_c = 5.03$		$\sigma_c = 4.10$	
	$\overline{r_{ii'}} = .17$		$\overline{r_{ii'}} = .59$	

example we see that components 2, 5, 7, 9, and 10 have the lowest correlations with total composite scores (r_{1c}) and therefore also the lowest average correlations with the other components $(\overline{r_{1i}})$. If we eliminate these components, not only do the remaining components have higher correlations with the new total composite scores and consequently higher average coefficients of correlation with the remaining components, but also the homogeneity of the composite $(\overline{r_{1i}})$ is substantially increased. As would be expected, when the number of components is reduced the standard deviation of composite scores is reduced, but not very much because the components selected for elimination have low intercorrelations. Frequently the process illustrated in Table 7-4 is repeated several times, eliminating in successive stages those components with the lowest correlations with the total composite until there remains a composite which is quite homogeneous. When the components are items in a test, this process is termed item analysis against total test scores.

The particular coefficient used for r_{1c} depends upon the nature of the data and upon the shortcuts we are willing to take in order to reduce the labor of computation. If the components are the items of a test each of which is scored as passing or failing, the biserial or the point biserial may be the most appropriate coefficient. If the components are continuous variables, we may wish to use the Pearsonian coefficient. Often the tetrachoric coefficient of correlation is used, dividing the total composite scores into approximately the upper and lower halves and similarly dichotomizing the scores on the components if they are not already dichotomized. Tetrachoric coefficients can easily be determined from Table 6-2 or other similar time-saving devices. It should be remembered, of course, that shortcuts always introduce errors. However, if we merely wish to eliminate those components which are most discrepant, the error of shortcut methods may not be too serious.

It should be recalled that our discussion of the process whereby the homogeneity of a composite can be increased was developed from Eq. (7-20), which presupposes that all components are expressed in standard-score form. If the components are not expressed as standard scores but all have standard deviations of the same magnitude, Eq. (7-18) applies but it resolves to Eq. (7-20). While it may be that in some cases the standard deviations of all components are equal, as when we deliberately equate the standard deviations of the scores in all components in order to make them comparable, in most instances they are not. For example, seldom if ever do we find all the items of a test having standard deviations of exactly the same value. Therefore in many if not most instances where we wish to increase the homogeneity of composites we shall be dealing with a situation reflected in Eqs. (7-18) and (7-19) rather than in Eq. (7-20).

It can be seen from Eq. (7-19) that as the components differ among themselves more and more in the magnitude of their standard deviations, the effect is to reduce the proportionality between r_{1c} and $\overline{r_{1i}}$. That is, the relationship between these two values, while still positive is not perfect. Therefore two components could have different values of $\overline{r_{1i}}$ and yet have the same value of r_{1c}.

However, in practice the differences in magnitude of the standard deviations of the components often are not great, and therefore the relationship between r_{1c} and $\overline{r_{1i}}$ is quite high. Hence in many instances the values of σ_i in Eq. (7-19) do not make a great deal of difference. Consequently the procedure illustrated in Table 7-3 will, in many situations, prove adequate in eliminating the less homogeneous components.

THE CORRELATION BETWEEN TWO COMPOSITE VARIABLES

We now turn to the relationship between scores on two composite variables. Let us term one composite i and say that it contains k components and the other composite j, saying that it contains m components. From Eq. (6-3) we can write the coefficient of correlation between scores on two composites as

$$
\begin{aligned}
r_{c_i c_j} &= r_{(x_{i,1} + \cdots + x_{i,k})(x_{j,1} + \cdots + x_{j,m})} \\
&= \frac{\Sigma(x_{i_1} + \cdots + x_{i_k})(x_{j_1} + \cdots + x_{j_m})}{n\sigma_{c_i}\sigma_{c_j}} \\
&= \frac{\Sigma x_{i_1}x_{j_1} + \cdots + \Sigma x_{i_1}x_{j_m} + \cdots + \Sigma x_{i_k}x_{j_1} + \cdots + \Sigma x_{i_k}x_{j_m}}{n\sigma_{c_i}\sigma_{c_j}}
\end{aligned}
$$

Since each of the k components of composite i is paired with each of the m components of composite j, the numerator of the above formula contains km terms. The multiplication of $(x_{i_1} + \cdots + x_{i_k})$ by

TABLE 7-5.   The Multiplication of $(x_{i_1} + \cdots + x_{i_k})$ by $(x_{j_1} + \cdots + x_{j_m})$

	x_{i_1}	x_{i_2}	$\cdots$	$x_{i_{k-1}}$	x_{i_k}
x_{j_1}	$x_{i_1}x_{j_1}$	$x_{i_2}x_{j_1}$	$\cdots$	$x_{i_{k-1}}x_{j_1}$	$x_{i_k}x_{j_1}$
x_{j_2}	$x_{i_1}x_{j_2}$	$x_{i_2}x_{j_2}$	$\cdots$	$x_{i_{k-1}}x_{j_2}$	$x_{i_k}x_{j_2}$
$\cdots$	$\cdots$	$\cdots$	$\cdots$	$\cdots$	$\cdots$
$x_{j_{m-1}}$	$x_{i_1}x_{j_{m-1}}$	$x_{i_2}x_{j_{m-1}}$	$\cdots$	$x_{i_{k-1}}x_{j_{m-1}}$	$x_{i_k}x_{j_{m-1}}$
x_{j_m}	$x_{i_1}x_{j_m}$	$x_{i_2}x_{j_m}$	$\cdots$	$x_{i_{k-1}}x_{j_m}$	$x_{i_k}x_{j_m}$

$(x_{j_1} + \cdots + x_{j_m})$ is shown in Table 7-5. Dividing the numerator and denominator by n, the number of cases, we have

$$
\begin{aligned}
r_{c_i c_j} &= \frac{\Sigma x_{i_1}x_{j_1}/n + \cdots + \Sigma x_{i_1}x_{j_m}/n + \cdots + \Sigma x_{i_k}x_{j_1}/n + \cdots + \Sigma x_{i_k}x_{j_m}/n}{\sigma_{c_i}\sigma_{c_j}} \\
&= \frac{\sigma_{i_1}\sigma_{j_1}r_{i_1j_1} + \cdots + \sigma_{i_1}\sigma_{j_m}r_{i_1j_m} + \cdots + \sigma_{i_k}\sigma_{j_1}r_{i_kj_1} + \cdots + \sigma_{i_k}\sigma_{j_m}r_{i_kj_m}}{\sigma_{c_i}\sigma_{c_j}}
\end{aligned}
$$

$$(7\text{-}22)$$

An example of the computation of the coefficient of correlation between scores on two composite variables by means of Eq. (7-22) is given in Table 7-6.

TABLE 7-6. Illustration of the Computation of the Coefficient of Correlation between Scores on Two Composites*

	x_{i_1}	x_{i_2}	x_{i_3}	x_{j_1}	x_{j_2}	σ
	Composite i			Composite j		
x_{i_1}		.40	.60	.20	.15	4
x_{i_2}			.50	.15	.10	2
x_{i_3}				.00	.30	5
x_{j_1}					.80	6
x_{j_2}						8

$$r_{c_i}r_{c_j} = \frac{(4)(6)(.20) + (4)(8)(.15) + (2)(6)(.15) + (2)(8)(.10) + (5)(6)(.00) + (5)(8)(.30)}{(9.24)(13.30)}$$

$$= \frac{25.00}{122.89}$$

$$= .20$$

* From Eq. (7-12), $\sigma_{c_i} = 9.24$; $\sigma_{c_j} = 13.30$.

If all the component variables are expressed in standard-score form, the values for the standard deviations in the numerator all become 1.00, and in the denominator we can substitute the standard deviation of composite scores from Eq. (7-13). This gives us

$$r_{c_{z,i}c_{z,j}} = \frac{r_{i_1j_1} + \cdots + r_{i_1j_m} + \cdots + r_{i_kj_1} + \cdots + r_{i_kj_m}}{\sqrt{k + k(k-1)\overline{r_{ii'}}} \sqrt{m + m(m-1)\overline{r_{jj'}}}}$$

where $\overline{r_{ii'}}$ is the average of the intercorrelations among the k components of composite i, and $\overline{r_{jj'}}$ is the average of the intercorrelations among the m components of composite j. Examination of Table 7-5 will show that there are km terms in the numerator. We can express the terms in the numerator as means and write

$$r_{c_{z,i}c_{z,j}} = \frac{km\overline{r_{ij}}}{\sqrt{k + k(k-1)\overline{r_{ii'}}} \sqrt{m + m(m-1)\overline{r_{jj'}}}}$$

where $\overline{r_{ij}}$ represents the average of the coefficients of the correlation among the k components of composite i and the m components of composite j, that is, the average of the cross correlations. Dividing the numerator and denominator by km, we have

$$r_{c_{z,i}c_{z,j}} = \frac{\overline{r_{ij}}}{\frac{1}{k}\sqrt{k + k(k-1)\overline{r_{ii'}}}\,\frac{1}{m}\sqrt{m + m(m-1)\overline{r_{jj'}}}}$$

$$= \frac{\overline{r_{ij}}}{\sqrt{\dfrac{k}{k^2} + \dfrac{k(k-1)}{k^2}\overline{r_{ii'}}}\,\sqrt{\dfrac{m}{m^2} + \dfrac{m(m-1)}{m^2}\overline{r_{jj'}}}}$$

$$= \frac{\overline{r_{ij}}}{\sqrt{\dfrac{1}{k} + \dfrac{k-1}{k}\overline{r_{ii'}}}\,\sqrt{\dfrac{1}{m} + \dfrac{m-1}{m}\overline{r_{jj'}}}} \tag{7-23}$$

If both composites are formed of a very large number of components, say that k and m are infinitely large numbers, then $1/k$ and $1/m$ very closely approximate zero and $(k-1)/k$ and $(m-1)/m$ very closely approximate 1.00. Symbolizing composite scores as $c_{z_{i,\infty}}$ and $c_{z_{j,\infty}}$ to indicate that the composites are formed of infinitely large numbers of components, we can write Eq. (7-23) as

$$r_{c_{z,i,\infty}c_{z,j,\infty}} = \frac{\overline{r_{ij}}}{\sqrt{\overline{r_{ii'}}}\,\sqrt{\overline{r_{jj'}}}} = \frac{\overline{r_{ij}}}{\sqrt{\overline{r_{ii'}}\,\overline{r_{jj'}}}} \tag{7-24}$$

Entering illustrative values of .10, .50, and .80 for $\overline{r_{ii'}}$, $\overline{r_{jj'}}$, and $\overline{r_{ij}}$ in Eq. (7-23) together with a number of different values of k and m and for simplicity letting $k = m$, the formula was solved for $r_{c_{z,i}c_{z,j}}$ and the values are plotted in Fig. 7-4. From this figure the following principles concerning the correlation between scores on two composite variables can be derived:

1. The higher are the correlations between the components of the two composites (the cross correlations), the higher is the correlation between the two composites.
2. The lower are the intercorrelations among the components (the less homogeneous the components are), the higher is the correlation between the two composites.
3. As the numbers of components in the two composites increase (assuming the additional components are the same as the original components in terms of their average intercorrelations and cross correlations), the correlation between the two composites increases. This effect is greater the lower are the intercorrelations among the components which comprise the two composites.

These principles are useful in a variety of ways for dealing with practical problems in psychological measurement. As we have seen, we frequently deal with composite variables and often are concerned with the relationship between such variables.

When we wish to increase the degree of relationship between two composites, we sometimes try to do so by increasing the number of components in them and expect thereby to improve precision of measurement. As we can see from Fig. 7-4, this increase in the correlation between

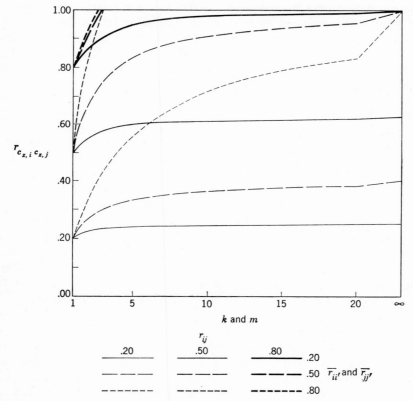

Figure 7-4 The effects on the correlation between scores on two composite variables ($r_{c_{z,i} c_{z,j}}$) of the number of components (k and m, where $k = m$), the intercorrelations among the components ($\overline{r_{ii'}}$ and $\overline{r_{jj'}}$, where $\overline{r_{ii'}} = \overline{r_{jj'}}$), and the cross correlations between the components of the two composites ($\overline{r_{ij}}$).

two composites is greatest when the correlations among the components are low, that is, when the composite is a heterogeneous one. Yet frequently the composites we deal with are homogeneous, and therefore increasing the number of components has relatively little effect upon the correlation between the two composites.

For example, the correlation between the ratings assigned by different raters to the same individual often is relatively low, perhaps .50 or less. Sometimes it is argued that this results from the fact that the trait being rated is so ambiguous that the different raters cannot agree on its meaning. As a remedy we may fractionate the trait into its different aspects and have each rater evaluate every individual on a number of subtraits. A composite in this case is the series of scales measuring these subtraits. The correlation between composites is the degree of relationship between the total rating assigned by two raters. The procedure of fractionation just described is not likely to improve the agreement between the raters, inasmuch as raters commonly manifest the so-called "halo error." That is, the ratings assigned by a rater on different scales usually are very highly correlated, perhaps .70 or above. Thus the composite which is formed of the ratings assigned by a rater on a number of scales is very likely to be quite homogeneous; therefore such a fractionation will only slightly, if at all, improve the degree of agreement between two raters.

In some situations we need two or more forms of the same test. The forms must differ in the specific items they contain, so that having taken one form an individual will not thereby obtain a relatively higher score on the second form due to specific memory or practice effects. Furthermore, the scores on both forms should be highly correlated so that we can be assured that they measure the same abilities or traits. It may be that we want several forms of a test so that if something happens to disturb a testing situation when an individual is taking the test, we can give him another. Or we may wish to administer a test before and after some treatment—experimental, therapeutic, or otherwise—in order to observe any change that might occur as a result of the treatment.

When we make up a test or a series of forms of a test, we begin by developing a series of items. We develop these items from the definition of the variable we propose to measure. When we assemble the items into different forms, we know from Eq. (7-23) that those items which are likely to be highly correlated should be placed into different forms and those items which are likely to be less correlated should be placed in the same form. For example, if we were developing two forms of a test designed to measure knowledge of American history and had two questions concerning the Civil War and two questions concerning the foreign policy of the Wilson administration, we should place one of each type of question in one form of the test and the other in the second form. It seems likely that the correlation between scores on the two Civil War items, and between the two Wilson administration items, will be higher than the correlation between the scores on either one or the other of the Civil War items and either one or the other of the Wilson administration items.

THE CORRELATION BETWEEN TWO COMPOSITES WHEN ONE IS A
PART OF THE OTHER

Let us now consider the special case of correlation between composites when one of them is a part of the other. Let us say we have a set of 1 through k components forming a composite and to this composite we add another consisting of $(k + 1)$ through m components. Listing our components, we have

$$x_1, x_2, \ldots , x_{k-1}, x_k, x_{k+1}, \ldots , x_{m-1}, x_m$$

The total number of components, then, is $k + m$. From these components we can form two composites, one of which includes the first k components (c_k) and the other of which includes all $k + m$ components (c_{k+m}). The correlation between these two composites is

$$r_{c_k c_{k+m}} = r_{(x_1+ \cdots +x_k)(x_1+ \cdots +x_k+x_{k+1}+ \cdots +x_m)}$$
$$= \frac{\Sigma(x_1{}^2 + x_1x_2 + \cdots + x_1x_k + x_1x_{k+1} + \cdots + x_1x_m + \cdots + x_kx_1 + \cdots + x_kx_{k-1} + x_k{}^2 + x_kx_{k+1} + \cdots + x_kx_m)}{n\sigma_{c_k}\sigma_{c_{k+m}}}$$

In the numerator we have all the 1 to k components paired with each other and then each one paired with each of the $(k + 1)$ to m components. The multiplication of $(x_1 + \cdots + x_k)$ by

$$(x_1 + \cdots + x_k + x_{k+1} + \cdots + x_m)$$

is shown in Table 7-7. Dividing the numerator and denominator by n,

TABLE 7-7. The Multiplication of $(x_1 + \cdots + x_k)$ by $(x_1 + \cdots + x_k + x_{k+1} + \cdots + x_m)$

	x_1	x_2	$\cdots$	x_{k-1}	x_k
x_1	$x_1{}^2$	x_1x_2	$\cdots$	$x_{k-1}x_1$	x_kx_1
x_2	x_1x_2	$x_2{}^2$	$\cdots$	$x_{k-1}x_2$	x_kx_2
$\cdots$	$\cdots$	$\cdots$	$\cdots$	$\cdots$	$\cdots$
x_{k-1}	x_1x_{k-1}	x_2x_{k-1}	$\cdots$	x_{k-1}^2	x_kx_{k-1}
x_k	x_1x_k	x_2x_k	$\cdots$	$x_{k-1}x_k$	$x_k{}^2$
x_{k+1}	x_1x_{k+1}	x_2x_{k+1}	$\cdots$	$x_{k-1}x_{k+1}$	x_kx_{k+1}
$\cdots$	$\cdots$	$\cdots$	$\cdots$	$\cdots$	$\cdots$
			$\cdots$		
			$\cdots$		
x_{m-1}	x_1x_{m-1}	x_2x_{m-1}	$\cdots$	$x_{k-1}x_{m-1}$	x_kx_{m-1}
x_m	x_1x_m	x_2x_m	$\cdots$	$x_{k-1}x_m$	x_kx_m

we have

$$
\begin{aligned}
r_{c_k c_{k+m}} &= \frac{\begin{array}{c} \dfrac{\Sigma x_1{}^2}{n} + \dfrac{\Sigma x_1 x_2}{n} + \cdots + \dfrac{\Sigma x_1 x_k}{n} + \dfrac{\Sigma x_1 x_{k+1}}{n} + \cdots + \dfrac{\Sigma x_1 x_m}{n} + \cdots \\[2mm] + \dfrac{\Sigma x_k x_1}{n} + \cdots + \dfrac{\Sigma x_k x_{k-1}}{n} + \dfrac{\Sigma x_k{}^2}{n} + \dfrac{\Sigma x_k x_{k+1}}{n} + \cdots \dfrac{\Sigma x_k x_m}{n} \end{array}}{\sigma_{c_k}\sigma_{c_{k+m}}} \\[4mm]
&= \frac{\begin{array}{c} \sigma_1{}^2 + \sigma_1\sigma_2 r_{12} + \cdots + \sigma_1\sigma_k r_{1k} + \sigma_1\sigma_{k+1} r_{1(k+1)} \\[1mm] + \cdots + \sigma_1\sigma_m r_{1m} + \cdots + \sigma_k\sigma_1 r_{k1} + \cdots \\[1mm] + \sigma_k\sigma_{k-1} r_{k(k-1)} + \sigma_k{}^2 + \sigma_k\sigma_{k+1} r_{k(k-1)} + \cdots + \sigma_k\sigma_m r_{km} \end{array}}{\sigma_{c_k}\sigma_{c_{k+m}}}
\end{aligned}
$$

Rearranging terms gives

$$
r_{c_k c_{k+m}} = \frac{\begin{array}{c} \sigma_1{}^2 + \cdots + \sigma_k{}^2 + 2\sigma_1\sigma_2 r_{12} + \cdots + 2\sigma_{k-1}\sigma_k r_{(k-1)k} \\[1mm] + \cdots + 2\sigma_1\sigma_{k+1} r_{1(k+1)} + \cdots + 2\sigma_k\sigma_m r_{km} \end{array}}{\sigma_{c_k}\sigma_{c_{k+m}}} \tag{7-25}
$$

In the numerator there are k terms of σ^2, $k(k-1)$ covariance terms of the 1 to k components, and km cross-covariance terms of the combination of the 1 to k with the $(k+1)$ to m components. Therefore in the numerator we have the sum of the k variances of the 1 to k components, the sum of the $k(k-1)$ covariances of the 1 to k components, and the sum of the km cross covariances of the 1 to k and the $(k+1)$ to m components. Substituting the number of values times their means for the sums of the values of each of these three sets of terms, we can write the formula as

$$
r_{c_k c_{k+m}} = \frac{k\overline{\sigma_k{}^2} + k(k-1)\overline{\sigma_k\sigma_{k'} r_{kk'}} + km\overline{\sigma_k\sigma_m r_{km}}}{\sigma_{c_k}\sigma_{c_{k+m}}} \tag{7-26}
$$

where σ_k and $\sigma_{k'}$ refer to the standard deviations of the 1 to k components, $r_{kk'}$ to their intercorrelations, σ_m to the standard deviations of the $(k+1)$ to m components, and r_{km} to the cross correlations between the 1 to k and the $(k+1)$ to m components. Note that there are km of these cross correlations, k being the number of components in the first composite and m being the number of components in the second set and not the total number of components. The total number of components is $k+m$.

If all components are expressed in standard-score form, all the standard deviations in Eq. (7-26) become 1.00 and we can substitute for the standard deviations of composite scores in the denominator from Eq. (7-13). We then have

$$
r_{c_{z,k} c_{z,k+m}} = \frac{k + k(k-1)\overline{r_{kk'}} + km\overline{r_{km}}}{\sqrt{k + k(k-1)\overline{r_{kk'}}}\ \sqrt{(k+m) + (k+m)(k+m-1)\bar{r}}} \tag{7-27}
$$

In this formula the correlations among all the $k+m$ components are symbolized as $\bar{r}$.

If the 1 to k and the $(k + 1)$ to m components are the same in terms of their average coefficients of correlation, then we can write the formula as

$$r_{c_{z,k}c_{z,k+m}} = \frac{k + k(k - 1)\bar{r} + km\bar{r}}{\sqrt{k + k(k - 1)\bar{r}}\,\sqrt{(k + m) + (k + m)(k + m - 1)\bar{r}}} \qquad (7\text{-}28)$$

Equation (7-28) is useful because it tells what will be the effects of eliminating components upon the order of individuals in composite scores. We are presuming, of course, that when we eliminate components those eliminated are the same as the original ones in terms of their average intercorrelations. This is likely to occur when we eliminate components at random. We may wish to eliminate components for purposes of economy. For example, in measuring reaction time we might be taking 100 measurements, but for purposes of saving testing time we might prefer to take fewer measurements. Would we greatly disturb the order of individuals in composite scores if we took only 50 measurements? In the evaluation of candidates for a job each candidate might be interviewed by eight people. Since this is an expensive procedure we might wish to reduce the number of interviews to four. But would this greatly affect the order of individuals in terms of composite interview ratings? Suppose we have an achievement test comprised of 300 items which very satisfactorily differentiates among students and reflects very well what they have learned in a course. However, we have to allow 3 hr of testing. Would we seriously change the order of individuals in total test score if we cut the test to 100 items and allow only 1 hr for it?

If the coefficient of correlation between scores of the reduced composite and scores on the total composite is, say, only .70 to .80, we probably should feel that the order of individuals is too greatly changed. Therefore we should be unwilling to shorten the composite to the degree proposed. However, if the coefficient of correlation between scores on the reduced and the original composite is, say, .95 or higher, we might hold that the order of individuals is not sufficiently changed to make any practical difference and consequently we should be willing to eliminate some of the components.

By plotting Eq. (7-28) we can see the effects of eliminating components upon the order of individuals in composite scores. This formula is plotted in Fig. 7-5. From this figure we can derive the following principles:

1. The more components that are eliminated from a composite variable, the greater is the order of individuals in composite scores changed from the order as given by the scores in the original composite.
2. The higher are the correlations among the components, that is, the more homogeneous is the composite, the less will be the change in the order of individuals when some components are eliminated.

3. The larger is the number of components in the original composite, the less will be the change in the order of individuals in composite scores when a given number of components is eliminated.

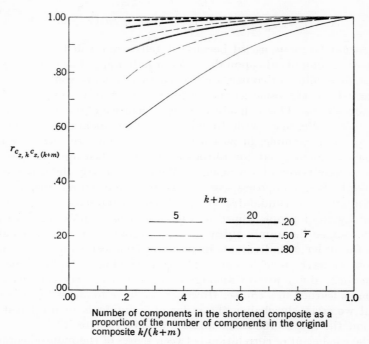

Figure 7-5   The effects on the order of individual differences ($r_{c_{z,k}c_{z,(k+m)}}$) in composite scores of reducing the number of components in the composite to k in relation to the intercorrelations among the components ($\bar{r}$) and of the number of components in the original composite ($k + m$).

COMPOSITES WHEN THE SCORES ON COMPONENT VARIABLES ARE AVERAGED

So far we have been discussing composites which are formed from the sum of scores of the components. But sometimes we have composites formed from the average of the scores on the components. Typically when we measure reaction time we take as the individual's score the average of a series of determinations of the speed of his response. With ratings we frequently do the same thing. If we have several raters we usually average their ratings, and if we have ratings on several scales we sometimes average them.

Let us now consider composites wherein the scores on the component variables are averaged. We can symbolize such scores as $\bar{X}$. If our composite is made up of 1 to k components, the raw composite score for any one person is

$$\bar{X} = \frac{X_1 + \cdots + X_k}{k}$$

and the composite score for any one person when each of the component variables is expressed in deviation-score form is

$$\bar{x} = \frac{x_1 + \cdots + x_k}{k}$$

THE MEAN OF AVERAGE COMPOSITE SCORES

The mean of average composite scores is

$$\bar{\bar{X}} = \frac{\Sigma \bar{X}}{n} = \frac{\bar{X}_a + \cdots + \bar{X}_n}{n}$$

where there are a to n individuals. Therefore,

$$\bar{\bar{X}} = \frac{(X_{1_a} + \cdots + X_{k_a})/k + \cdots + (X_{1_n} + \cdots + X_{k_n})/k}{n}$$

$$= \frac{(1/k)[(X_{1_a} + \cdots + X_{k_a}) + \cdots + (X_{1_n} + \cdots + X_{k_n})]}{n}$$

Rearranging scores by tests rather than by individuals gives

$$\bar{\bar{X}} = \frac{(1/k)[(X_{1_a} + \cdots + X_{1_n}) + \cdots + (X_{k_a} + \cdots + X_{k_n})]}{n}$$

$$= \frac{1}{k}\left(\frac{X_{1_a} + \cdots + X_{1_n}}{n} + \cdots + \frac{X_{k_a} + \cdots + X_{k_n}}{n}\right)$$

$$= \frac{1}{k}(\bar{X}_1 + \cdots + \bar{X}_k) = \frac{\bar{X}_1 + \cdots + \bar{X}_k}{k} \qquad (7\text{-}29)$$

The mean of average composite scores is simply the mean of the means of the scores on the components.

THE STANDARD DEVIATION OF AVERAGE SCORES

The average composite deviation score for any one person is

$$\bar{x} = \frac{x_1 + \cdots + x_k}{k}$$

Squaring both sides of the equation, we have

$$\bar{x}^2 = \frac{(x_1 + \cdots + x_k)^2}{k^2}$$

$$= \frac{1}{k^2}(x_1^2 + \cdots + x_k^2 + 2x_1 x_2 + \cdots + 2x_{k-1} x_k)$$

Let us now sum these equations for all n individuals and divide by the number of cases:

$$\frac{\Sigma \bar{x}^2}{n} = \frac{(1/k^2)\Sigma(x_1^2 + \cdots + x_k^2 + 2x_1x_2 + \cdots + 2x_{k-1}x_k)}{n}$$

In the left-hand side of this equation we have the sum of the deviation scores squared divided by the number of cases. This is a variance. Therefore we can write

$$\sigma_{\bar{x}}^2 = \frac{1}{k^2} \frac{\Sigma(x_1^2 + \cdots + x_k^2 + 2x_1x_2 + \cdots + 2x_{k-1}x_k)}{n}$$

$$= \frac{1}{k^2}\left(\frac{\Sigma x_1^2}{n} + \cdots + \frac{\Sigma x_k^2}{n} + 2\frac{\Sigma x_1x_2}{n} + \cdots + 2\frac{\Sigma x_{k-1}x_k}{n}\right)$$

$$= \frac{1}{k^2}(\sigma_1^2 + \cdots + \sigma_k^2 + 2\sigma_1\sigma_2 r_{12} + \cdots + 2\sigma_{k-1}\sigma_k r_{(k-1)k}) \qquad (7\text{-}30)$$

This is the formula for the variance of average scores on a series of variables. The standard deviation of average scores, then, is

$$\sigma_{\bar{x}} = \frac{1}{k}\sqrt{\sigma_1^2 + \cdots + \sigma_k^2 + 2\sigma_1\sigma_2 r_{12} + \cdots + 2\sigma_{k-1}\sigma_k r_{(k-1)k}} = \frac{\sigma_c}{k} \qquad (7\text{-}31)$$

If all the components are in standard-score form, we can write Eq. (7-31) parallel to Eq. (7-13) as

$$\sigma_{\bar{z}} = \frac{1}{k}\sqrt{k + k(k - 1)\overline{r_{ii'}}}$$

$$= \sqrt{\frac{k}{k^2} + \frac{k(k - 1)}{k^2}\overline{r_{ii'}}}$$

$$= \sqrt{\frac{1}{k} + \frac{k - 1}{k}\overline{r_{ii'}}} \qquad (7\text{-}32)$$

If we compare Eq. (7-31) with (7-7), the formula for the standard deviation of a summed composite, we shall see that the only difference between the two is the term $1/k$. The standard deviation of an average composite, then, is merely the standard deviation of a summed composite divided by the number of components. That is,

$$\sigma_{\bar{x}} = \frac{\sigma_{c_x}}{k} \qquad (7\text{-}33)$$

THE CORRELATION BETWEEN AN OUTSIDE VARIABLE AND AN AVERAGE COMPOSITE

The correlation between scores on an outside variable and those on an average composite is

$$r_{0\bar{x}} = r_{0[(x_1 + \cdots + x_k)/k]}$$

$$= \frac{\Sigma x_0[(x_1 + \cdots + x_k)/k]}{n\sigma_0\sigma_{\bar{x}}}$$

$$= \frac{(1/k)\Sigma x_0(x_1 + \cdots + x_k)}{n\sigma_0\sigma_{\bar{x}}}$$

$$= \frac{(1/k)\Sigma(x_0x_1 + \cdots + x_0x_k)}{n\sigma_0\sigma_{\bar{x}}}$$

Substituting for $\sigma_{\bar{x}}$ from Eq. (7-33) gives

$$r_{0\bar{x}} = \frac{(1/k)(\Sigma x_0x_1 + \cdots + \Sigma x_0x_k)}{n\sigma_0(1/k)\sigma_{c_x}}$$

$$= \frac{\Sigma x_0x_1/n + \cdots + \Sigma x_0x_k/n}{\sigma_0\sigma_{c_x}}$$

$$= \frac{\sigma_0\sigma_1r_{01} + \cdots + \sigma_0\sigma_kr_{0k}}{\sigma_0\sigma_{c_x}}$$

$$= \frac{\sigma_1r_{01} + \cdots + \sigma_kr_{0k}}{\sigma_{c_x}} \tag{7-34}$$

which is exactly the same as Eq. (7-14), the correlation between an outside variable and a summed composite. Hence whether we sum or average the components which form a composite, the correlation between the composite and an outside variable is the same.

THE CORRELATION BETWEEN TWO AVERAGE COMPOSITES

The correlation between scores on two average composites is

$$r_{\bar{x}\bar{y}} = r\left[\frac{(x_1 + \cdots + x_k)}{k}\right]\left[\frac{(y_1 + \cdots + y_m)}{m}\right]$$

$$= \frac{\Sigma[(x_1 + \cdots + x_k)/k][(y_1 + \cdots + y_m)/m]}{n\sigma_{\bar{x}}\sigma_{\bar{y}}}$$

$$= \frac{(1/km)\Sigma(x_1 + \cdots + x_k)(y_1 + \cdots + y_k)}{n\sigma_{\bar{x}}\sigma_{\bar{y}}}$$

Substituting for $\sigma_{\bar{x}}$ and $\sigma_{\bar{y}}$ from Eq. (7-33) gives

$$r_{\bar{x}\bar{y}} = \frac{(1/km)(\Sigma x_1y_1 + \cdots + \Sigma x_1y_m + \cdots + \Sigma x_ky_1 + \cdots + \Sigma x_ky_m)}{n(1/k)\sigma_{c_x}(1/m)\sigma_{c_y}}$$

$$= \frac{\Sigma x_1y_1/n + \cdots + \Sigma x_1y_m/n + \cdots + \Sigma x_ky_1/n + \cdots + \Sigma x_ky_m/n}{\sigma_{c_x}\sigma_{c_y}}$$

$$= \frac{\sigma_{x_1}\sigma_{y_1}r_{x_1y_1} + \cdots + \sigma_{x_1}\sigma_{y_m}r_{x_1y_m} + \cdots + \sigma_{x_k}\sigma_{y_1}r_{x_ky_1} + \cdots + \sigma_{x_k}\sigma_{y_m}r_{x_ky_m}}{\sigma_{c_x}\sigma_{c_y}} \tag{7-35}$$

This is exactly the same as Eq. (7-22), the correlation between two summed composites. Hence whether we sum or average the components which form composites, the correlation between two composites is the same.

If all the components of both x and y in Eq. (7-35) are given in standard-score form, we can write the formula as

$$r_{\bar{z}_x \bar{z}_y} = \frac{r_{x_1 y_1} + \cdots + r_{x_1 y_m} + \cdots + r_{x_k y_1} + \cdots + r_{x_k y_m}}{\sigma_{c_{z,x}} \sigma_{c_{z,y}}} \quad (7\text{-}36)$$

In the numerator we have each of the k components of x paired with each of the m components of y. Therefore there are km correlation terms in the numerator which are to be summed. This sum is $\Sigma r_{x_i y_i}$. The mean of these terms is

$$\overline{r_{x_i y_i}} = \frac{\Sigma r_{x_i y_i}}{km} \quad \text{or} \quad km\overline{r_{x_i y_i}} = \Sigma r_{x_i y_i}$$

We can substitute $km\overline{r_{x_i y_i}}$ for the sum in the numerator of Eq. (7-36). If we also substitute for the standard deviations in the denominator from Eq. (7-13), we have

$$r_{\bar{z}_x \bar{z}_y} = \frac{km\overline{r_{x_i y_i}}}{\sqrt{k + k(k-1)\overline{r_{x_i x_{i'}}}}\ \sqrt{m + m(m-1)\overline{r_{y_i y_{i'}}}}}$$

Dividing the numerator and denominator by k and m gives

$$r_{\bar{z}_x \bar{z}_y} = \frac{\overline{r_{x_i y_i}}}{\frac{1}{k}\sqrt{k + k(k-1)\overline{r_{x_i x_{i'}}}}\ \frac{1}{m}\sqrt{m + m(m-1)\overline{r_{y_i y_{i'}}}}}$$

$$= \frac{\overline{r_{x_i y_i}}}{\sqrt{\frac{k}{k^2} + \frac{k(k-1)}{k^2}\overline{r_{x_i x_{i'}}}}\ \sqrt{\frac{m}{m^2} + \frac{m(m-1)}{m^2}\overline{r_{y_i y_{i'}}}}}$$

$$= \frac{\overline{r_{x_i y_i}}}{\sqrt{\frac{1}{k} + \frac{k-1}{k}\overline{r_{x_i x_{i'}}}}\ \sqrt{\frac{1}{m} + \frac{m-1}{m}\overline{r_{y_i y_{i'}}}}} \quad (7\text{-}37)$$

THE CORRELATION BETWEEN A SUMMED COMPOSITE AND AN AVERAGE COMPOSITE

It should be obvious that the order of individuals in a summed composite is precisely the same as that in an average composite since in the latter case we merely divide each person's score by a constant k, the number of components. The correlation between a composite when the components merely are summed and a composite when those same components are averaged is

$$r_{c\bar{x}} = r_{(x_1 + \cdots + x_k)[(x_1 + \cdots + x_k)/k]}$$

$$= \frac{\Sigma(x_1 + \cdots + x_k)[(x_1 + \cdots + x_k)/k]}{n\sigma_c\sigma_{\bar{x}}}$$

Rearranging terms and substituting for $\sigma_{\bar{x}}$ from Eq. (7-33), we have

$$r_{c\bar{x}} = \frac{(1/k)\Sigma(x_1 + \cdots + x_k)(x_1 + \cdots + x_k)}{n\sigma_c(1/k)\sigma_c}$$

Dividing the numerator and the denominator by $1/k$ and substituting the symbol x_c, the sum of the scores on the components, for $x_1 + \cdots + x_k$ gives

$$r_{c\bar{x}} = \frac{\Sigma x_c x_c}{n\sigma_c\sigma_c}$$

$$= \frac{\Sigma x_c^2/n}{\sigma_c^2}$$

$$= \frac{\sigma_c^2}{\sigma_c^2}$$

$$= 1.00$$

Hence the order of individuals in summed composite scores is precisely the same as the order in average composite scores. Since the summed and average composite scores are perfectly correlated, it is apparent that all we have said about the correlations of summed composite scores also holds for average composite scores. Therefore in practice we may not wish to average composite scores, since it involves an additional computation and does not affect the order of individuals.

Summary

Many of the scores used in psychological measurement are composites made up of the sum of the scores on a series of component variables. The mean of composite scores is merely the sum of the means of the components, and the variance is the sum of the variances of the components plus the sum of their covariances, a covariance being the product of the standard deviations of the two variables and the coefficient of correlation between them.

In many instances the units in which the components are expressed are so different from component to component that it does not make sense to add them together in forming composite scores. Since in certain terms standard scores on different variables are comparable, scores on the components often are transformed into standard scores before adding them together to form composite scores. When composite scores are formed from components expressed as standard scores, the mean of the composite scores is zero, and their variance is the number of components plus the sum of their intercorrelations.

The correlation between a composite and a variable outside of it is a function of the correlations between the components and the outside variable, the inter-correlations among the components, and the number of components. This correlation is higher the higher are the correlations between the components and the outside variable, the lower are the intercorrelations among the components, and the larger is the number of components.

One way to increase the homogeneity of a composite is to eliminate those components which have the lowest correlations with the other components. If there are many components, it is a long task to calculate all their intercorrelations. However, the magnitude of the correlation between a component and the total composite is a function of the magnitude of the correlations between that component and the other components. Therefore by elimination of those components which have the lowest correlations with the composite, the homogeneity of the composite can be increased.

The correlation between two composites is a function of the cross correlations between the components of the two composites, the intercorrelations among the components of each composite, and the number of components in each composite. The correlation is higher the higher are the cross correlations, the lower the intercorrelations among the components, and the larger the number of components.

Sometimes we desire to shorten the length of a test, decreasing the number of component items in it. The formula for the correlation between two composites, one composite being a part of the other, tells how much the order of individuals in composite scores will be disturbed by decreasing the number of components. This formula indicates that the order of individuals will be least disturbed when the number of components eliminated is small, the intercorrelations among the components is high, and the original composite contains many components.

When composites are formed of the average of a set of components rather than of their sum, the mean of composite scores is the average of the means of the components, and the standard deviation is simply the standard deviation of summed composite scores divided by the number of components. Average and summed composite scores are perfectly correlated. The formulae for the correlation between average composite scores and scores on an outside variable and for the correlation between two average composites are precisely the same as those for summed composites.

Selected Readings

Guilford, J. P.: "Fundamental Statistics in Psychology and Education," 3d ed., McGraw-Hill, 1956.

Gulliksen, H.: "Theory of Mental Tests," Wiley, 1950.

Horst, A. P.: The prediction of personal adjustment, Social Science Research Council Bulletin 48, 1941.

Peters, C. C., and W. R. Van Voorhis: "Statistical Procedures and Their Mathematical Bases," McGraw-Hill, 1940.

Spearman, C.: Correlations of sums and differences, *Brit. J. Psychol.*, **5**:417–426, 1913.

Thurstone, L. L.: "The Reliability and Validity of Tests," Edwards, 1931.

chapter 8   The Concept of

Reliability of Measurement

The tests we use in psychological measurement give us quantitative descriptions of individuals in terms of the extent to which they possess or manifest various psychological traits and abilities. Ordinarily we are interested in these quantitative descriptions or scores not for themselves alone but rather for their usefulness in permitting us to make comparisons among individuals on a given trait and within individuals on different traits, for predicting other types of behavior, and for evaluating the effects of various factors upon an individual's performance. As a consequence, when we measure an individual we hope to obtain a score that will give us a precise characterization of him.

If we administer the same test several times to the same individual, we usually find that he does not obtain exactly the same score on all applications. Sometimes the scores change in a systematic fashion, increasing or decreasing in magnitude or fluctuating regularly in a cyclical fashion. On other occasions the scores earned by an individual seem to fluctuate in a random and unsystematic fashion. For example, when we measure the height of a person several times with the same ruler, the first time we measure him our operations might tell us that his height is 5.76 ft, and on subsequent times they might tell us his height is 5.83,

5.79, 5.85, or 5.80 ft. Similarly, when we administer a psychological test to an individual on several different occasions, he might obtain scores of 83, 86, 85, 81, and 84.

When this state of affairs occurs, it means that we cannot depend too much upon any single score earned by an individual since on another application of the same test he might earn quite a different score. It is from this common observation of unsystematic variation in the scores earned by an individual on repeated applications of the same test that the problem termed *reliability of measurement* arises. It will be our task in this chapter to consider the types of variation that may occur in the scores earned by an individual on a given test and to formalize the concept of reliability of measurement. Only if we formalize the concept can we deal with it both theoretically and practically.

THE IMPORTANCE OF UNSYSTEMATIC VARIATION IN TEST SCORES

When an individual obtains different scores on subsequent administrations of the same test and the variation among these scores is unsystematic, we can say that the quantitative descriptions given by the test are not reliable. Reliability of measurement, then, refers to the degree of self-consistency among the scores earned by an individual. If the test yields scores for an individual which differ markedly from one occasion to another, they are of little value. Such a test does not give reliable or self-consistent scores and therefore we can predict only with a low degree of accuracy the score an individual will obtain on any one administration of a test from any other administration of it. Unreliable scores are of little value when we wish to compare two or more individuals on the same test, to assign individuals to groups or classes, to predict other types of behavior, to compare different traits or abilities of an individual, or to assess the effects of various systematic factors upon an individual's performance. Let us consider examples of each of these so that we can see the importance of reliability of measurement.

RELIABILITY AND THE COMPARISON AMONG INDIVIDUALS ON THE SAME TEST

Sometimes we wish to know whether one person is superior to another in the traits or abilities measured by a particular test. If we know that people vary in their scores from one repetition of the test to another by as much as 10 points and the difference between the scores of two persons is 30 points, we probably should be willing to conclude that the one person is indeed superior to the other and the difference would hold even if we tested them on another occasion. We should know that if we administered the test a second time to the two people, the individual who was superior on the first occasion undoubtedly would be superior on the second. The one who was superior on the first application of the test might earn a score as much as 10 points lower on the second test and the one who was inferior on the first test might improve his score by as much as 10 points, but there would still be at least a 10-point difference between the two individuals in their scores. However, we should not be so willing to say that the one person is superior to the other if we found that people vary as much as 20 points from one application of the test to another. In this case, if we tested both persons twice, the individual who earned the higher score on the first application of the test might well earn the lower score on the second application. The extent to which we are willing to trust the difference between the scores earned by two individuals on a test as reflecting a real or stable difference between them in the trait being measured by the test, then, is a function of the reliability of that test.

RELIABILITY AND THE ASSIGNMENT OF INDIVIDUALS TO GROUPS OR CLASSES

Suppose that pupils in a school are to be placed in reading sections on the basis of the scores they earn on a reading achievement test, with those earning scores of 60 and above being assigned to the accelerated section, those with scores of 50 to 59 to the average section, and those with scores of 49 and below to the retarded section. Now further suppose that variation in scores of as much as six points occurs when an individual takes the test a number of times. A pupil who earns a score of 55 on the test will be assigned to the average section. However, if he had taken the test on another occasion he might have earned a score as high as 61 and have been assigned to the accelerated section, or he might have earned a score as low as 49 and have been assigned to the retarded section. It is therefore obvious that the degree of reliability of measurement of this test is insufficient to assign pupils to sections with very much certainty. On the other hand, if the variation among scores in subsequent administrations of the test is only one point, then a very large proportion of pupils can be assigned with a high degree of certainty. Consequently we can see that the reliability of measurement is an important consideration in terms of the precision with which individuals can be assigned to groups or classes.

RELIABILITY AND PREDICTION

Scores on tests often are used to predict other types of behavior. For example, scores on intelligence tests commonly are used to predict success in academic work. If the particular intelligence test used in making predictions of this kind happens to be highly unreliable, then from the score earned by an individual on one occasion a high degree of scholastic success might be anticipated for him, but from the score he earned on another occasion just the opposite conclusion might be reached. It would, therefore, be difficult under such circumstances to make predictions with any satisfactory degree of certainty. Consequently we can see that accuracy of prediction from one variable to another is limited by the degree of reliability with which these variables are measured.

RELIABILITY AND THE COMPARISON OF TRAITS AND ABILITIES
OF AN INDIVIDUAL

In certain circumstances it is necessary to know on which of two traits an individual is superior. For example, as an aid to counseling a student we may wish to know whether he is superior in mechanical or in clerical aptitude. Suppose when we apply tests of mechanical and clerical aptitude to the same individuals, standardized scores in each test vary as much as 20 points from one application to another. If we administer both tests to a student on a single occasion and find that on the mechanical aptitude test his score is 70 and on the clerical aptitude test his score is 85, we cannot say with much certainty that his mechanical aptitude is superior to his clerical aptitude. However, if the variation in scores on repeated applications of the tests were only five points, we should be much more willing to draw this conclusion. Therefore, the confidence we place on the differences among the scores earned by an individual on different tests is a function of the degree of reliability of those tests.

RELIABILITY AND THE ASSESSMENT OF THE EFFECTS OF SYSTEMATIC
FACTORS ON AN INDIVIDUAL'S PERFORMANCE

We may wish to ascertain whether a change in performance from one administration of a test to a second can be ascribed to some systematic factors that have been introduced between testing periods or whether it is better ascribed to the unsystematic variation that occurs between repeated applications of the test. If we know the extent of this unsystematic variation and find that it is greater than the amount of change in scores, then we shall not be willing to say that the change in score is the result of the factors in question. On the other hand, if the amount of unsystematic variation is less than the amount by which the individual's score changes, then we can conclude with considerable confidence that the change in scores is the result of the factors that have been introduced.

Suppose when we administer a test a number of times to an individual under the same conditions we find his scores vary about 20 points. Thus on subsequent administrations of the same test a person might earn a score as low as 50 and as high as 70, and another person might earn a score as low as 80 and as high as 100. Now we administer the test to a person, submit him to some treatment, say some special instruction, and test him again. If after the treatment his score increases by 15 points, we should be very hesitant to say that the increase is due to the treatment, because changes of this magnitude occur frequently just in the normal course of events when there are no special changes in conditions between testing periods. However, if the variation between subsequent applications of the test when there are no special conditions is only five points, then we should feel that the treatment was beneficial.

SYSTEMATIC AND UNSYSTEMATIC VARIATION IN TEST SCORES

As we have seen, there are two major types of variation in the scores earned by an individual over repeated testing. One type we termed *systematic variation* and the other *unsystematic variation*. We must examine both types of variation so that we can differentiate unsystematic from systematic variations in order to develop the concept of reliability of measurement.

SYSTEMATIC VERSUS UNSYSTEMATIC VARIATION IN SCORES

Suppose we examine the different scores obtained by an individual on successive applications of the same test. It might be that a trend appears in the scores. Thus if we measure the height of an individual at different hours of the day we are likely to find that from the morning to the evening the values become smaller and smaller. We might attribute this phenomenon to a gradual sagging of the backbone. Similarly, if we administer the same arithmetic test over and over to the same individual, his scores may gradually increase. This would suggest that the series of testing situations operate as practice periods and the individual gradually is improving his skill in solving the arithmetic problems.

Sometimes, however, when we examine the various scores obtained by an individual on successive repetitions of a given test, no trend of any kind can be discerned even though the scores differ on the different testing occasions. Rather, the scores seem to vary among themselves in a random fashion. If we have an individual react as quickly as possible in a specified manner to each stimulus in a series of stimuli, we shall find that some of his responses are more rapid than others. When we compare the times taken to respond to stimuli that occur early in the series with those that occur later, we may find that on the average they are the same. We might attribute variation in reaction-time scores to unsystematic moment-to-moment changes in the environmental conditions, the smoothness of the operation of the reaction-time apparatus, the individual's motivation, and his attention.

There are, then, two kinds of variation in scores. One is systematic and the other unsystematic. Systematic variations are characterized by an orderly progression or pattern, with the scores obtained by an individual changing from one occasion to the next in some trend. Systematic changes appear as a regular increase or decrease in scores, or they may follow some cycle. Unsystematic variation, on the other hand, is characterized by a complete absence of order. The scores of an individual fluctuate from one occasion to the next in a completely haphazard manner.

The two types of variation, of course, may occur simultaneously. Thus we may find that on the average the scores of an individual increase as he is repeatedly tested with the same instrument, and around this trend his scores appear to vary in a random fashion, sometimes being above the trend and sometimes below it.

FACTORS CAUSING VARIATION IN SCORES

Having observed a particular kind of variation in test scores, we attempt to explain it. On the basis of the nature of the variation, and of our knowledge about conditions prior to and during the testing, we draw inferences about the kinds of factors which cause the variation. It is inappropriate here to discuss at length the philosophical problems of causation, but what we can say is that essentially we observe phenomena which are associated in one manner or another and which occur simultaneously or successively in time and then say that the one caused the other. For example, when we administer a test to an individual on a number of occasions, arranging circumstances so that he reviews the content of the test just before he takes it each time, if his scores show a regular and systematic improvement we attribute this improvement to the practice.

SYSTEMATIC VERSUS UNSYSTEMATIC FACTORS

Just as the members of a particular population of objects can be classified in a variety of different ways, so can the phenomena with which we are here concerned, namely, multiple factors including factors which affect test scores. We can classify people according to sex, age, or place of birth. Similarly, we can classify factors which affect test scores as environmental or individual factors, acquired or native determiners of behavior, unimportant or important, or—for our present purposes—factors having systematic or unsystematic effects. Classification of the factors according to whether their effects on test scores are systematic or unsystematic will help us to understand their mode of operation, to identify specific kinds of determiners, and above all to help us to formalize the concept of reliability of measurement.

A *systematic factor* is one which produces systematic changes in scores. Learning, training, and growth produce regular and progressive increases in scores. Fatigue, forgetting, and senescence result in regular and progressive decreases in scores. Mood and living habits may produce regular cyclical changes in scores. When systematic factors are at work, then, scores show a regular disposition or arrangement—an order.

An *unsystematic factor* is one which produces unsystematic changes in scores. Moment-to-moment variations in attention result in random fluctuations in reaction time. An inconsistent and balky pen sometimes permits the student taking an examination to write easily and on other occasions slows the speed of writing. The marks given to an elementary school pupil as he progresses through the various grades are sometimes higher and sometimes lower, depending upon whether the teacher to whom he happens to be assigned tends to be lenient or strict in her evaluations of pupils' performance. When unsystematic factors are at work, then, scores fluctuate in a random fashion and do not manifest any consistent pattern.

In some circumstances we may consider the effects of a given factor as being systematic and in others as unsystematic. For example, suppose we test a group of individuals on a number of occasions in the same room, a room in which there is only one light fixture. On any given testing occasion we can say that the lighting has a systematic effect on scores, since we can show that the further an individual is from the light the poorer is his score. Let us say that on each testing occasion the seating of an individual is done in a random fashion. Then over the different testing occasions the scores of an individual vary in a random fashion because sometimes he is nearer to the light and sometimes further away from it. We should therefore say that on any given testing occasion, illumination operates as a systematic factor on individuals, but for a given individual over different testing occasions it operates as an unsystematic factor.

INFERENCES ABOUT FACTORS AFFECTING SCORES

The factors which affect scores seem to be almost infinite in number and variety. An individual's performance is a function of the numerous qualities with which he was endowed at birth, elaborated upon by the process of maturation and by his numerous experiences together with the many environmental influences operating upon him at any given moment. The inferences we draw in attempting to explain variation in scores are a function of the knowledge we have about these factors. In some instances our inferences have quite substantial foundation because our knowledge is direct and extensive. In other instances our knowledge may be indirect and not complete, so that we are less sure of our inferences. Finally, we may have such limited knowledge about conditions that our inferences are little more than guesses.

Suppose we give an individual a test of knowledge of French vocabulary and find his score is zero. We then have him take an elementary course in French and retest him. Now his score is higher. He continues to take more and more courses in French, and after he completes each course we again administer the test. Undoubtedly we shall find a continuous increase in his scores, and with a great deal of certainty we could attribute his increase in scores to the training to which he has been deliberately subjected.

We administer to an individual a test of arithmetic on a number of different occasions and observe that while his scores vary over the different occasions they do not manifest any particular trend but rather vary in an unsystematic fashion. Sometimes we have tested him in the morning and sometimes late in the afternoon. We note that on some occasions the illumination in the testing room was not so bright as it was on other occasions and sometimes the room was noisy and sometimes it was quiet. As test administrators sometimes we were alert and careful in giving instructions and in controlling the time permitted the individual to take the test, and sometimes we were concerned with other matters and were careless. We observed that on some occasions the individual came to the test highly motivated and on other occasions he was bored with the entire procedure. Over the testing period we observed a variety of different factors operating, factors that obviously could affect the individual's performance. Since these factors were largely independent of each other, we should expect that sometimes their effects would cancel each other out, whereas fate would decree that on other occasions the preponderance would have a facilitating effect and on still others a depressing effect upon the individual's performance. In view of the fact that the individual's scores vary in an unsystematic fashion, it seems reasonable to infer that this variation can be attributed to the joint effects of the factors we observed varying in an unsystematic fashion.

Suppose we have before us determinations of the IQ of a child from several different testings and note that they were substantially lower when the tests were administered during the summer months. We have no knowledge whatsoever about the state the child was in when he was tested nor of the conditions prior to or coincident with the different administrations of the test. There are a variety of inferences we might make to explain the variation in scores. One which might appear reasonable to us is that this child's performance on intelligence tests is influenced by the degree of intellectual stimulation he receives, so that during the summer months when he is away from school his scores are lower. This explanation accounts for the change in scores but is a pure guess.

THE DEFINITION OF RELIABILITY OF MEASUREMENT

Having examined the kinds of variation that occur in scores and the types of factors that cause them, we are now in a position to define reliability of measurement. We shall do so in terms of the extent of unsystematic variation in scores. In order to specify our definitions we shall then present the concept of *parallel tests,* which permits a more precise definition of reliability. On the basis of our definition of reliability and of the concept of parallel tests, we shall be able to indicate the ways in which the extent of reliability can be measured and to make some theoretical-mathematical developments of reliability which in turn will enable us to give still more precise definitions of reliability.

RELIABILITY AND THE OPERATIONS OF MEASUREMENT

While we have indicated the general area of phenomena to which the term "reliability of measurement" refers, we have not yet given a definition of it. It will be recalled that the problem of reliability of measurement arises out of the unsystematic variation in scores earned by an individual when we obtain a number of measurements indicative of the degree to which he possesses or manifests some particular trait or quality. Reliability of measurement, then, pertains to the precision with which some trait is measured by means of specified operations. Consequently our concern is not with one particular instrument but rather with the operations of measurement which stem from the definition of our variable. The theoretical and practical implications of this will be clearer later when we discuss parallel tests and the estimation of the extent of reliability of measurement.

As we saw in Chap. 2, from the definition of a given variable a variety of different operations of measurement may follow. For example, if we define ability to perform simple addition as the speed and accuracy with which single-digit numbers are added together, we can utilize a test comprised of a series of items such as $3 + 4 = $ _____, $9 + 2 = $ _____, and $1 + 7 = $ _____, as well as a series comprised of items such as $4 + 3 = $ _____, $2 + 9 = $ _____, and $7 + 1 = $ _____. Let us therefore define reliability of measurement simply as the extent of unsystematic variation in the quantitative descriptions of the amount of some trait an individual possesses or manifests when that trait is measured a number of times.

Basic to any formal mathematical statement of reliability of measurement, and to the development of pertinent formulae, is the concept of parallel tests. There have been many definitions given for parallel tests, some rational and some mathematical. We shall begin by giving a rational definition, and this ultimately will lead us to three different mathematical formulations or models of reliability.

We have defined reliability of measurement as the extent of unsystematic variation in scores of an individual on some trait when that trait is measured a number of times. To ascertain the extent of this unsystematic variation we need to obtain for an individual a series of scores by the application of a number of sets of operations all of which follow from the definition of the variable. In conceptualizing these operations we do not need to stipulate that the same specific measuring device is always used. On the other hand, we do not have to deny that the same measuring device is always used. What we are concerned with, then, is a series of operations of measurement or tests which measure the same traits to the same degree, that is, tests which evoke the same psychological processes. Tests of this kind are termed parallel tests.

In essence, what we are saying is that reliability can be defined as the extent of unsystematic variation of an individual's scores on a series of parallel tests, and that by parallel tests we mean different sets of operations all of which follow from a particular definition of a trait. While this definition of reliability may give an adequate general orientation to the problem, it is in fact too loose and vague to be of any direct value, either as a basis for theoretical developments or as a guide to indicate practical ways for estimating the reliability of tests. We shall find it necessary to take some theoretical position before we can define reliability of measurement with sufficient precision to be useful.

RELIABILITY OF MEASUREMENT AND PARALLEL TESTS

Suppose we have a series of tests k in number and we have scores on all these k tests for one or more individuals. If we were measuring with perfect reliability, then any given individual would obtain precisely the same score on all the k parallel tests. In other words, there would be no variation at all in his scores over the k tests. On the other hand, if we were measuring with less than perfect reliability, then his scores would be different on the different parallel tests, the variation among his scores being completely unsystematic. The less the variation the greater the reliability of measurement, and the greater the variation the less the reliability of measurement. Consequently it is through the use of parallel tests that we are able to ascertain the extent to which we are measuring a trait reliably.

DESCRIPTION OF THE DEGREE OF RELIABILITY OF MEASUREMENT

We have just seen that reliability of measurement refers to the extent of unsystematic variation in an individual's scores over parallel tests. Our task now is to set up indices which give quantitative descriptions of the extent of such variation. Such indices will be useful for comparing different tests so we can ascertain which gives us the most precise or stable scores, and will permit us to ascertain whether the reliability with which a test measures is sufficient for our purposes. The two indices which are used are the *standard error of measurement* and the *reliability coefficient*. The standard error of measurement is an index of the extent to which an individual's scores vary over a number of parallel tests, and the reliability coefficient is an index of the extent to which scores on any one parallel test can predict scores on any other.

THE STANDARD ERROR OF MEASUREMENT

In Table 8-1 we have a representation of parallel tests. Here we have the scores of n individuals on k different parallel tests. In any given column we have the scores of the n individuals on one parallel test, and in any given row we have the scores of any one individual over the k

TABLE 8-1.   The Situation with Raw Scores on Parallel Tests

Individuals	Parallel tests					$\bar{X}_i$	S_i
	1	2	$\cdots$	$k-1$	k		
a	X_{1_a}	X_{2_a}	$\cdots$	$X_{(k-1)_a}$	X_{k_a}	$\bar{X}_a$	S_a
b	X_{1_b}	X_{2_b}	$\cdots$	$X_{(k-1)_b}$	X_{k_b}	$\bar{X}_b$	S_b
$\cdots$	$\cdots$	$\cdots$	$\cdots$	$\cdots$	$\cdots$	$\cdots$	$\cdots$
			$\cdots$				
$n-1$	$X_{1_{n-1}}$	$X_{2_{n-1}}$	$\cdots$	$X_{(k-1)_{n-1}}$	$X_{k_{n-1}}$	$\bar{X}_{n-1}$	S_{n-1}
n	X_{1_n}	X_{2_n}	$\cdots$	$X_{(k-1)_n}$	X_{k_n}	$\bar{X}_n$	S_n
$\bar{X}$	$\bar{X}_1$	$\bar{X}_2$	$\cdots$	$\bar{X}_{k-1}$	$\bar{X}_k$		
σ_x	σ_1	σ_2	$\cdots$	σ_{k-1}	σ_k		

parallel tests. We could compute the mean and standard deviation of the scores in any given column. These values are the mean and standard deviation of the scores on that one parallel test and are represented in the last two rows of Table 8-1, which are labeled $\bar{X}$ and σ_x.

In a similar fashion we could compute the mean and standard deviation of the scores in any given row. These values are the mean and the standard deviation of the scores of that individual. These means and standard deviations are represented in the last two columns in the table, labeled $\bar{X}_i$ and S_i. The symbol S_i is used rather than σ_i to distinguish it as being the standard deviation of one individual's scores over k parallel tests. S_i is termed the standard error of measurement.* When this standard deviation is large it means that an individual's scores differ considerably among themselves, and the reliability of measurement is poor. When this standard deviation is zero it means that an individual obtains precisely the same score on all parallel tests, and reliability of measurement for him is perfect.

THE RELIABILITY COEFFICIENT

Reliability of measurement also can be thought of in terms of predictability, the degree to which scores on one parallel test predict scores on another. When the variation in an individual's scores over parallel tests is great, this means that the prediction of his score on one parallel test from his score on another is poor. On the other hand, if there is no variation at all among an individual's scores, then it means that we could predict perfectly an individual's score on one parallel test from his score on another. Casting reliability in terms of the coefficient of correlation between parallel tests provides another way of describing the precision of measurement. The coefficient of correlation between parallel tests is termed the reliability coefficient. When the coefficient is low it means that an individual's scores over k parallel tests show a great deal of variation, and when it is high it means that an individual's scores on the k parallel tests are very nearly the same.

THEORETICAL MODELS OF RELIABILITY OF MEASUREMENT

We defined reliability of measurement as the extent of unsystematic variation in the scores of an individual on some trait when that trait was measured a number of times. Parallel tests we defined as sets of operations which follow directly from the definition of the trait. In other words, parallel tests are tests which measure the same traits. With this

* The standard error of measurement has been defined in a variety of ways other than that given here. For example, sometimes the standard error of measurement is taken as the standard deviation of scores on one parallel test of those individuals all of whom have the same score on another parallel test. This would be the error of predicting scores on one parallel test from scores on another. Other definitions of the term are used in connection with specific theoretical or mathematical formulations of reliability of measurement.

definition of parallel tests we were then able to specify our definition of reliability of measurement by saying that it is the extent of unsystematic variation of the scores of an individual over a number of parallel tests.

However, these definitions of reliability of measurement and of parallel tests are still too vague to permit us to develop specific procedures for describing or estimating the precision with which a trait is measured. Because the statement of the problem of reliability of measurement is vague, it is not surprising to find that different people have come to take different positions on it. We have, then, a variety of different theoretical models of reliability of measurement which lead us to somewhat different formal statements about it and to different mathematical developments of it. These various notions can be reasonably well subsumed under one or another of three different major views which we may call the *concept of true and error scores,* an *eclectic concept of true scores and parallel tests,* and the *concept of domain sampling.**

THE THEORY OF TRUE AND ERROR SCORES

One way of thinking about and describing unsystematic variation in scores is to conceive of the individual as possessing a certain amount of the trait being measured by a particular test and the score he actually earned on the test as being an imperfect function of this quality. His performance on any given administration of a test does not reflect with complete accuracy the amount of the trait he possesses, because of the effects of unsystematic or chance factors. The score an individual actually obtains on a test is termed his *fallible score,* and the amount of the trait being measured that he in fact possesses is termed his *true score.* The difference between the fallible and true scores is termed his *error score.* The error score sometimes causes the fallible score to be too high and sometimes causes it to be too low. The fallible scores an individual obtains on a series of parallel tests, then, vary in a random fashion around his true score.

BASIC EQUATIONS IN THE CONCEPT OF TRUE AND ERROR SCORES

The relationship between fallible, true, and error scores can be symbolized by the following equation:

$$x_i - x_\infty = e_i \qquad (8\text{-}1)$$

* Historically it can be said that Spearman and Yule were the originators of the theory of true and error scores. Other strong adherents to this point of view are Thurstone and Guilford. Brown and Kelley may be said to have notions similar to the eclectic concept of true scores and parallel tests. This view also has been stressed by Guilliksen. The last notion, that of domain sampling, is newer and has been developed by Tryon. See the selected references at the end of this chapter to the works of these writers.

where x_i is the fallible score earned on one administration of the test, x_∞ the true score, and e_i the error score on that particular administration of the test. The terms of this equation may be arranged as follows:

$$x_i = x_\infty + e_i \tag{8-2}$$

If we administer many parallel tests of the same trait to the same individual, say k parallel tests, there will be an equation for each repetition as follows:

$$\begin{aligned}
x_1 &= x_\infty + e_1 \\
x_2 &= x_\infty + e_2 \\
&\cdots\cdots\cdots \\
x_k &= x_\infty + e_k
\end{aligned} \tag{8-3}$$

These equations show that the individual's true score remains the same over the k parallel tests but his fallible score changes because the extent of error on the different applications of the test is different, the errors being sometimes positive and sometimes negative. This is merely symbolizing mathematically what we have said about fallible, true, and error scores.

Equation (8-2) does not carry the condition that scores on a test are due only to a single factor within the individual. The fact that a single term x_∞ has been used to describe the amount of the trait an individual possesses should not be taken to imply that individual differences in scores on a given test are determined by a single factor. The true score could be a summation of true scores on a number of different traits, and Eq. (8-2) might be written as

$$x = x_{A_\infty} + x_{B_\infty} + \cdots + x_{N_\infty} + e \tag{8-4}$$

where A to N are the factors determining trait x. The term x_∞ therefore merely stands for the sum of all systematic factors that are operating. Furthermore, we should not take Eq. (8-4) to imply that all factors have equal weight in determining the score of one individual on a test. More properly (8-4) should be written as

$$x = W_A x_{A_\infty} + W_B x_{B_\infty} + \cdots + W_N x_{N_\infty} + e \tag{8-5}$$

If we find a systematic change in fallible scores, it means that there is an increase or a decrease in the number of factors entering into Eq. (8-5), or that there is a change in the relative weights (W) of the several factors. We can see in Eq. (8-5) that as the number of factors or their relative weights change, so would the fallible score x.

FUNDAMENTAL ASSUMPTIONS IN THE THEORY OF TRUE AND ERROR SCORES

In order to develop the concept of reliability on the basis of the theory of true and error scores, it is necessary to make three fundamental assumptions. One of these assumptions has to do with true scores, another with error scores, and the last with the way in which these two scores are combined.

Assumption 1: *The Individual Possesses Stable Characteristics or Traits That Persist through Time.* In order for the concept of true and error scores to be meaningful some assumption such as the foregoing must be made. If the individual changed continuously from moment to moment, there would be no stability whatsoever in his characteristics or traits. It is therefore necessary for the theory of true and error scores to consider the individual as possessing stable characteristics that are different from the error factors which produce differences in fallible scores on different parallel tests. These stable characteristics of the individual are his true scores on various tests. They are characteristics which are assumed in order to understand and to predict the relationships between stimuli and responses, and may be considered to be intellectual constructs.

Assumption 2: *Errors Are Completely Random.* From the essential notion of the theory of true and error scores it follows that variations in fallible scores on parallel tests are due entirely to unsystematic factors, the effects of which change from moment to moment. It must therefore be assumed that error scores are completely random and consequently are independent of all other characteristics. It follows, then, that the error scores on any one administration of a test are uncorrelated with scores on any other variable. Therefore

$$r_{e_1 e_2} = \cdots = r_{e_{k-1} e_k} = r_{x_\infty e_1} = \cdots = r_{x_\infty e_k}$$
$$= r_{y e_1} = \cdots = r_{y e_k} = .00 \quad (8\text{-}6)$$

where there are 1 to k parallel tests and y is any variable other than these parallel tests.

Assumption 3: *Fallible Scores Are the Result of the Addition of True and Error Scores.* A review of Eqs. (8-1) to (8-5) will show that they all involve the addition of true and error scores. Thus Eq. (8-2) states that the fallible score is equal to the true score *plus* the error score. Equation (8-5) is a more complex statement, but even here we see a simple sum. It is apparent that a number of other states of affairs could be assumed. For example, fallible scores might be taken as the product or the quotient of true and error scores. The formulation given, however, appears to be the most reasonable as judged from the logical developments of Eq. (8-2). But most of all it is more comprehensible and concise. If we can explain phenomena on simple grounds and make satisfactory predictions with a simple formulation, there is no point in seeking a more complex formulation. Hence we use a simple sum in our basic equation, and in our more elaborate forms of Eq. (8-2) we continue to use sums. Furthermore, many complex formulations involving the multiplication or division of factors can be transformed to additive functions if the values are transformed, as by logarithms. Hence it is argued that it is reasonable to assume that fallible scores are the result of the addition of true and error scores.

PARALLEL TESTS IN THE CONCEPT OF TRUE AND ERROR SCORES

It will be recalled that we defined parallel tests as tests measuring exactly the same traits. Therefore in terms of the concept of true and error scores it would follow that when an individual is measured by a series of parallel tests, his true scores on all of them are precisely the same. If his true scores differed from one test to another, then by definition the tests would not be measuring the same trait. His fallible scores, of course, may vary from one parallel test to another since the error factors operating on the different occasions of testing may differ. This is the situation we represented earlier in Eqs. (8-3). In the concept of true and error scores the situation with respect to scores on parallel tests is that represented in Table 8-2. In the rows we have the scores of each person over the k parallel tests, and in the columns the scores of the n individuals on one parallel test.

Since different individuals possess different amounts of the trait being measured on any given parallel test, we find a variation among individuals on true scores. Inasmuch as we are dealing with parallel tests, any given individual has exactly the same true score on all parallel tests. In other words, the distributions of true scores on all parallel tests are precisely the same. Consequently we can say that the means and standard deviations of true scores on all parallel tests are exactly the same. That is,

$$\bar{X}_{\infty_1} = \cdots = \bar{X}_{\infty_k} \tag{8-7}$$

and
$$\sigma_{\infty_1} = \cdots = \sigma_{\infty_k} \tag{8-8}$$

Since by definition the error scores e vary in a completely random fashion, the distribution of error scores for any one individual (the values in any row) necessarily is equal to the distribution of error scores for any other individual (the values in any other row). Hence when the number of parallel tests, k, is very large, the standard deviation of the error scores of each person over the k parallel tests necessarily is equal

TABLE 8-2. The Situation with Scores on Parallel Tests in Terms of the Theory of True and Error Scores

Individuals	Parallel tests				
	1	2	$\cdots$	$k-1$	k
a	$x_{1_a} = x_{\infty_a} + e_{1_a}$	$x_{2_a} = x_{\infty_a} + e_{2_a}$	$\cdots$	$x_{k-1_a} = x_{\infty_a} + e_{(k-1)_a}$	$x_{k_a} = x_{\infty_a} + e_{k_a}$
b	$x_{1_b} = x_{\infty_b} + e_{1_b}$	$x_{2_b} = x_{\infty_b} + e_{2_b}$	$\cdots$	$x_{k-1_b} = x_{\infty_b} + e_{(k-1)_b}$	$x_{k_b} = x_{\infty_b} + e_{k_b}$
$\cdots$	$\cdots$	$\cdots$	$\cdots$	$\cdots$	$\cdots$
$n-1$	$x_{1_{n-1}} = x_{\infty_{n-1}} + e_{1_{n-1}}$	$x_{2_{n-1}} = x_{\infty_{n-1}} + e_{2_{n-1}}$	$\cdots$	$x_{(k-1)_{n-1}} = x_{\infty_{n-1}} + e_{(k-1)_{n-1}}$	$x_{k_{n-1}} = x_{\infty_{n-1}} + e_{k_{n-1}}$
n	$x_{1_n} = x_{\infty_n} + e_{1_n}$	$x_{2_n} = x_{\infty_n} + e_{2_n}$	$\cdots$	$x_{(k-1)_n} = x_{\infty_n} + e_{(k-1)_n}$	$x_{k_n} = x_{\infty_n} + e_{k_n}$

to the standard deviation of the error scores of every other person. That is,

$$S_a = \cdots = S_n \tag{8-9}$$

Furthermore, since the error scores vary in a completely random fashion, when the number of individuals is very large the distribution of error scores in any column necessarily is equal to the standard deviation of the error scores in any other column. Hence the standard deviations of error scores on all parallel tests necessarily are equal. That is,

$$\sigma_{e_1} = \cdots = \sigma_{e_k} \tag{8-10}$$

Finally, since the error scores vary in a completely random fashion equally in the rows and columns of Table 8-2, the distributions of error scores in the rows necessarily are equal to the distributions of error scores in the columns. That is,

$$S_a = \cdots = S_n = \sigma_{e_1} = \cdots = \sigma_{e_k} \tag{8-11}$$

In the concept of true and error scores, by definition errors are factors that sometimes cause the fallible scores to be higher than the true scores and sometimes cause them to be lower. This means, then, that the error scores are sometimes positive and sometimes negative; and because they vary in a random fashion they are positive as frequently as they are negative, and every positive error of a given amount is matched by a negative error of the same amount. Consequently the mean of error scores is zero. This would be true whether we consider the mean of the error scores in any row of Table 8-2 or the mean of the error scores in any column. Hence

$$\bar{e}_a = \cdots = \bar{e}_n = \bar{e}_1 = \cdots = \bar{e}_k = 0 \tag{8-12}$$

THE MEAN OF SCORES ON PARALLEL TESTS

An individual's fallible score is a composite score, being the sum of his true and error scores. In Eq. (7-4) we saw that the mean of composite scores is equal to the sum of the means of the components. Hence we can write

$$\bar{X}_1 = \bar{X}_\infty + \bar{e}_1$$
$$\bar{X}_2 = \bar{X}_\infty + \bar{e}_2$$
$$\cdots \cdots \cdots \cdots$$
$$\bar{X}_{k-1} = \bar{X}_\infty + \bar{e}_{k-1}$$
$$\bar{X}_k = \bar{X}_\infty + \bar{e}_k$$

However, as we have just seen in Eq. (8-12), the mean of the error scores on a test is zero. Hence in the above equations the terms $\bar{e}_1, \cdots, \bar{e}_k$ are all zero. Consequently in each of the foregoing equations the mean of the fallible scores equals the mean of the true scores so that

$$\bar{X}_1 = \cdots = \bar{X}_k = \bar{X}_\infty \tag{8-13}$$

From Eq. (8-13) we can say that the means of the fallible scores on all parallel tests are equal to each other and are equal to the mean of the true scores.

THE STANDARD DEVIATION OF SCORES ON PARALLEL TESTS

Again considering fallible scores as composite scores, we can write the variance of fallible scores from Eq. (7-6) as

$$\sigma_x{}^2 = \sigma_{x_\infty+e}^2 = \sigma_{x_\infty}{}^2 + 2\sigma_{x_\infty}\sigma_e + \sigma_e{}^2$$

From Eq. (8-6) we know that the correlation between true and error scores is .00. Therefore the entire second term in the above equation becomes zero and drops out. We can then write the variances of a series of parallel tests as

$$\sigma_{x_1}{}^2 = \sigma_{x_\infty}{}^2 + \sigma_{e_1}{}^2$$
$$\sigma_{x_2}{}^2 = \sigma_{x_\infty}{}^2 + \sigma_{e_2}{}^2$$
$$\cdots \cdots \cdots \cdots$$
$$\sigma_{x_{k-1}}^2 = \sigma_{x_\infty}{}^2 + \sigma_{e_{k-1}}^2$$
$$\sigma_{x_k}{}^2 = \sigma_{x_\infty}{}^2 + \sigma_{e_k}{}^2$$

From Eq. (8-10) we know that the standard deviations of error scores for all parallel tests are equal to each other. Hence in each of the above equations we can write $\sigma_e{}^2$ for the standard deviations of error scores. Therefore all the above equations are equal and we can write them as

$$\sigma_{x_1}{}^2 = \cdots = \sigma_{x_k}{}^2 = \sigma_{x_\infty}{}^2 + \sigma_{x_e}{}^2 \tag{8-14}$$

Equation (8-14) shows us that the standard deviations of all parallel tests are equal to each other.

THE CORRELATIONS AMONG PARALLEL TESTS

From Eq. (8-3) we can write the correlations between any two parallel tests i and i' as

$$r_{x_i x_{i'}} = r_{(x_\infty+e_i)(x_\infty+e_{i'})}$$
$$= \frac{\Sigma(x_\infty + e_i)(x_\infty + e_{i'})}{n\sigma_{x_i}\sigma_{x_{i'}}}$$

Since we know from Eq. (8-14) that the standard deviations of all parallel tests are equal, we can write $\sigma_x{}^2$ for $\sigma_{x_i}\sigma_{x_{i'}}$:

$$r_{x_i x_{i'}} = \frac{\Sigma(x_\infty + e_i)(x_\infty + e_{i'})}{n\sigma_x{}^2}$$

$$= \frac{\Sigma(x_\infty{}^2 + x_\infty e_i + x_\infty e_{i'} + e_i e_{i'})}{n\sigma_x{}^2}$$

$$= \frac{\Sigma x_\infty{}^2/n + \Sigma x_\infty e_i/n + \Sigma x_\infty e_{i'}/n + \Sigma e_i e_{i'}/n}{\sigma_x{}^2}$$

Since the sum of the cross products of deviation scores divided by the number of cases is equal to the coefficient of correlation between the two variables times their standard deviations, we can write the last three terms in the numerator in this manner:

$$r_{x_i x_{i'}} = \frac{\sigma_{x_\infty}{}^2 + r_{x_\infty e_i}\sigma_{x_\infty}\sigma_{e_i} + r_{x_\infty e_{i'}}\sigma_{x_\infty}\sigma_{e_{i'}} + r_{e_i e_{i'}}\sigma_{e_i}\sigma_{e_{i'}}}{\sigma_x{}^2}$$

From Eq. (8-6) we know that the correlation between error scores and other variables is .00. Therefore the last three terms in the numerator become zero and drop out. Hence

$$r_{x_i x_{i'}} = \frac{\sigma_{x_\infty}{}^2}{\sigma_x{}^2} \tag{8-15}$$

In a similar fashion we can show that the coefficient of correlation between any pair of parallel tests other than x_i and $x_{i'}$ is equal to the ratio of the variance of true scores to the variance of fallible scores. Consequently we can write

$$r_{x_1 x_2} = \cdots = r_{x_{k-1} x_k} = \frac{\sigma_{x_\infty}{}^2}{\sigma_x{}^2} = r_{xx} \tag{8-16}$$

We conclude from Eq. (8-16) that all parallel tests are correlated with each other to the same degree. Therefore we can write the coefficient of correlation between parallel tests as r_{xx}. Inasmuch as the coefficient of correlation between scores on parallel tests is the reliability coefficient, we can also see from Eq. (8-16) that in terms of the concept of true and error scores the reliability coefficient is the ratio of the variance of true scores to the variance of fallible scores.

THE CORRELATION BETWEEN SCORES ON PARALLEL TESTS AND SCORES ON ANY OTHER TEST

Let us now examine the correlation between scores on any one parallel test x_i and scores on any other variable y:

$$r_{x_i y} = r_{(x_\infty + e_i) y}$$
$$= \frac{\Sigma(x_\infty + e_i)y}{n\sigma_{x_i}\sigma_y}$$
$$= \frac{\Sigma x_\infty y / n + \Sigma e_i y / n}{\sigma_{x_i}\sigma_y}$$

Since the sum of cross products of deviation scores divided by the number of cases is equal to the correlation coefficient times the two standard deviations,

$$r_{x_i y} = \frac{r_{x_\infty y}\sigma_{x_\infty}\sigma_y + r_{e_i y}\sigma_{e_i}\sigma_y}{\sigma_{x_i}\sigma_y}$$

From Eq. (8-6) we know that the correlation between error scores and scores on any other variable is .00. Therefore the entire second term in the numerator becomes zero and drops out. Hence

$$r_{x_i y} = \frac{r_{x_\infty y}\sigma_{x_\infty}\sigma_y}{\sigma_{x_i}\sigma_y}$$
$$= \frac{r_{x_\infty y}\sigma_{x_\infty}}{\sigma_{x_i}}$$
$$= r_{x_\infty y}\frac{\sigma_{x_\infty}}{\sigma_{x_i}}$$

From Eq. (8-16) we know that the ratio of the variance of true scores to the variance of fallible scores is equal to the reliability coefficient. Hence

$$r_{x_i y} = r_{x_\infty y}\sqrt{r_{xx}} \tag{8-17}$$

By a similar derivation we can show that the above equation holds for any parallel test other than x_i. Consequently

$$r_{x_1 y} = \cdots = r_{x_k y} = r_{x_\infty y}\sqrt{r_{xx}} \tag{8-18}$$

Hence we can conclude that all parallel tests correlate to the same degree with any other variable.

CHARACTERISTICS OF PARALLEL TESTS

Let us now summarize our knowledge about parallel tests.

1. The mean of the scores is exactly the same for all parallel tests.
2. The standard deviation of the scores is exactly the same for all parallel tests.
3. The scores on all parallel tests are correlated with each other to exactly the same degree.
4. The scores on all parallel tests are correlated to exactly the same degree with the scores on any other variable.

It will be recalled that these characteristics were derived from the basic equation in the concept of true and error scores, Eq. (8-2), and from the three fundamental assumptions involved in this theory. If a set of tests satisfies these criteria, then they are parallel tests; and if it does not, they are not parallel tests.

RELIABILITY IN TERMS OF THE CONCEPT OF TRUE AND ERROR SCORES

Reliability of measurement, we said, refers to the extent of variation in an individual's scores over a series of parallel tests. We saw that the standard error of measurement and the reliability coefficient both give descriptions of the degree of reliability. Let us now examine the relationship between these two indices in terms of the concept of true and error scores. We can develop Eq. (8-16) as follows:

$$r_{xx} = \frac{\sigma_{x_\infty}^2}{\sigma_x^2}$$

$$= \frac{\sigma_x^2 - \sigma_e^2}{\sigma_x^2}$$

$$= \frac{\sigma_x^2}{\sigma_x^2} - \frac{\sigma_e^2}{\sigma_x^2}$$

$$= 1 - \frac{\sigma_e^2}{\sigma_x^2}$$

$$\frac{\sigma_e^2}{\sigma_x^2} = 1 - r_{xx}$$

$$\sigma_e^2 = \sigma_x^2(1 - r_{xx}) \tag{8-19}$$

$$\sigma_e = \sigma_x \sqrt{1 - r_{xx}} \tag{8-20}$$

Therefore the standard deviation of the distribution of error scores on any one administration of a test is equal to the standard deviation of fallible scores on that administration times the square root of 1 minus the reliability coefficient. In Eq. (8-11) we showed that the standard deviation of error scores on any one administration of a test is equal to the standard deviation of the error scores of any one individual over k parallel tests. That is, $\sigma_e = S$. Hence we can write Eq. (8-20) as the standard error of measurement:

$$S = \sigma_x \sqrt{1 - r_{xx}} \tag{8-21}$$

The variability of an individual's scores over a number of parallel tests, then, also is equal to the standard deviation of the fallible scores on any one administration times the square root of 1 minus the reliability coefficient.

ESTIMATING TRUE SCORES

We have seen from Eq. (8-13) that the mean of true scores is equal to the mean of fallible scores on any parallel test. If we rearrange the terms in Eq. (8-16), we have an equation which permits us to calculate the variance of true scores:

$$\sigma_{x_\infty}^2 = \sigma_x^2 r_{xx} \tag{8-22}$$

If we have two parallel tests, then, by using their standard deviation and the correlation between them it is quite simple to determine the characteristics of the distribution of true scores of the trait they measure.

However, we cannot determine exactly the true score for any one individual. But let us see whether we can predict his true score from his fallible score. The coefficient of correlation between fallible and true scores is

$$
\begin{aligned}
r_{xx_\infty} = r_{(x_\infty + e)x_\infty} &= \frac{\Sigma(x_\infty + e)x_\infty}{n\sigma_x\sigma_{x_\infty}} \\
&= \frac{\Sigma(x_\infty^2 + x_\infty e)}{n\sigma_x\sigma_{x_\infty}} \\
&= \frac{\Sigma x_\infty^2 + \Sigma x_\infty e}{n\sigma_x\sigma_{x_\infty}} \\
&= \frac{\Sigma x_\infty^2/n + \Sigma x_\infty e/n}{\sigma_x\sigma_{x_\infty}} \\
&= \frac{\sigma_{x_\infty}^2 + \sigma_{x_\infty}\sigma_e r_{x_\infty e}}{\sigma_x\sigma_{x_\infty}}
\end{aligned}
$$

From the second assumption in the theory of true and error scores as given in Eq. (8-6) we know that the correlation between error scores and scores on any other variable is .00. Therefore the second term in the numerator of the above equation becomes zero and drops out:

$$
\begin{aligned}
r_{xx_\infty} &= \frac{\sigma_{x_\infty}^2}{\sigma_x\sigma_{x_\infty}} \\
&= \frac{\sigma_{x_\infty}}{\sigma_x}
\end{aligned}
$$

Substituting from Eq. (8-16), we have

$$r_{xx_\infty} = \sqrt{r_{xx}} \tag{8-23}$$

Traditionally this value is termed the *index of reliability*. It is the coefficient of correlation between fallible and true scores and indicates how good fallible scores are as measures of true scores. It is apparent that when the reliability of a test is low, fallible scores are poor indices of true scores; and when reliability is high, true scores can be very accurately predicted from fallible scores.

AN ECLECTIC CONCEPT OF TRUE SCORES AND PARALLEL TESTS

For some the notion of random error and the assumptions involved in the theory of true and error scores are too restrictive and tenuous, and therefore they prefer to approach the matter of reliability of measurement from a similar but more eclectic point of view. In this concept true scores are not conceived of as some quality inherent in the individual, but are merely taken as the average of an individual's scores over an infinite number of parallel tests. Again true scores are an intellectual construct since we could never obtain scores on an individual over an infinite number of tests, but the construct is different from that of true scores in the concept of true and error scores.

The equation for true scores of any individual, then, is

$$x_\infty = \bar{x}_a = \frac{x_1 + \cdots + x_k}{k} \qquad (8\text{-}24)$$

where x_1 to x_k refer to scores on parallel tests and k is an infinitely large number. More exactly, we should say that x_∞ is the value that is approached as the number of parallel tests is increased without limit. Consequently it is not necessary to make the first assumption of the theory of true and error scores. While the second assumption in that theory is implied here, it is not really necessary. To be sure, it makes the concept of reliability somewhat clearer to conceive of errors as being completely random, but we do not have to so stipulate for this development. Similarly, the third assumption, the additive character of scores, is not necessary but also may be implied.

THE CORRELATION BETWEEN SCORES ON PARALLEL TESTS AND SCORES ON ANY OTHER TEST

Our general definition of parallel tests is that they are tests which measure the same traits to the same degree. We need no other definition to begin our development. The question we must ask and answer is how to determine whether two or more tests do in fact measure the same traits to the same degree. One approach is to examine the content or nature of the tests. Suppose we have two tests both of which involve the same types of arithmetic problems. In one the problems are $3 + 4 = $ _____, $9 + 2 = $ _____, and $1 + 7 = $ _____; and in the other the problems are $4 + 3 = $ _____, $2 + 9 = $ _____, and

$7 + 1 = $ _____. Even though the specific problems contained in the two tests are different, they are so very nearly the same that we certainly should be willing to say that the two tests measure the same traits and therefore are parallel tests. However, if one test involved putting pegs into holes and the other involved solving algebraic formulae we should not be willing to say that they are parallel. The problems posed by these two tests are so very different that as psychologists we should say that they elicit quite different psychological processes and therefore measure quite different traits.

Hence we could use our judgment as psychologists as a way for gauging the extent to which two or more tests are parallel, our judgment being based upon the similarity in the nature and content of the two tests. This judgmental process is so subjective, however, that the opinions of two different psychologists with respect to the parallelism of two or more tests might be quite different. Furthermore, a given individual may not be certain of his own judgment. Therefore we should like to have a more objective way of indicating the degree of parallelism of two tests.

Let us approach the problem a bit obliquely. Suppose we have a test and we wish to know what traits it measures. Obviously an examination of its nature and content would give us some information. We could obtain an even better notion if we knew something of the ways in which its scores are related to scores on a wide variety of other tests. By noting the nature of those tests with which our test is more highly related and those with which it tends to be unrelated, we can obtain some general notions of the traits measured by our test.

For example, suppose scores on our test are rather highly correlated with scores on tests involving placing dots into small circles, tracing irregular pathways with a pencil, placing pegs into holes, and throwing darts. In addition, suppose scores on our test at best bear only very low correlations on the one hand with tests involving speed and accuracy of motion such as blind positioning movements and on the other hand with tests of goodness of vision such as visual acuity. Speed and accuracy of movements or goodness of vision alone are relatively unrelated to scores on our test, but when they occur in combination in a test we find a substantial relationship with our test. On the basis of the pattern of correlations our test has with these other tests, we probably should term it a test of eye-hand coordination.

If we had a second test and it, too, showed precisely the same pattern of correlations with other tests, we should also term it a test of eye-hand coordination. We should therefore say that two or more tests measure the same traits if they have precisely the same pattern of correlations with a wide variety of other tests. Since parallel tests by definition are tests that measure the same traits, if two or more tests are parallel they must have precisely the same patterns of correlations with other tests. In other words, all tests that are parallel are correlated to the same degree with any other given test.

THE CORRELATIONS AMONG PARALLEL TESTS

Let us now examine the correlations among parallel tests. Actually the intercorrelations among parallel tests can be taken as being merely a special case of the proposition we just discussed: that for a series of tests to be considered parallel they must be correlated to the same degree with any other given test.

Let us illustrate this in a somewhat roundabout way. Suppose we have k parallel tests but we hold out one of them, x_1, for a moment and consider it as an outside test. Pursuant to our earlier rationale, tests x_2 to x_k all must be correlated equally with x_1 since they are parallel. That is,

$$r_{x_1 x_2} = r_{x_1 x_3} = \cdots = r_{x_1 x_k}$$

Therefore we know that x_1 is correlated to the same degree with all the other tests. Now let us hold out test x_2 and consider it as an outside test. Then pursuant to our first criterion of parallel tests,

$$r_{x_2 x_1} = r_{x_2 x_3} = \cdots = r_{x_2 x_k}$$

Therefore we know that x_2 is correlated to the same degree with all the other tests. We also know that x_1 and x_2 are correlated to the same degree with all the other tests x_3 to x_k and are correlated with each other to this same degree. Proceeding in this fashion, we can demonstrate that on the basis of the first criterion of parallel tests the intercorrelations among parallel tests must be equal. Consequently we can say that for a series of tests to be considered as being parallel they must correlate with each other to precisely the same degree.

THE MEANS AND STANDARD DEVIATIONS OF PARALLEL TESTS

As we have just seen, in the concept of statistically equivalent parallel tests the nature of the correlations between parallel tests and other tests and the intercorrelations among parallel tests follow logically from the general definition of parallel tests (tests which measure precisely the same traits), which is the basis of this eclectic notion. However, there is nothing in this definition which in and of itself provides indications of a logic which leads to statements about the nature of the means and standard deviations of parallel tests. In the concept of true and error scores these characteristics mathematically follow from the basic equations and assumptions.

As a consequence it is perhaps not surprising to find that there is some divergence of opinion among those who adhere to the notions of this eclectic point of view relative to the means and standard deviations of parallel tests. Since the basic definition of parallel tests tells us nothing about the means and standard deviations, we must deal with them on different grounds.

It is sometimes said that the means and standard deviations of parallel tests must be assumed to be equal. Yet the basis for such an assumption is obscure. Let us therefore approach the matter differently.

As we said, reliability of measurement is indicated by the extent of variation among an individual's scores over a series of parallel tests. Thus if we wished to know the reliability with which the weights of objects are measured we should weigh objects on a series of balances. Suppose that on one balance, weight is expressed in pounds, on another in kilograms, on another in arrobas, and on another in ssu. Obviously variation among weight scores would be meaningless since the units in which weight is expressed differ from one parallel balance to another. Therefore we should have to transmute the values of weight on all parallel balances to the same scale and examine the variation among the scores of each object on these transmuted values.

Similarly, with a series of parallel tests all measuring the same psychological trait, variation in an individual's scores over these tests would be meaningless unless scores on all tests were expressed in the same units. In Chap. 3 we outlined the rationale for rendering units of measurement on different tests comparable by use of standard or standardized scores. If this rationale is accepted, then the means and standard deviations of scores on all parallel tests become equal because we make them so by a process of transformation. However, even though all parallel tests have the same means and standard deviations, it should be clear that equality of means and standard deviations of raw scores is not a criterion of parallel tests in this eclectic concept as it is in the theory of true and error scores.

THE MEANS OF TRUE SCORES

Let us now examine the means of true scores. From Eq. (8-24) we can write the true score of any individual a as

$$X_{\infty_a} = \frac{X_{1_a} + \cdots + X_{k_a}}{k} = \frac{\Sigma X_a}{k} = \bar{X}_a \qquad (8\text{-}25)$$

From Eq. (7-29), the formula for the mean of average scores, we can write the mean of the true scores for all n individuals as

$$\bar{X}_\infty = \frac{1}{k}(\bar{X}_1 + \cdots + \bar{X}_k)$$

Since we are taking the means of all parallel tests to be equal through transformation, that is, $\bar{X}_1 = \cdots = \bar{X}_k = \bar{X}$, and there are k parallel tests,

$$\bar{X}_\infty = \frac{1}{k} k\bar{X} = \bar{X} \qquad (8\text{-}26)$$

Hence the mean of true scores is precisely equal to the mean of fallible scores.

THE VARIANCE OF TRUE SCORES

Now let us consider the variance of true scores. This we can write as

$$\sigma_{x_\infty}{}^2 = \sigma^2_{(x_1 + \cdots + x_k)/k}$$

As we see, we are concerned with the standard deviation of the average of a composite of scores. This we considered in Eq. (7-30). Therefore we can write

$$\sigma_{x_\infty}{}^2 = \frac{1}{k^2}\left(\sigma_{x_1}{}^2 + \cdots + \sigma_{x_k}{}^2 + 2\sigma_{x_1}\sigma_{x_2}r_{x_1 x_2} + \cdots + 2\sigma_{x_{k-1}}\sigma_{x_k}r_{x_{k-1}x_k}\right)$$

By our transformation process we have made all the standard deviations of the parallel tests equal (σ_x), and we have shown that the intercorrelations among parallel tests are equal (r_{xx}). Consequently we can write the above equation as

$$\sigma_{x_\infty}{}^2 = \frac{1}{k^2}\left[k\sigma_x{}^2 + k(k-1)\sigma_x{}^2 r_{xx}\right]$$

$$= \frac{k}{k^2}\sigma_x{}^2 + \frac{k(k-1)}{k^2}\sigma_x{}^2 r_{xx}$$

$$= \frac{1}{k}\sigma_x{}^2 + \frac{k-1}{k}\sigma_x{}^2 r_{xx}$$

Since k is a very large number, for all practical purposes $1/k = 0$ and the entire first term becomes zero and drops out, and $(k-1)/k = 1$. Hence

$$\sigma_{x_\infty}{}^2 = \sigma_x{}^2 r_{xx} \qquad (8\text{-}27)$$

or

$$\frac{\sigma_{x_\infty}{}^2}{\sigma_x{}^2} = r_{xx} \qquad (8\text{-}28)$$

In this eclectic development, as in the concept of true and error scores, we see that the variance of true scores is equal to the variance of fallible scores times the reliability coefficient, and the reliability coefficient is equal to the ratio of the variance of true scores to the variance of fallible scores.

ESTIMATING TRUE SCORES

By means of Eqs. (8-26) and (8-27) we can calculate the characteristics of the distribution of true scores. But again we cannot determine the true score of an individual. The best we can do is to estimate it from his fallible score. Therefore let us develop the correlation between fallible and true scores:

$$
\begin{aligned}
r_{x_1 x_\infty} &= r_{x_1(x_1+x_2+\cdots+x_k)/k} \\
&= \frac{\Sigma x_1[(x_1 + x_2 + \cdots + x_k)/k]}{n\sigma_{x_1}\sigma_{x_\infty}} \\
&= \frac{(1/k)\Sigma x_1(x_1 + x_2 + \cdots + x_k)}{n\sigma_{x_1}\sigma_{x_\infty}} \\
&= \frac{(1/k)(\Sigma x_1{}^2/n + \Sigma x_1 x_2/n + \cdots + \Sigma x_1 x_k/n)}{\sigma_{x_1}\sigma_{x_\infty}} \\
&= \frac{(1/k)(\sigma_{x_1}{}^2 + \sigma_{x_1}\sigma_{x_2}r_{x_1 x_2} + \cdots + \sigma_{x_1}\sigma_{x_k}r_{x_1 x_k})}{\sigma_{x_1}\sigma_{x_\infty}}
\end{aligned}
$$

However, the standard deviations of the scores on all parallel tests are equal through transformation so that $\sigma_{x_1} = \cdots = \sigma_{x_k} = \sigma_x$, and the intercorrelations among all the parallel tests are equal so that

$$r_{x_1 x_2} = \cdots = r_{x_1 x_k} = r_{xx}$$

Since we are dealing with a composite variable, it will be recalled that there are $k - 1$ of these correlation terms. Hence

$$
\begin{aligned}
r_{xx_\infty} &= \frac{(1/k)[\sigma_x{}^2 + (k-1)\sigma_x{}^2 r_{xx}]}{\sigma_x\sigma_{x_\infty}} \\
&= \frac{(1/k)\sigma_x{}^2 + [(k-1)/k]\sigma_x{}^2 r_{xx}}{\sigma_x\sigma_{x_\infty}}
\end{aligned}
$$

Since k is a very large number, $1/k$ so closely approximates zero that it can be considered to be zero and the entire first term of the numerator becomes zero and drops out; and $(k-1)/k$ so closely approximates 1 that it can be considered to be 1. Hence

$$r_{xx_\infty} = \frac{\sigma_x{}^2 r_{xx}}{\sigma_x\sigma_{x_\infty}}$$

Substituting for σ_{x_∞} from Eq. (8-27) gives

$$r_{xx_\infty} = \frac{\sigma_x{}^2 r_{xx}}{\sigma_x{}^2 \sqrt{r_{xx}}}$$

Dividing the numerator and denominator by σ_x^2 and $\sqrt{r_{xx}}$, we have

$$r_{xx_\infty} = \sqrt{r_{xx}} \qquad (8\text{-}29)$$

This value indicates the accuracy with which we can predict true from fallible scores. It will be observed that this formula, which is termed the index of reliability, is precisely the same as that [Eq. (8-23)] which we developed on a different conceptual basis in connection with the theory of true and error scores.

RELIABILITY IN TERMS OF THE ECLECTIC CONCEPT

In this electric concept the standard error of measurement, the variation among the scores of any one individual over the k parallel tests, would be

$$S_a = \sigma_{x_a - x_{\infty,a}}$$

As a variance this is

$$S_a^2 = \sigma^2_{x_a - x_{\infty,a}} = \frac{\Sigma(x_a - x_{\infty a})^2}{k}$$

$$= \frac{(x_{1_a} - x_{\infty a})^2 + \cdots + (x_{k_a} - x_{\infty a})^2}{k}$$

$$= \frac{1}{k}(x_{1_a}^2 - 2x_1 x_{\infty a} + x_{\infty a}^2 + \cdots + x_{k_a}^2 - 2x_1 x_{\infty a} + x_{\infty a}^2) \qquad (8\text{-}30)$$

$$S_a^2 = \frac{1}{k}(\Sigma x_a^2 - 2\Sigma x_a x_{\infty a} + \Sigma x_{\infty a}^2) \qquad (8\text{-}31)$$

At this point we can take either of two courses, both of which result in the same formula. However, they involve different conceptualizations and so we shall deal with them separately.

There is nothing in the definition of true scores or parallel tests in this eclectic concept which permits us to make any statement about whether the standard error of measurement is the same for all individuals or whether it varies in magnitude from one individual to another. Perhaps as a result of the influence of the theory of true and error scores the assumption is frequently made that the standard error of measurement is equal for all individuals. Obviously the specific values of x_1 to x_k and x_∞ vary from individual to individual, but pursuant to this assumption the sum of their squares and cross products as given in Eq. (8-30) would be the same for all individuals.

A second way of approaching the matter is to make no assumption at all about the equality of the standard error of measurement for all individuals. If we do not make any assumption, then our task is simply to determine the mean of the standard errors of all individuals. Let us begin by pursuing this second course.

Note that in Eq. (8-31), which is the variance of any one individual's fallible scores over k parallel tests, x_∞ is a constant. Therefore we can write $\Sigma x_{\infty_a}^2$ as $kx_{\infty_a}^2$. Hence

$$S_a^2 = \frac{1}{k}(\Sigma x_a^2 - 2x_a x_{\infty_a} + kx_{\infty_a}^2)$$

$$= \frac{1}{k}[(x_{1_a}^2 + \cdots + x_{k_a}^2) - 2(x_{1_a}x_{\infty_a} + \cdots + x_{k_a}x_{\infty_a}) + kx_{\infty_a}^2]$$

$$(8\text{-}32)$$

If we average these standard deviations for all a to n individuals, we have

$$\overline{S^2} = \frac{\frac{1}{k}[(x_{1_a}^2 + \cdots + x_{k_a}^2) - 2(x_{1_a}x_{\infty_a} + \cdots + x_{k_a}x_{\infty_a}) + kx_{\infty_a}^2] + \cdots + \frac{1}{k}[(x_{1_n}^2 + \cdots + x_{k_n}^2) - 2(x_{1_n}x_{\infty_n} + \cdots + x_{k_n}x_{\infty_n}) + kx_{\infty_n}^2]}{n} \quad (8\text{-}33)$$

Rearranging terms, grouping scores by tests rather than by individuals, gives

$$\overline{S^2} = \frac{\frac{1}{k}[(x_{1_a}^2 + \cdots + x_{1_n}^2) + \cdots + (x_{k_a}^2 + \cdots + x_{k_n}^2) - 2(x_{1_a}x_{\infty_a} + \cdots + x_{1_n}x_{\infty_n}) - \cdots - 2(x_{k_a}x_{\infty_a} + \cdots + x_{k_n}x_{\infty_n}) + k(x_{\infty_a}^2 + \cdots + x_{\infty_n}^2)]}{n}$$

$$= \frac{\frac{1}{k}(\Sigma x_1^2 + \cdots + \Sigma x_k^2 - 2\Sigma x_1 x_\infty - \cdots - 2\Sigma x_k x_\infty + k\Sigma x_\infty^2)}{n}$$

$$= \frac{1}{k}\left(\frac{\Sigma x_1^2}{n} + \cdots + \frac{\Sigma x_k^2}{n} - 2\frac{\Sigma x_1 x_\infty}{n} - \cdots - 2\frac{\Sigma x_k x_\infty}{n} + k\frac{\Sigma x_\infty^2}{n}\right)$$

$$= \frac{1}{k}(\sigma_{x_1}^2 + \cdots + \sigma_{x_k}^2 - 2\sigma_{x_1}\sigma_{x_\infty}r_{x_1 x_\infty} - \cdots - 2\sigma_{x_k}\sigma_{x_\infty}r_{x_k x_\infty} + k\sigma_{x_\infty}^2)$$

Recalling that the standard deviations of all parallel tests are equal by transformation of their scores and that there are k parallel tests, we can write $\sigma_{x_1}^2 + \cdots + \sigma_{x_k}^2$ as $k\sigma_x^2$. Also there are k covariance terms, all of which are equal [Eq. (8-29)], which we can write as $k2\sigma_x\sigma_{x_\infty}r_{xx_\infty}$. Therefore

$$\overline{S^2} = \frac{1}{k}(k\sigma_x^2 - k2\sigma_x\sigma_{x_\infty}r_{xx_\infty} + k\sigma_{x_\infty}^2)$$

$$= \sigma_x^2 - 2\sigma_x\sigma_{x_\infty} + r_{xx_\infty} + \sigma_{x_\infty}^2$$

Making appropriate substitutions for σ_{x_∞} from Eq. (8-27) and for r_{xx_∞} from Eq. (8-29), we have

$$\begin{aligned}
\overline{S^2} &= \sigma_x{}^2 - 2\sigma_x\sigma_x \sqrt{r_{xx}} \sqrt{r_{xx}} + \sigma_x{}^2 r_{xx} \\
&= \sigma_x{}^2 - 2\sigma_x{}^2 r_{xx} + \sigma_x{}^2 r_{xx} \\
&= \sigma_x{}^2 - \sigma_x{}^2 r_{xx} \\
&= \sigma_x{}^2(1 - r_{xx})
\end{aligned} \tag{8-34}$$

The above formula gives the average of the standard errors of measurement when the standard error is expressed in terms of variance. By using $\overline{S^2}$ as a description of the extent of unsystematic variation in individuals' scores over parallel tests, we make no commitment about the nature of the variation. There is no theoretical or practical reason why we should make such a commitment, and to use an average value such as $\overline{S^2}$ is perfectly adequate for any descriptive purposes. Indeed, it could well be that some individuals are more resistant to the influence of unsystematic factors than are others. In any event, this is a question that can be left open to empirical investigation.

Let us say we are willing to assume that the magnitude of the standard error of measurement, S^2, is the same for all individuals. Then as we pointed out earlier, while the sums of the terms in the brackets of Eq. (8-30) would be the same for all individuals, the specific values of x_1 to x_k and x_∞ would vary from individual to individual. Therefore when we sum the standard errors as we did in Eq. (8-33), the total of each term in brackets would be the same, and we should make our development from Eq. (8-32) but as

$$\frac{\Sigma S^2}{n} = \frac{(1/k)[\Sigma(x_1{}^2 + \cdots + x_k{}^2) - 2\Sigma(x_1 x_\infty + \cdots + x_k x_\infty) + k\Sigma x_\infty{}^2]}{n}$$

Since we are taking S^2 to be a constant, that is, the same for each person, we could write $\Sigma S^2/n$ as S^2, because the sum of a constant divided by the number of times it is summed to itself is equal to the constant. To continue the development,

$$\begin{aligned}
S^2 &= \frac{(1/k)(\Sigma x_1{}^2 + \cdots + \Sigma x_k{}^2 - 2\Sigma x_1 x_\infty - \cdots - 2\Sigma x_k x_\infty + k\Sigma x_\infty{}^2)}{n} \\
&= \frac{1}{k}\left(\frac{\Sigma x_1{}^2}{n} + \cdots + \frac{\Sigma x_k{}^2}{n} - 2\frac{\Sigma x_1 x_\infty}{n} - \cdots - 2\frac{\Sigma x_k x_\infty}{n} + k\frac{\Sigma x_\infty{}^2}{n}\right) \\
&= \frac{1}{k}\left(\sigma_{x_1}{}^2 + \cdots + \sigma_{x_k}{}^2 - 2\sigma_{x_1}\sigma_{x_\infty}r_{x_1 x_\infty} - \cdots - \sigma_{x_k}\sigma_{x_\infty}r_{x_k x_\infty}\right. \\
&\qquad\qquad\qquad\qquad\qquad\qquad\qquad\qquad \left. + k\sigma_{x_\infty}{}^2\right)
\end{aligned} \tag{8-35}$$

The variances of all parallel tests through transformation are equal to each other so that $\sigma_{x_1}{}^2 + \cdots + \sigma_{x_k}{}^2 = k\sigma_x{}^2$. From Eq. (8-29) we know that the correlations between scores on all parallel tests and x_∞ are the same. Substituting for r_{xx_∞} from Eq. (8-29), we could write the terms

$$-2\sigma_x\sigma_{x_\infty}r_{x_1x_\infty} - \cdots - 2\sigma_{x_k}\sigma_{x_\infty}r_{x_kx_\infty} = -2k\sigma_x\sigma_{x_\infty}\sqrt{r_{xx}}$$

Finally, from Eq. (8-29) we know that we can write $\sigma_{x_\infty}{}^2$ as $\sigma_x{}^2r_{xx}$ and σ_{x_∞} as $\sigma_x\sqrt{r_{xx}}$. Therefore we can write Eq. (8-35) as

$$
\begin{aligned}
S^2 &= \frac{1}{k}[k\sigma_x{}^2 - 2k\sigma_x\sigma_x\sqrt{r_{xx}}\sqrt{r_{xx}} + k\sigma_x{}^2r_{xx}] \\
&= \sigma_x{}^2 - 2\sigma_x{}^2r_{xx} + \sigma_x{}^2r_{xx} \\
&= \sigma_x{}^2 - \sigma_x{}^2r_{xx} \\
&= \sigma_x{}^2(1 - r_{xx})
\end{aligned}
\tag{8-36}
$$

It is apparent from Eqs. (8-34) and (8-36) that whether we assume the standard error of measurement to be the same for all individuals or make no assumption at all about it but compute the average of the standard errors for all individuals, the values are precisely the same. It will also be observed that the formula for the standard error of measurement is precisely the same whether we develop it from the rationale of this eclectic concept of true scores and parallel tests [Eqs. (8-34) and (8-36)] or from the rationale of the theory of true and error scores [Eq. (8-20)].

THE CONCEPT OF DOMAIN SAMPLING

We now turn to the third view of reliability of measurement, which arises from a notion of sampling from a specified domain of behavior. The point of view adopted is that when we define a trait we are describing a domain of behavior, a category of behaviors all of which have some property in common. To measure the trait we provide a series of items or situations each of which elicits one or another of the behaviors in the domain. The operations of measurement we develop to measure a trait do not tap all the possible behaviors in the domain but only a sample of them. Reliability of measurement, then, is conceived of as referring to the extent of variation among an individual's scores on a number of different comparable samples of items or situations, all of which are drawn from the same domain, or to the extent of correlation between scores on two or more such samples.

THE THEORETICAL BASIS OF THE CONCEPT OF DOMAIN SAMPLING

The concept of domain sampling conceives of a trait as being a group of behaviors all of which have some property in common. This group of behaviors constitutes a domain of behavior and differs from other groups of behaviors or domains which have other properties in common. Some domains of behavior may be quite general, whereas others may be quite specific. Thus the domain "aggression" includes a wide variety of behaviors from murderous acts and injury to others, through hitting and cursing, to malicious gossiping and hostile glances. On the other hand, the domain "simple addition" involves only the addition of pairs of single-digit numbers. Some domains completely include other domains, whereas in other instances there is only partial overlap. The domain "social interaction" completely includes the domain "aggression" since all aggression involves the interaction among people, whereas the domain "verbal fluency" would only partially overlap the domain "aggression" to include acts of cursing and malicious gossiping but not murderous acts, hitting, angry glances, and the like.

Pursuant to the point of view of domain sampling we can say that the exigencies of testing time and the like prevent us from tapping all the behaviors in a domain. Therefore a given test or measuring device does not measure all the possible behaviors in a domain but only a sample of them. Consequently when we measure a trait we are only sampling from a larger domain.

For example, suppose we wish to measure the trait "interest in active occupations," which we define as "preference for occupations which involve moving about from one place to another." We can conceive of many items in which people are asked whether they would like or dislike such occupations as bus driver, traveling salesman, airline pilot, patrolman, and solicitor. From the many possible items, we choose for our test only a certain number, say 50. Consequently our test is comprised of a sample of 50 items from the total domain of items.

As another example let us consider the measurement of reaction time to a light. We can conceive of a large number of presentations of the light to subjects, and these many presentations constitute the domain of reaction time to this particular light. However, because of the limitations of the experimental period when we actually measure reaction time we might present the light only 25 times. Hence we have taken a sample of responses from the many possible numbers of responses which constitute the domain.

THE STATISTICAL DESCRIPTION OF A DOMAIN

Suppose we wish to describe the nature of the items or situations that comprise a domain. Since the domain is comprised of a number of components, a description of it would involve statements about the distributional characteristics of the components, the relationships among the components, and the relationships between the components and other variables. The components of any domain vary among themselves in these characteristics. They differ among themselves in their means, standard deviations, and covariances. Therefore in order to provide a statistical description of the components j, we should have to describe their average characteristics. In describing a particular domain, then, we should give the following values:

$$\overline{\bar{X}_j} = \text{average of means of scores on components}$$
$$\overline{\sigma_{x_j}{}^2} = \text{average of variances of scores on components}$$
$$\overline{\sigma_{x_j}\sigma_{x_{j'}}r_{x_j x_{j'}}} = \text{average of covariances among components}$$
$$\overline{\sigma_{x_j}\sigma_y r_{x_j y}} = \text{average of covariances between components and any other}$$
$$\text{variable } y \text{ outside the domain}$$

We may wonder why covariances are used to describe the relationships rather than just the coefficients of correlation. Reference to Eqs. (7-18) and (7-22) will show that in determining relationships involving composites, knowledge of the intercorrelations among components is not sufficient and knowledge of covariances is also necessary.

SAMPLING FROM A DOMAIN

From a particular domain we could draw samples of any given size. In our test of "interest in active occupations" we could have 10 items, 38, 50, 164, or any other number. Similarly, in our reaction-time test we could take three reactions, or 17, 25, 45, or whatever we wish. If our domain is infinitely large we could draw an infinite number of such samples.

Let us say that we draw k samples from our domain, each sample being composed of M items or situations. We then have 1 to k samples each composed of I to M components. Such scores can be represented as follows:

$$X_1 = X_{1_I} + \cdots + X_{1_M}$$
$$\cdots\cdots\cdots\cdots\cdots\cdots \qquad (8\text{-}37)$$
$$X_k = X_{k_I} + \cdots + X_{k_M}$$

In deviation-score form we write these equations as

$$x_1 = x_{1_I} + \cdots + x_{1_M}$$
$$\cdots\cdots\cdots\cdots\cdots\cdots$$
$$x_k = x_{k_I} + \cdots + x_{k_M}$$

If the sample we draw from the domain is representative of it, then its characteristics are exactly the same as those of the total domain. Now suppose every one of the k samples we draw is perfectly representative of the total domain in terms of the averages of the means, variances, and covariances of the component items or situations j; then the following four conditions would hold:

1. The averages of the means of the scores on the components are the same for all samples and are equal to the average of the means of the scores on the components in the total domain:

$$\overline{X_{1_j}} = \cdots = \overline{X_{k_j}} = \overline{X_j} \tag{8-38}$$

2. The averages of the variances of the scores on the components are the same for all samples and are equal to the average of the variances of the scores on the components in the total domain:

$$\overline{\sigma^2_{x_{1,j}}} = \cdots = \overline{\sigma^2_{x_{k,j}}} = \overline{\sigma_{x_j}}^2 \tag{8-39}$$

3. The averages of the covariances among the components in all samples are equal and are equal to the average of the *cross* covariances between the components in the domain:

$$\overline{\sigma_{x_{1,j}}\sigma_{x_{1,j'}}r_{x_{1,j}x_{1,j'}}} = \cdots = \overline{\sigma_{x_{k,j}}\sigma_{k,j'}r_{x_{k,j}x_{k,j'}}} = \cdots = \overline{\sigma_{x_{1,j}}\sigma_{x_{2,j}}r_{x_{1,j}x_{2,j}}}$$
$$= \cdots = \overline{\sigma_{x_{k-1,j}}\sigma_{x_{k,j}}r_{x_{k-1,j}x_{k,j}}} = \cdots = \overline{\sigma_{x_j}\sigma_{x_{j'}}r_{x_jx_{j'}}} \tag{8-40}$$

4. The averages of the covariances between the components and any other variable are the same in all samples and are equal to the average of the covariances among the components and any other variable in the total domain:

$$\overline{\sigma_{x_{1,j}}\sigma_y r_{x_{1,j}y}} = \cdots = \overline{\sigma_{x_{k,j}}\sigma_y r_{x_{k,j}y}} = \overline{\sigma_{x_j}\sigma_y r_{x_jy}} \tag{8-41}$$

A DOMAIN AS AN INTELLECTUAL CONSTRUCT

We might argue that it is impossible to draw a number of samples of a given size from a domain and expect them all to be precisely equal in terms of average mean, variance, and covariance. Indeed, if we were dealing with an actual population of behaviors, this would be true. But in the theory of domain sampling the domain is conceived of not as a domain of actual or even potential items or situations, but rather as an intellectual construct. Conceptually we are dealing only with those samples drawn from the domain that are representative of the total domain.

Suppose we conceive of a domain as a group of actual behaviors. We should begin by defining our variable, following the rationale we outlined in Chap. 2, ending up with a verbal statement of the nature and characteristics of the trait we propose to measure. Taking this verbal statement as a set of specifications or a blueprint, we should then develop operations for measuring the trait. We should say that from the many behaviors which fall in the domain we have defined, behaviors all of which have in common the property with which we are concerned, the operations of measurement only sample them.

Let us return to our example of the measurement of the trait "interest in active occupations." It might be that we develop some 1,000 items from the definition of our trait. But the practicalities of testing being what they are, we might say that we can only have an inventory consisting of 50 items. Therefore we should draw from the total pool of 1,000 items 50 of them, which we should form into our measuring device. This measuring device, then, samples 50 out of the 1,000 possibilities.

Now we might say that these 1,000 items constitute our domain and that all the items are equally good because they all stem from the definition of our variable. Therefore the choice of any particular 50 items should be determined purely on a chance basis, with the likelihood of any given item's being chosen being precisely the same as that of any other item. In a similar fashion we could pick out other samples of 50 items, taking them as being parallel to our first since all samples are chosen in a purely random fashion. Reliability of measurement, then, would be determined by the variation in an individual's scores over these various parallel tests or by the intercorrelations among them.

If we adopt this point of view, then it is necessary to deal with the problem of the extent to which each of the samples is representative of the total domain. But this implies two propositions: first, that we can precisely describe the totality of the domain, and secondly, that all items or situations are equally good for measuring the trait.

If we wish to describe statistically the characteristics of the items in the domain we wish to measure, we should do so in terms of whatever characteristics appear to be important, such as the means and variances of the items and their covariances. We should describe the items in terms of the averages of their means, variances, and covariances and compare these values with those of the total domain.

But which items constitute our domain? The 50 we finally selected? The 1,000 which form our original pool of items? Or what? Certainly if we had given more time and effort to the matter we might have developed not just 1,000 items but 10,000 such items, or 100,000 or 1 million. Indeed, in many instances we could conceive of there being a limitless number of possible items that could be developed from the definition of our trait, and therefore our domain would be limitless.

Now there are some domains about which it might be said that there is a definite and specific number of possible items which can be readily identified. Suppose we wish to measure the trait "simple addition," which we define as "the addition together of pairs of single-digit numbers." Since there are 10 single-digit numbers ranging from 0 to 9, if they are taken two at a time there are only 100 possible items. We might therefore take the position that these 100 items constitute the total domain. However, there is nothing in our definition which stipulates that items cannot be repeated, so that again we have a limitless number of possible items in our domain. Consequently we might be led to conclude that all domains are comprised of an infinite number of items.

Furthermore, sampling from a domain, as we have just described it, presupposes that we consider all the available items as being equally good "representatives" of the domain. However, in practice it is very unlikely that we should consider all the items we can think of as being equally good. Let us return to our example of the inventory for measuring "interest in active occupations." Undoubtedly we should not consider all the items in our pool of 1,000 to be equally good as measures of "active occupations." For example, we might discard the item "patrolman," because while patrolmen do move about they do not do so to any great extent. Obviously, therefore, even though we develop all the items from the definition of our trait, some of them do not seem to fit the definition quite so well as others. As a consequence we find it relatively easy to distinguish among items in terms of how well they fit our definition and to discard those which fit it less well. In addition, we might find it easy to distinguish between more and less acceptable items on other grounds. The item "solicitor" we might discard because it has certain immoral implications; and if we were testing boys we might discard the item "airline pilot" because the occupation is so glamorous for boys that they would all choose it and the item would not differentiate among individuals. So on one basis or another we should find 50 items which we believe to be better than the remaining 950, and as a consequence the basis of our choice of items would not be random; rather, it would be systematic.

Let us also reconsider our example of the measurement of reaction time. We might say that all presentations of the stimulus are comparable and elicit the same kind of behavior. Therefore we should present the stimulus as many times as we found convenient and should take as an individual's score the average of his reaction times. However, it is very probable that we should not do this. As psychologists we should say that the first few reaction times are not representative of the individual's speed of response, because at the beginning he is becoming familiar with the apparatus; and that after many reactions the individual becomes fatigued or bored, and again simple reaction time alone is not being measured. So it is likely that we should discard perhaps the first 10 responses and take only the next 25 for our determination. Again we find ourselves in a position wherein we can say that some of the items or situations are more representative of the domain than are others, and our final selection of samples is not determined by chance.

We have stretched things a bit to make our point. In drawing items situations from an actual or potential pool, the decision of whether or not to include a given item or situation is not always easy. Of the items develop from the definition of our variable we can say that some are more representative of the domain as we have defined it than are others, but in many instances there will be doubt. In any event it is obvious that items or situations to greater or lesser degrees fit into the domain, and there is no boundary which clearly differentiates items pertaining to the domain from those which do not. It is certain that by one means or another we do ultimately select a set of operations of measurement which samples something, and the method of selection ordinarily is not based on chance. Usually the items or situations selected are those which best fit our ideas about the nature of the domain.

The best definition of the domain or variable, then, is given by the particular sample of items or situations which we finally select. Or if we wish, we can say that the domain is defined by the particular sample we select. This is, of course, an operational definition of our trait. Consequently, our domain is not a collection of actual items or situations but rather is an intellectual construct. It is a conceptualized domain of behavior that has the same characteristics as those in our actual sample or test as are indicated by the average means, variances, and covariances.

This is the basic proposition of the concept of domain sampling. The domain is characterized by a set of items or situations which on the average have the same means, variances, and covariances as those of our test. Parallel samples drawn from the domain are those which also have the same average means, variances, and covariances, and those which do not have these same average characteristics are not parallel. Recall that the domain and the sample drawn from it, other than those items or situations which constitute our actual test, are constructs and not actual items or situations. The conceptualized domain contains an infinitely large number of components.

DEFINING A DOMAIN BY THE SELECTION OF ITEMS WHICH ARE RELATED TO SOME OTHER MEASURE OF THE TRAIT

There is nothing implicit in the concept of domain sampling which restricts us to the process we have just discussed of defining a domain in verbal terms, developing a series of items from that definition, and finally selecting those which in our opinion best satisfy the definition. Indeed, in practice we often develop a measuring instrument in quite different ways. These other procedures yield collections of items or situations all of which are said to measure the same characteristics, as indicated by the fact that they are related to some other measure or measures of that characteristic.

Suppose, for example, we wish to measure leadership. We could define leadership as "the formal role in a group wherein the individual supervises and directs the behavior of other members of that group." Pursuant to this definition we could obtain two groups of individuals: those who have achieved the formal role of leader and those who have not. Thus we might obtain a group of 100 high school boys who have been elected president of their class or club, captain of their team, or the like. Paired with them we could have another 100 boys equal in age and in group or team membership, but none of whom have achieved the role of formal leader.

Now we administer a series of items to all boys. For example, we might have them describe themselves on an adjective checklist, each boy checking those adjectives which he believes describe him. We use an adjective checklist rather than some other type of device because we believe that "self-perception" is more likely to be related to leadership behavior. However, we do not know or have any ideas about what particular self-perceptions will be related to leadership behavior, so for each adjective or item we observe the difference in responses of the two groups of boys. We could set some particular difference as being significant and could use in our final adjective checklist only those items which meet this criterion. If there are more "significant" items than we need, we utilize those for which the differences in the responses of the two groups of boys are the greatest since they are most closely related to the property we wish to measure.

Our domain, then, is comprised of a series of adjectives all of which have in common the property of differentiating those individuals who have manifested leadership from those who have not. In the development of our original pool of items there need have been no selection on the basis of any definition of leadership. Perhaps all we did was to take a random sample of adjectives which describe personal characteristics in the hope that some of them would be useful for our particular purposes.

In this same manner we might develop an inventory designed to measure "interests of students in the physical sciences." We begin by collecting a series of items asking for expressions of interest in all sorts of occupations, hobbies, and school subjects. As we develop our items we merely select those which have to do with activities which people like or dislike. We then administer our interest items to a group of college students majoring in the physical sciences and to others majoring in other subjects. By comparing the responses of the two groups to each of the questions, we select as representative of our final domain of "interest of students in the physical sciences" those items on which the difference between the responses of the two groups meet some criterion of significance.

Both in the adjective checklist and in the interest inventory the items or situations themselves are not necessarily developed or selected on the basis of some definition of the specific domain or variable we are interested in measuring. Rather, they may be chosen on some other grounds, that is, from a more general domain, such as personally descriptive adjectives in the one case and activities in the other. The final selection of items for the domains, however, is based upon the degree to which the items have the common property of being related to some other measure of the trait in which we are interested.

A test developed in this way can be treated as a sample from a domain in just the same way as a test wherein the items are developed from a verbal definition of a trait. As a matter of fact, when we develop a series of items from a verbal definition of a trait we often do not entirely trust our subjective judgment of whether a given item really follows from the definition or not. Therefore we sometimes eliminate items which are not related to some other independent measure of the same trait or which are related to it to a low degree. In other cases we may not trust our own judgment concerning a single item, but we do trust our collective judgment concerning the large bulk of items. In this case we may compute the score for each person on the total of all items in the available pool and eliminate those items which are unrelated to, or are related only to a low degree with, total scores.

PARALLEL TESTS IN THE CONCEPT OF DOMAIN SAMPLING

Clearly implicit both in the theory of true and error scores and in the eclectic concept of true scores and parallel tests is the notion that it is possible to develop a set of actual tests which precisely meet the mathematical criteria of parallelism. Indeed, a set of actual parallel tests is necessary to estimate reliability, and an infinite number of actual parallel tests would be necessary to obtain a precise statement of the degree of reliability.

In the concept of domain sampling, parallel tests are viewed as being intellectual constructs, and a set of actual tests which meet certain criteria of parallelism is not necessary to estimate the degree of reliability of measurement. It is not denied that tests which meet the criteria of parallelism in terms of having precisely equal means, standard deviations, and intercorrelations, as well as the same patterns of correlations with other tests, can exist. This is a matter left open for empirical investigation and has no bearing upon either the theory of reliability or the estimation of the degree of reliability.

In our mathematical formulations of the concept of domain sampling we have denoted parallel samples drawn from a domain as 1 to k, each sample containing M items, situations, etc. Any one sample can be our actual test or measuring instrument, and the remainder are intellectual constructs. For convenience let us designate sample 1 as the actual test and samples 2 to k as the parallel constructs.

THE MEANS OF SCORES ON PARALLEL TESTS

From Eq. (7-4) we know that the mean of composite scores is equal t
the sum of the means of the components. Since from Eq. (8-38) we kno'
that the means of the components in all samples are the same, we can cor
clude that the means of the scores on all parallel samples are the sam(
That is,

$$\bar{X}_1 = \cdots = \bar{X}_k = \bar{X}_i \qquad (8\text{-}4\colon$$

where i refers to any parallel test, whereas we have used j to refer to an
component in a parallel test.

THE VARIANCES OF SCORES ON PARALLEL TESTS

From Eq. (7-8), the formula for the variance of a composite, we ca
write the variances of the scores on our parallel tests as follows:

$$\sigma_{x_1}{}^2 = M\overline{\sigma_{x_{1,j}}^2} + M(M-1)\overline{\sigma_{x_{1,j}}\sigma_{x_{1,j}}r_{x_{1,j}x_{1,j'}}}$$
$$\cdots\cdots\cdots\cdots\cdots\cdots\cdots\cdots \qquad (8\text{-}4\colon$$
$$\sigma_{x_k}{}^2 = M\overline{\sigma_{x_{k,j}}^2} + M(M-1)\overline{\sigma_{x_{k,j}}\sigma_{x_{k,j}}r_{x_{k,j}x_{k,j'}}}$$

Since from Eqs. (8-39) and (8-40) we know that the averages of th
variances of the components in all parallel samples as well as their c(
variances are equal, all the above equations are equal. That is,

$$\sigma_{x_1}{}^2 = \cdots = \sigma_{x_k}{}^2 = \sigma_{x_i}{}^2 \qquad (8\text{-}4\cdot$$

THE CORRELATIONS AMONG PARALLEL TESTS

In the concept of domain sampling each parallel sample or test is
composite. From Eq. (7-22), the formula for the correlation between tw
composites, we can write the correlation between any two parallel tes
1 and 2, each of which is composed of I to M components, as

$$r_{x_1x_2} = r_{(x_{1,I}+\cdots+x_{1,M})(x_{2,I}+\cdots+x_{2,M})}$$
$$= \frac{\sigma_{x_{1,I}}\sigma_{x_{2,I}}r_{x_{1,I}x_{2,I}} + \cdots + \sigma_{x_{1,M}}\sigma_{x_{2,M}}r_{x_{1,M}x_{2,M}}}{\sigma_{x_1}\sigma_{x_2}}$$

In the numerator there are M^2 terms, so we can express the sum in th
numerator as the number of terms M^2 times their mean. Therefore

$$r_{x_1x_2} = \frac{M^2\overline{\sigma_{x_{1,j}}\sigma_{x_{2,j}}r_{x_{1,j}x_{2,j}}}}{\sigma_{x_1}\sigma_{x_2}}$$

From Eq. (8-40) we know that the average of the cross covariance (
the components of any two parallel tests is equal to the average covarian(

among the components of any one parallel test, and from Eq. (8-44) we know that the standard deviations of all parallel tests are equal so that we can write the denominator of the above equation, $\sigma_{x_1}\sigma_{x_2}$, as $\sigma_{x_1}^2$:

$$r_{x_1 x_2} = \frac{M^2 \overline{\sigma_{x_{1,j}}\sigma_{x_{1,j'}}r_{x_{1,j}x_{1,j'}}}}{\sigma_{x_1}^2}$$

Instead of using parallel tests 1 and 2 we could have used any other pair and should have come out with the above equation. Therefore we can say that all the correlations among parallel samples or tests (the reliability coefficient) are equal, and can write the coefficient as r_{xx}. Hence

$$r_{xx} = \frac{M^2 \overline{\sigma_{x_{i,j}}\sigma_{x_{i,j'}}r_{x_{i,j}x_{i,j'}}}}{\sigma_{x_i}^2} \tag{8-45}$$

TRUE SCORES IN THE CONCEPT OF DOMAIN SAMPLING

In the concept of domain sampling a true score is defined as the sum, or more conveniently as the average, of an individual's scores on an infinitely large number of representative samples or parallel tests. If the number of parallel tests is increased without limit, then they will completely include all the components in the domain, and consequently the true score is the domain score. The equation for the true score for an individual is

$$X_\infty = \bar{X}_a = \frac{X_1 + \cdots + X_k}{k} \tag{8-46}$$

and

$$x_\infty = \bar{x}_a = \frac{x_1 + \cdots + x_k}{k} \tag{8-47}$$

THE CHARACTERISTICS OF TRUE SCORES IN THE
CONCEPT OF DOMAIN SAMPLING

It will be observed that the definition of true scores in the concept of domain sampling as given in Eq. (8-47) above is precisely the same as that for the eclectic concept of true scores and parallel tests in Eq. (8-24). In the eclectic concept we mathematically derived from the nature of parallel tests the characteristics of true scores, that is, their means and standard deviations, their correlations with fallible scores, and their scores on any other test. From the point of view of the eclectic concept we were led by logical considerations to say that the means and standard deviations of scores on parallel tests and the intercorrelations among them are equal. From the point of view of domain sampling we were led to the same conclusion, although the demonstration was mathematical. Consequently, the mathematical derivations we performed in connection with the eclectic concept relative to the characteristics of true scores would also hold with domain sampling, and we need not repeat them.

Therefore pursuant to domain sampling we can say:

1. The mean of true scores is equal to the mean of fallible scores on any one parallel test [from Eq. (8-26)].
2. The variance of true scores is equal to the variance of fallible scores times the reliability coefficient [from Eq. (8-27)]. Therefore [parallel to Eq. (8-28)] the reliability coefficient is equal to the ratio of the variance of true scores to the variances of fallible scores.
3. The correlation between true and fallible scores, the index of reliability, is equal to the square root of the reliability coefficient [from Eq. (8-29)]. This value in domain sampling is termed domain validity since it indicates how well scores on the total domain can be predicted from scores on a test measuring the same traits.

RELIABILITY IN TERMS OF THE CONCEPT OF DOMAIN SAMPLING

Let us now consider the standard error of measurement in terms of the concept of domain sampling. The variance of any one individual's scores over k parallel tests, the square of the standard error of measurement, is

$$S_a{}^2 = \sigma_{x_a - \bar{x}_a} = \frac{\Sigma (x_a - \bar{x}_a)^2}{k}$$

From Eq. (8-47) we can substitute x_∞ for the average of the individual's scores on the k parallel tests:

$$S_a{}^2 = \frac{\Sigma (x_a - x_{\infty_a})^2}{k} \tag{8-48}$$

In the concept of domain sampling, ordinarily no position is taken on whether the standard error of measurement is the same for all individuals or whether it varies in magnitude from person to person. Therefore in order to obtain a description of the variation in individual's scores over parallel tests we should probably wish to calculate the average standard error. We should determine the standard error of each person from Eq. (8-48) and then average the standard errors for all persons. We have already developed the appropriate formula in connection with the eclectic concept of true scores and parallel tests in Eq. (8-34). Hence we can write for the concept of domain sampling the formula for the average of the standard errors in exactly the same way as

$$\overline{S^2} = \sigma_x{}^2 (1 - r_{xx}) \tag{8-49}$$

THE IMPORTANCE OF THE VARIOUS POINTS OF VIEW CONCERNING RELIABILITY OF MEASUREMENT

Even though true scores are defined differently in each of the three concepts of reliability of measurement that we discussed and the developments we made in each are different, we nevertheless arrived at exactly the same conclusions about the characteristics of parallel tests and of true scores. In all three approaches parallel tests are seen as tests with the same means, standard deviations, and intercorrelations. True scores are seen as having the same means as fallible scores and having standard deviations equal to the standard deviation of fallible scores times the square root of 1 minus the reliability coefficient.

We might therefore question whether it is worthwhile considering different theoretical approaches to reliability of measurement. If they all lead to the same conclusions, why bother about the fact that they have quite different bases? However, as we shall see in the following chapter, the differences among them in terms of their basic conceptualizations are of great importance when we come to empirically estimate the reliability of a test. The various ways for estimating reliability of measurement will be seen to differ in appropriateness and precision, depending upon which point of view we adopt with respect to reliability. Therefore a given estimate of the reliability of a test may be viewed as being too high, exactly right, or too low, depending upon whether we hold to the theory of true and error scores, the eclectic concept of true scores and parallel tests, or the theory of domain sampling.

Summary

When a test is administered a number of times to an individual, ordinarily he does not obtain the same score each time. Sometimes the scores vary systematically, showing an upward or downward trend or cyclical variations, which we attribute to the effects of systematic factors. In addition, there are random variations in scores which we attribute to the effects of unsystematic factors. This unsystematic variation among measurements within an individual on the same trait is termed reliability of measurement.

Reliability of measurement can be taken to be the variation in an individual's scores over a series of parallel tests. Parallel tests are tests which measure the same trait to the same degree. Two indices of reliability are the standard error of measurement, which is the standard deviation of an individual's scores over many parallel tests, and the reliability coefficient, which is the correlation between two parallel tests. When measurements are highly reliable the standard error is small and the reliability coefficient is high, and when measurements are unreliable the standard error is large and the reliability coefficient is low.

Reliability of measurement has been conceived of in a variety of ways in the attempt to specify its definition, to understand its effects, and to measure its extent. These different views are reasonably well represented by three theoretical models: the theory of true and error scores, which is the classic psychometric theory; the eclectic theory of true scores and parallel tests; and the theory of domain sampling.

According to the theory of true and error scores, the score an individual earns on a test (his fallible score) is a composite of the amount of the trait he actually possesses (his true score) and an error of measurement. This theory assumes that individuals possess stable characteristics or traits that persist over time, that errors are completely random and therefore uncorrelated with any other variable, and that fallible scores are the result of the addition of true and error scores.

From these assumptions it follows mathematically that tests which are parallel to each other have the same mean and standard deviation, correlate with each other to exactly the same degree, and correlate to the same degree with any other variable. It also follows that the standard error of measurement is the same for all individuals, and the reliability coefficient is the ratio of the variance of true scores to the variance of fallible scores. If the assumptions are granted, it is possible to develop formulae for estimating true from fallible scores (the index of reliability) and for determining the variance of true scores.

The second point of view about reliability of measurement, the eclectic theory of true scores and parallel tests, makes no assumptions about either true or error scores. A true score is defined simply as the average of an individual's scores over an infinitely large number of parallel tests. It follows logically from the definition of parallel tests that the intercorrelations among such tests must all be the same, and that they must all correlate to the same degree with any other variable. There is nothing in this concept which indicates the characteristics of the means and standard deviations of parallel tests. However, in order to determine the variation in scores over a series of different tests their scores must be comparable. If comparability is accomplished by the use of standard scores, then the mean and standard deviation of all parallel tests will be the same.

In this theory, true scores are considered as being composites. By using the formulae for composites, and taking the number of component parallel tests as being infinitely large, it is possible to derive formulae for the prediction of true scores from fallible scores and for the variance of true scores. Though derived from a completely different conceptual basis, these formulae are precisely the same as those derived from the concept of true and error scores. It is also possible to show mathematically that the reliability coefficient is equal to the ratio of the variance of true scores to the variance of fallible scores. However, it does not follow that the magnitude of the standard error of measurement is the same for all individuals.

The third theory, domain sampling, conceives of a trait as being a domain of behaviors all of which have some property in common. This domain is infinitely large, so that in measuring the trait we can draw only a sample from the domain. The score on the sample is the individual's fallible score, and his score on the entire domain is his true score. Both fallible and true scores are therefore taken to be composites. Parallel tests are regarded as being samples from the domain that are representative of it. That is, the averages of the means and standard deviations of the components, the averages of the covariances among the components, and the averages of the covariances between the components and any other variable outside the domain are taken to be the same for all parallel tests and for the entire domain.

From these notions it follows mathematically, using formulae for composites and taking the number of components to be infinitely large, that parallel tests have the same means and standard deviations, correlate with each other to the same degree, and correlate to the same degree with any other variable. Formulae can be derived for estimating true from fallible scores and for calculating the standard deviation of true scores. Though arrived at from an entirely different theoretical position, these formulae are exactly the same as those given by the other two concepts. Again the reliability coefficient can be shown to be the ratio of the variance of true scores to the variance of fallible scores. But as with the eclectic theory, it does not follow that for all individuals the standard error of measurement has the same value.

Selected Readings

Brown, W.: Some experimental results in the correlation of mental abilities, *Brit. J. Psychol.*, **3**:296–322, 1910.

Gulliksen, H.: "Theory of Mental Tests," Wiley, 1950.

Horst, A. P.: A generalized expression for the reliability of measures, *Psychometrika*, **14**:21–31, 1949.

Jackson, R. W. B., and G. A. Ferguson: Studies on the reliability of tests, Department of Education, University of Toronto, Bulletin 12, 1941.

Spearman, C.: Correlation calculated from faulty data, *Brit. J. Psychol.*, **3**:271–295, 1910.

Thurstone, L. L.: "The Reliability and Validity of Tests," Edwards, 1931.

Tryon, R. C.: Reliability and behavior domain validity: reformulation and historical critique, *Psychological Bull.*, **54**:229–249, 1957.

Yule, G. U.: "An Introduction to the Theory of Statistics," Griffin, 1922.

chapter 9   Factors in

Reliability and the Empirical

Estimation of the Reliability

of Measurement

Having some notion of what is meant by reliability of measurement, and having examined the various theoretical approaches which have been made to the problem, we are now in a position to examine it in more detail. In this chapter we shall consider the effects of the number of measurements and of the range of individual differences upon reliability, the effects of reliability of measurement upon the range of individual differences and upon the correlation between tests, and finally ways and means for determining or estimating the degree of reliability of measurement.

RELIABILITY AND THE NUMBER OF MEASUREMENTS

We have seen that when an individual's scores on a series of parallel tests vary unsystematically among themselves, that is, manifest a low degree of reliability of measurement, the score on any one test has limited value. When this situation occurs it would seem that the obvious thing to do is to take a person's scores on a number of parallel tests and average them. It would be expected that an average score such as this would provide a more characteristic quantitative description of the individual than would the score he earns on any single parallel test.

Let us state this another way. Suppose we form a number of composites of parallel tests, each composite containing the same number of tests, k, and average the scores in each composite. We then have a series of parallel composites. We should expect the variation (standard error of measurement) among the average scores on parallel composites to be less than the variation among the scores on single parallel tests, and the correlations (reliability coefficient) among parallel composites to be higher than the correlations among single parallel tests. In other words, as we increase the number of measurements which enter into the determination of a score there should be an increase in the reliability of measurement.

SCORES ON PARALLEL COMPOSITES

Suppose we have a large number of tests which are parallel to each other. From this large pool of tests we pick out a number of groups of tests, the number of tests in each group being the same. We then have a series of parallel composites which we can designate as x_A, x_B, to x_N, in each composite there being k tests. Any two composites can be designated as J and J'. For any one individual a, his scores on these N composites are

$$x_{A_a} = \frac{x_{A_{1,a}} + \cdots + x_{A_{k,a}}}{k}$$

$$x_{B_a} = \frac{x_{B_{1,a}} + \cdots + x_{B_{k,a}}}{k}$$

$$\cdots \cdots \cdots \cdots \cdots \cdots \cdots$$

$$x_{N_a} = \frac{x_{N_{1,a}} + \cdots + x_{N_{k,a}}}{k}$$

(9-1)

As we increase the number of measurements, k becomes larger and larger.

THE VARIANCE OF PARALLEL COMPOSITES

From Eq. (7-30) we can write the variance of a parallel composite, that is, an average composite of k tests, as

$$\sigma_J{}^2 = \frac{1}{k^2} \left(\sigma_{J_1}{}^2 + \cdots + \sigma_{J_k}{}^2 + 2\sigma_{J_1}\sigma_{J_2}r_{J_1J_2} + \cdots + 2\sigma_{J_{k-1}}\sigma_{J_k}r_{J_{k-1}J_k} \right)$$

In Chap. 8 we saw that no matter what our theoretical conception of reliability of measurement may be, the standard deviations of all parallel tests are equal and so are their intercorrelations. Therefore the above equation can be written as

$$\sigma_J^2 = \frac{1}{k^2}\left[k\sigma_{x_i}^2 + k(k-1)\sigma_{x_i}^2 r_{x_i x_{i'}}\right]$$

where i refers to any one of the 1 to k parallel tests. To continue, we have

$$\sigma_J^2 = \sigma_{x_i}^2\left[\frac{k}{k^2} + \frac{k(k-1)}{k^2}\,r_{x_i x_{i'}}\right]$$

$$= \sigma_{x_i}^2\left(\frac{1}{k} + \frac{k-1}{k}\,r_{x_i x_{i'}}\right)$$

We come to precisely this same result if we use any of the A to N composites. Therefore we can say that the standard deviations of all composites, each made up of the same number of parallel tests, are equal. That is,

$$\sigma_A^2 = \cdots = \sigma_N^2 = \sigma_J^2 = \sigma_x^2\left(\frac{1}{k} + \frac{k-1}{k}\,r_{xx}\right) \tag{9-2}$$

where σ_x refers to the standard deviation of single parallel tests and r_{xx} to the reliability coefficient of single parallel tests.

THE RELIABILITY COEFFICIENT AND THE NUMBER OF MEASUREMENTS

The reliability coefficient is the correlation between parallel tests. If we wish to ascertain the reliability of a composite of parallel tests, we need to have at least two composites formed of the same number of components. The correlation between two such parallel composites J and J', that is, the reliability coefficient of the average scores on k parallel tests, is

$$r_{JJ'} = r\left[\frac{(x_{J,1} + \cdots + x_{J,k})}{k}\right]\left[\frac{(x_{J',1} + \cdots + x_{J',k})}{k}\right]$$

$$= \frac{\Sigma[(x_{J_1} + \cdots + x_{J_k})/k][(x_{J'_1} + \cdots + x_{J'_k})/k]}{n\sigma_J\sigma_{J'}}$$

$$= \frac{(1/k^2)\Sigma(x_{J_1} + \cdots + x_{J_k})(x_{J'_1} + \cdots + x_{J'_k})}{n\sigma_J\sigma_{J'}}$$

$$= \frac{(1/k^2)(\Sigma x_{J_1}x_{J'_1} + \cdots + \Sigma x_{J_k}x_{J'_k})}{n\sigma_J\sigma_{J'}}$$

$$= \frac{(1/k^2)(\Sigma x_{J_1}x_{J'_1}/n + \cdots + \Sigma x_{J_k}x_{J'_k}/n)}{\sigma_J\sigma_{J'}}$$

$$= \frac{\overline{k}^2(\sigma_{x_{J,1}}\sigma_{x_{J',1}}r_{x_{J,1}x_{J',1}} + \cdots + \sigma_{x_{J,k}}\sigma_{x_{J',k}}r_{x_{J,k}x_{J',k}})}{\sigma_J\sigma_{J'}}$$

Since the standard deviations of and the intercorrelations among parallel tests are equal, all the terms in the brackets in the numerator are equal to each other. Since there are k^2 such terms (each of the k component parallel tests of J being paired with each of the k component parallel tests of J'), they can be written as $k^2\sigma_x^2 r_{xx}$. Furthermore, we know from Eq. (9-2) that the standard deviations of all parallel composites are equal. Hence

$$r_{JJ'} = \frac{(1/k^2)k^2\sigma_x^2 r_{xx}}{\sigma_x^2\{1/k + [(k-1)/k]r_{xx}\}}$$

$$= \frac{r_{xx}}{1/k + [(k-1)/k]r_{xx}} \tag{9-3}$$

Multiplying the numerator and denominator by k gives

$$r_{JJ'} = \frac{kr_{xx}}{1 + (k-1)r_{xx}} \tag{9-4}$$

If we had used any two composites other than J and J', we should have come to the same result. Therefore we can say that the correlation between all parallel composites is the same.

Equation (9-4) is called the Spearman-Brown formula after the two men who first developed it.

If each parallel composite contains only one parallel test, then Eq. (9-4) resolves to the coefficient of correlation between two single parallel tests:

$$r_{JJ'} = \frac{1r_{xx}}{1 + 0r_{xx}} = \frac{r_{xx}}{1} = r_{xx}$$

When each composite contains an infinitely large number of parallel tests, $1/k$ very closely approximates zero and $(k-1)/k$ very closely approximates 1. Therefore in this case Eq. (9-3), which is merely another form of Eq. (9-4), the Spearman-Brown formula, resolves to

$$r_{JJ'} = \frac{r_{xx}}{0 + 1r_{xx}} = \frac{r_{xx}}{r_{xx}} = 1.00$$

Hence if the average scores are based upon composites of an infinitely large number of parallel tests, the reliability coefficient of these scores is unity, and we measure with perfect reliability.

Let us now examine the relationship between the magnitude of the reliability coefficient and the number of measurements. In Fig. 9-1 the relationship for three values of the reliability coefficient of single parallel tests, r_{xx}, is plotted. It can be seen in this figure that as the number of measurements increases the reliability coefficient increases, the increase being greater in those cases where the reliability of single parallel tests is low. Furthermore, it will be seen that in general the greatest increase in reliability occurs with the first increase in the additional measurements entering into the composite of scores.

Suppose we have a test that has a reliability coefficient of .70. If we increase the length of the test five times, we find that the reliability coefficient of the lengthened test, from Eq. (9-4), is .92. Thus, for example, if we find that the reliability of the ratings assigned by single raters is .70, the average of the ratings assigned by five parallel raters is .92, a significant increase in reliability. This presumes, of course, that the standard deviations of the ratings assigned by the different raters are precisely the same and the intercorrelations among the ratings assigned by

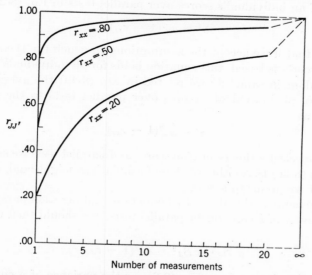

Figure 9-1 The relationship between the reliability coefficients and the number of measurements.

the different raters also are equal. If this is not precisely the case, then Eq. (9-4) provides only an estimate of the reliability resulting from an increased number of measurements.

The Spearman-Brown formula (9-4) also can be used to estimate the effects on reliability of reducing the number of measurements. Suppose a test composed of 100 items has a reliability coefficient of .80. If this test takes too long to administer, we might wish to shorten it and use only 50 items. We should then want to estimate the reliability coefficient of a test one-half as long as the original test. In this case k in Eq. (9-4) is .5 and $k - 1$ is $-.5$. Applying Eq. (9-4) would show us that a test half as long as the original test would have a reliability coefficient of .67. We presume, of course, that the standard deviations of and intercorrelations among the eliminated items are equal in magnitude to the standard deviations of and intercorrelations among the items which are retained.

THE NUMBER OF MEASUREMENTS AND THE STANDARD ERROR
OF MEASUREMENT

Let us now ask what effect an increase in the number of measurements
has upon the standard error of measurement. That is, how does the variation among the scores of an individual over a series of single parallel tests
compare with the variation among his scores over parallel composites?

On the basis of the theory of true and error scores we developed the
variance of an individual's scores over parallel tests in Eq. (8-20) as

$$S^2 = \sigma_x^2(1 - r_{xx})$$

We saw that if we accept the assumptions on which the theory of true
and error scores is based, this equation holds for all individuals. With the
theory of domain sampling we related in Eq. (8-49) the average of the
variances of all individual's scores over parallel tests to the reliability
coefficient as

$$\overline{S^2} = \sigma_x^2(1 - r_{xx})$$

With the eclectic theory of true scores and parallel tests we saw in Eqs.
(8-34) and (8-36) that either of these formulations might hold, depending
upon what we prefer to assume.

Let us generalize the above two equations, taking each parallel test to
be a composite of k component parallel tests. We should then write them
as

$$S_J^2 \text{ or } \overline{S_J^2} = \sigma_J^2(1 - r_{JJ})$$

Substituting for σ_J^2 from Eq. (9-2) for the variance of a composite of
parallel tests and for r_{JJ} from Eq. (9-4) for the reliability coefficient of
such a composite, we have

$$
\begin{aligned}
S_J^2 \text{ or } \overline{S_J^2} &= \sigma_x^2\left(\frac{1}{k} + \frac{k-1}{k}r_{xx}\right)\left[1 - \frac{kr_{xx}}{1+(k-1)r_{xx}}\right] \\
&= \sigma_x^2\frac{1+(k-1)r_{xx}}{k}\left[\frac{1+(k-1)r_{xx}}{1+(k-1)r_{xx}} - \frac{kr_{xx}}{1+(k-1)r_{xx}}\right] \\
&= \sigma_x^2\frac{1+(k-1)r_{xx}}{k}\frac{1+(k-1)r_{xx} - kr_{xx}}{1+(k-1)r_{xx}} \\
&= \sigma_x^2\frac{1+kr_{xx} - r_{xx} - kr_{xx}}{k} \\
&= \frac{\sigma_x^2}{k}(1 - r_{xx})
\end{aligned}
\tag{9-5}
$$

Equation (9-5) shows us the effects of increasing the number of measurements upon the standard error of measurement. This equation is
plotted as Fig. 9-2. It can be seen in this figure that as the number of

measurements that enter into the average composite scores increases, the variation among the individual's scores on parallel composites decreases. Hence it is apparent that such average composite scores give a much more characteristic description of the individual than do scores on a single test.

By way of example, if the reliability of ratings assigned by a single rater is .70 and the standard deviation of the ratings assigned by any individual rater is 10, the standard deviation of the ratings assigned to

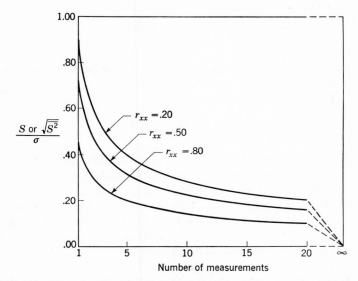

Figure 9-2   The relationship between the standard error of measurement and the number of measurements.

one individual by many raters (the variation of an individual's ratings over raters), as calculated from Eqs. (8-20), (8-34), (8-36), or (8-49), would be 5.5. However, if we take as the individual's ratings the average of the ratings assigned by a group of five parallel raters, the standard deviation of the average composite ratings assigned the individual by a number of parallel groups of raters (each group containing five raters), as calculated from Eq. (9-5), would be only 2.4.

THE NUMBER OF MEASUREMENTS NECESSARY TO ACHIEVE A
DESIRED DEGREE OF RELIABILITY

Sometimes we wish to achieve a particular degree of reliability of measurement but the reliability of the only test available is insufficiently high. If there are a number of parallel tests available, then we could administer several of them and take as the scores the average composite, thereby increasing reliability. However, there is always a cost when the number of measurements is increased, in terms of the time, effort, or money involved in developing parallel tests and in the increased testing itself. Hence we should prefer to increase the number of measurements by the least amount required. Therefore we need to have formulae available to estimate the number of measurements required to achieve a particular degree of reliability.

These formulae are obtained by solving Eqs. (9-4) and (9-5) for k. Equation (9-4) then becomes

$$k = \frac{r_{JJ}(1 - r_{xx})}{r_{xx}(1 - r_{JJ})} \tag{9-6}$$

where r_{xx} is the reliability coefficient of single parallel tests and r_{JJ} is the reliability coefficient of the magnitude desired.

Equation (9-5) becomes

$$k = \frac{\sigma_x^2}{S_J^2} (1 - r_{xx}^2) \tag{9-7}$$

where S_J^2 is the square of the standard error of measurement desired.

For example, suppose that the reliability coefficient of ratings assigned by a single rater is .50 and we wish to have ratings with a reliability coefficient of .90. Equation (9-6) tells us we need to employ nine such raters. Suppose we wish to have ratings that would vary for an individual only one-tenth as much as the variation among individuals. Equation (9-7) tells us we need five such raters. Before we use either Eq. (9-6) or Eq. (9-7) to determine the number of measurements needed to achieve a given degree of reliability, we should recall the conditions stipulated in their development. It is very unlikely that these conditions will hold exactly, and therefore these formulae should be taken as giving only estimates.

THE EFFECTS OF THE RANGE OF INDIVIDUAL DIFFERENCES ON THE MAGNITUDE OF THE RELIABILITY COEFFICIENT

Occasionally we wish to determine the reliability of a test for a particular group but do not have available the entire range of individuals. Thus suppose we have a test that was administered in order to determine norms, and the mean and standard deviation of the scores were found to be 80 and 15, respectively. Further suppose we could only obtain a selected group with a mean of 90 and a standard deviation of 10 to whom we could administer the test several times in order to get an estimate of the reliability of measurement. Obviously the "reliability" group is more restricted in terms of range of scores than is the "norm" group. Sometimes we have the reverse problem. We know the reliability of a test when administered to a more heterogeneous group, but we wish to know whether it would yield sufficiently reliable scores when used with a group that is more homogeneous.

To derive the formula appropriate for this purpose we need to know the standard deviation of scores on any one parallel test of those individuals all of whom have the same true score. Note that this standard deviation is different from the standard error of measurement. The standard error of measurement refers to the standard deviation of one individual's scores over many parallel tests. The standard deviation we wish here is the standard error of prediction of scores on any single test from true scores. It is, therefore, in accordance with Eq. (6-13), a partial standard deviation. From Eq. (6-13) we can write

$$\sigma_{x \cdot x_\infty} = \sigma_x \sqrt{1 - r_{xx_\infty}^2}$$

Substituting for r_{xx_∞} from Eq. (8-23) or (8-29) gives

$$\sigma_{x \cdot x_\infty} = \sigma_x \sqrt{1 - r_{xx}} \tag{9-8}$$

Suppose that, instead of the range of scores described by σ_x, we have a different range of scores described by the standard deviation σ_x' with the reliability coefficient r_{xx}'. If we are willing to assume that the correlation between true scores and scores on any single parallel test is homoscedastic, then the value $\sigma_{x \cdot x_\infty}$ holds throughout the entire range of scores so that

$$\sigma_{x \cdot x_\infty} = \sigma_x \sqrt{1 - r_{xx}} = \sigma_x' \sqrt{1 - r_{xx}'}$$

Therefore

$$\frac{\sigma_x}{\sigma_x'} = \frac{\sqrt{1 - r_{xx}'}}{\sqrt{1 - r_{xx}}}$$

Solving for r_{xx}', the reliability coefficient for the individuals whose range of scores is σ_x' rather than σ_x, we have

$$r_{xx}' = 1 - \left(\frac{\sigma_x}{\sigma_x'}\right)^2 (1 - r_{xx}) \tag{9-9}$$

The relationship between reliability and the range of scores is shown graphically in Fig. 9-3. The figure shows that as the range of talent is reduced, the magnitude of the reliability coefficient is correspondingly reduced. For example, suppose with a particular group of individuals we find that a test has a reliability coefficient of .70. Now suppose we apply this test to another group which has a smaller range of talent. Let us say that the standard deviation of the scores of the second group is only three-fourths the size of the standard deviation of the scores of the original group. The reliability coefficient computed from the group with the smaller standard deviation would be only about .47. If the standard deviation of the group with the restricted range of scores is only 60 per cent of the size of the standard deviation of the original group, the reliability coefficient would fall to about .16. Figure 9-3 shows that a small reduction in range of scores has only a slight effect upon the reliability

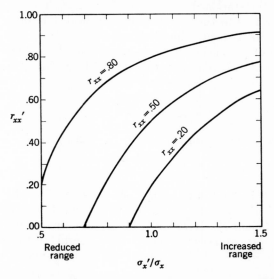

Figure 9-3　The relationship between the range of scores and the reliability coefficient.

coefficient but when the reduction is greater than about 10 per cent or more, the reduction in the magnitude of the reliability coefficient is quite significant. Furthermore, reduction in the range of scores is far more serious with tests that initially have lower reliability coefficients than with those that have higher coefficients.

RELIABILITY AND THE RANGE OF INDIVIDUAL DIFFERENCES

The extent to which individuals differ among themselves in scores on a test often is a matter of considerable consequence. These differences in scores are important not only in describing the extent to which a trait varies within a group but also in evaluating the differences between groups.

Suppose, for example, that the scores of school children on a reading test are expressed in terms of class level. If the situation were such that the reading scores of some fifth-grade children were as low as the second-grade level whereas those of others were as high as the eighth-grade level, undoubtedly the recommended mode of instruction would be substantially different from that in a situation where the range of scores is only from the fourth- to the sixth-grade levels. Therefore, if for some reason the scores yielded by the test erroneously indicate a large rather than a small range of reading ability, the conclusion we should reach about the most appropriate methods of instruction would be wrong.

Suppose we find that the average scores of younger and older men on an intelligence test are respectively 80 and 76. If the standard deviations of the scores of both groups are 20, we do not consider the difference to be particularly important. The differences between individuals in either the one or the other group are so large that by comparison the difference between the two groups seems small and inconsequential. However, suppose for some reason or another the test we use indicates greater differences among individuals in intellectual ability than actually exists. If a more correct description of the variation among individuals in both groups were represented by a standard deviation of 5 rather than of 20, then the difference of four points between the means would assume considerable significance. Whereas before we should conclude that the effect of age on intellectual ability is of little consequence, now we should conclude that age is an important factor.

As it turns out, the reliability of a test affects the range of scores it yields. If the reliability of a test is increased, the standard deviation of the scores decreases.

If a test were perfectly reliable, then the standard deviation of the scores would be described by σ_{x_∞} rather than σ_x. The relationship between σ_{x_∞} and σ_x is

$$\sigma_{x_\infty} = \sigma_x \sqrt{r_{xx}}$$

This we developed as Eq. (8-22) for the theory of true and error scores and as Eq. (8-27) for the eclectic concept of true scores and parallel tests and for the theory of domain sampling. Let us solve this for σ_x:

$$\sigma_x = \frac{\sigma_{x_\infty}}{\sqrt{r_{xx}}} \tag{9-10}$$

Since the reliability coefficient of fallible scores, r_{xx}, is less than 1.00, it is apparent that the standard deviation of fallible scores is necessarily greater than the standard deviation of true scores. True scores, of course, are the scores a test would yield if it were perfectly reliable. For example, if the standard deviation of true scores is 10 and the reliability coefficient is .49, then by Eq. (9-10) the standard deviation of fallible scores is

$$\sigma_x = \frac{10}{\sqrt{.49}} = \frac{10}{.70} = 14.29$$

Let us increase the reliability of a test from r_{xx} to r'_{xx}. We have, then, increased the reliability coefficient by the ratio r'_{xx}/r_{xx}. We should like to know the effects upon the standard deviation of the scores, the change from σ_x to σ'_x. The change in the standard deviation is indicated by the ratio σ'_x/σ_x. When we change the reliability of a test, true scores, of course, remain the same and we are changing only the fallible scores. Hence for any given test

$$\sigma_{x_\infty} = \sigma_x \sqrt{r_{xx}} = \sigma'_x \sqrt{r'_{xx}}$$

Consequently, from Eq. (9-10) we can write the ratio

$$\frac{\sigma'_x}{\sigma_x} = \frac{\sigma'_{x_\infty}/\sqrt{r'_{xx}}}{\sigma_{x_\infty}/\sqrt{r_{xx}}}$$

$$= \frac{\sqrt{r_{xx}}}{\sqrt{r'_{xx}}} = \sqrt{\frac{r_{xx}}{r'_{xx}}} \quad (9\text{-}11)$$

Suppose, for example, we increase the reliability of a test from .50 to .80. Then

$$\frac{\sigma'_x}{\sigma_x} = \sqrt{\frac{.50}{.80}} = \sqrt{.625} = .79$$

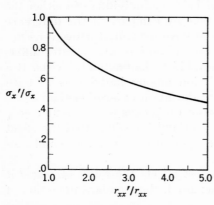

Figure 9-4 The effect of increasing the reliability of a test from r_{xx} to r'_{xx} on the standard deviation of scores.

That is, because of the increase in the reliability of the test, the standard deviation of the scores it yields now is only 79 per cent as great as that of the original test, and we have reduced the variation among individuals by 21 per cent.

The effect of increasing the reliability of measurement upon the range of individual differences is shown in Fig. 9-4. In this figure we can see that as we increase the reliability of measurement we decrease the extent of variation among individuals. By increasing reliability we more and more closely approximate the true variation among individuals.

RELIABILITY OF MEASUREMENT AND THE CORRELATION BETWEEN TWO VARIABLES

The degree to which variables are related is a matter of prime importance in many psychological problems, both practical and theoretical.

The higher the relationship between two variables, the more accurately can scores on the one be predicted from scores on the other, and the greater the extent to which individual differences in both variables are determined by the same factors.

Suppose, for example, we wish to predict grades in a shop course from scores on a mechanical aptitude test. If we find that the coefficient of correlation between the two variables is only .10, we conclude that success in this type of training cannot be predicted by this particular test with sufficient accuracy to be useful. However, if for some reason grades and test scores were in error and with the reduction of these errors the correlation were found to be .60, we should arrive at the opposite conclusion.

Suppose we are interested in the extent to which speed of response is an inherited characteristic. To ascertain the effects of inheritance on this trait we might measure the reaction times of fathers and sons and ascertain the degree of relationship between the two. If we find that the coefficient of correlation between the reaction times of fathers and that of their sons is only .20, we conclude that genetic constitution is not a very important factor in speed of response. However, if for some reason reaction times were in error and with the reduction in these errors the correlation were found to be .80, we should arrive at the opposite conclusion.

Let us begin our evaluation of the effects of reliability of measurement upon the correlation between variables by deriving the formula for the correlation between true scores on two variables. Because true scores are conceived of differently in the various concepts of reliability of measurement, we shall have to make more than one derivation. It will be recalled that in the concept of true and error scores a true score is thought of as the difference between a fallible and an error score [Eq. (8-2)], and in both the eclectic concept and the notion of domain sampling a true score is considered to be the average of scores on an infinitely large number of parallel tests [Eqs. (8-24) and (8-46)].

In terms of the theory of true and error scores, the correlation between true scores on two variables x and y is

$$r_{x_\infty y_\infty} = r_{(x-e_x)(y-e_y)}$$

where e_x and e_y are, respectively, the errors of measurement on variables x and y.

$$r_{x_\infty y_\infty} = \frac{\Sigma(x - e_x)(y - e_y)}{n\sigma_{x_\infty}\sigma_{y_\infty}}$$

Substituting for the standard deviations of true scores from Eq. (8-22) and multiplying the terms in the numerator, we have

$$
\begin{aligned}
r_{x_\infty y_\infty} &= \frac{\Sigma(xy - xe_y - ye_x + e_x e_y)}{n\sigma_x \sqrt{r_{xx}}\, \sigma_y \sqrt{r_{yy}}} \\
&= \frac{\Sigma xy/n - \Sigma xe_y/n - \Sigma ye_x/n - \Sigma e_x e_y/n}{\sigma_x \sigma_y \sqrt{r_{xx} r_{yy}}} \\
&= \frac{\sigma_x \sigma_y r_{xy} - \sigma_x \sigma_{e_y} r_{xe_y} - \sigma_y \sigma_{e_x} r_{ye_x} + \sigma_{e_x} \sigma_{e_y} r_{e_x e_y}}{\sigma_x \sigma_y \sqrt{r_{xx} r_{yy}}}
\end{aligned}
$$

From Eq. (8-6) we know that in terms of the theory of true and error scores the correlations of error scores with any other scores are zero. Hence the last three terms in the numerator are zero and drop out. Consequently,

$$
\begin{aligned}
r_{x_\infty y_\infty} &= \frac{\sigma_x \sigma_y r_{xy}}{\sigma_x \sigma_y \sqrt{r_{xx} r_{yy}}} \\
&= \frac{r_{xy}}{\sqrt{r_{xx} r_{yy}}}
\end{aligned}
\tag{9-12}
$$

Equation (9-12) gives the correlation between true scores on two tests, that is, the correlation between scores on two traits if both were measured with perfect reliability. It is termed the *correction for attenuation* since it corrects the empirically obtained correlation between two variables for chance or unsystematic factors that reduce or attenuate the true relationship.

Let us now develop the coefficient of correlation between true scores on two variables when, as in the eclectic concept and the theory of domain sampling, they are conceived of as the average of scores on an infinitely large number of parallel tests.

Equation (7-37) gives us the correlation between two composites of scores each of which is averaged, and the scores on all components have the same standard deviations. In our present terms we should write this as

$$
r_{\bar{x}\bar{y}} = \frac{\overline{r_{x_i y_i}}}{\sqrt{\dfrac{1}{k} + \dfrac{k-1}{k}\, \overline{r_{x_i x_{i'}}}}\, \sqrt{\dfrac{1}{m} + \dfrac{m-1}{m}\, \overline{r_{y_i y_{i'}}}}}
$$

where $\overline{r_{x_i x_{i'}}}$ is the average of the correlations among parallel tests of x, $\overline{r_{y_i y_{i'}}}$ is the average of the correlations among parallel tests of y, and $\overline{r_{x_i y_i}}$ is the average of the coefficients of correlation between the k parallel tests of x and the m parallel tests of y. But we have seen that parallel tests correlate to the same degree with each other and also that they correlate to the same degree with any other test. Therefore

$$
\overline{r_{x_i x_{i'}}} = r_{xx} \qquad \overline{r_{y_i y_{i'}}} = r_{yy} \qquad \overline{r_{x_i y_i}} = r_{xy}
$$

Therefore

$$r_{\bar{x}\bar{y}} = \frac{r_{xy}}{\sqrt{\dfrac{1}{k} + \dfrac{k-1}{k} r_{xx}} \sqrt{\dfrac{1}{m} + \dfrac{m-1}{m} r_{yy}}}$$

Since true scores are the average of the scores on an infinitely large number of tests, $1/k$ and $1/m$ closely approximate 0, and $(k-1)/k$ and $(m-1)/m$ closely approximate 1. $r_{\bar{x}\bar{y}}$, then, would be written as $r_{x_\infty y_\infty}$. Hence

$$r_{x_\infty y_\infty} = \frac{r_{xy}}{\sqrt{r_{xx} r_{yy}}}$$

This is precisely the same as Eq. (9-12), the correlation between true scores on two tests that we derived in terms of the concept of true and error scores. Therefore Eq. (9-12), termed the correction for attenuation, is precisely the same for all theoretical formulations of reliability of measurement.

Suppose we find the coefficient of correlation between the scores on two tests to be .28. From the magnitude of this coefficient we might be led to say that the two traits measured by these tests are related to a rather low degree. But if we knew that the reliability coefficients of the two tests were respectively .30 and .40 by applying the formula for the correction for attenuation Eq. (9-12), we should estimate that had we measured the two traits with perfect reliability the coefficient of correlation between their scores would have been

$$r_{x_\infty y_\infty} = \frac{.28}{\sqrt{(.30)(.40)}} = \frac{.28}{\sqrt{.12}} = \frac{.28}{.35} = .80$$

Now we should conclude that the two traits are quite substantially related.

Because its application ordinarily increases the magnitude or relationships, and in some cases quite substantially, the correction for attenuation is most attractive. However, it is important to note that the usefulness of the formula, and indeed of any of the formulae involving reliability coefficients, is a function of the adequacy with which the reliability coefficients are determined. The formula for the correction for attenuation is quite sensitive to variations in the magnitudes of the reliability coefficients. If our determination of the degree of reliability of measurement is incorrect, even though the error be relatively small, our estimates of relationships between perfectly reliable scores may be substantially in error. For example, suppose our estimates of the reliability coefficients of the two tests considered in the previous paragraph were not .30 and .40 but were just slightly higher, being respectively .40 and .50. By applying Eq. (9-12) we should find our estimate of the correlation between perfectly reliable scores to be

$$r_{x_\infty y_\infty} = \frac{.28}{\sqrt{(.40)(.50)}} = \frac{.28}{\sqrt{.20}} = \frac{.28}{.45} = .62$$

This value is considerably lower than our previous estimate of .80, and by using it we should probably conclude that the two traits are only moderately related.

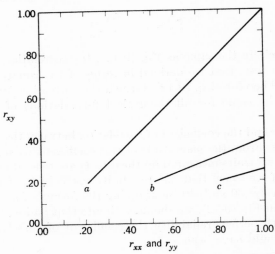

Figure 9-5 The effects of increasing the reliability of tests on their intercorrelation, when $r_{xx} = .20$ and the initial reliability coefficients r_{xx} and r_{yy} both are (a) .20, (b) .50, and (c) .80.

Suppose our estimates of the reliability coefficients were in the other direction and the coefficients, instead of being .30 and .40, were .20 and .30. When Eq. (9-12) is applied we find our estimate of the coefficient of correlation between perfectly reliable scores to have the absurd value of 1.17:

$$r_{x_\infty y_\infty} = \frac{.28}{\sqrt{(.20)(.30)}} = \frac{.28}{\sqrt{.06}} = \frac{.28}{.24} = 1.17$$

Again we see the need to apply the formula for the correction for attenuation with caution.

Let us now examine the effects of increasing the reliability of measurement upon the correlation between two variables. We can begin by solving Eq. (9-12) for r_{xy}. This gives us

$$r_{xy} = r_{x_\infty y_\infty} \sqrt{r_{xx} r_{yy}} \qquad (9\text{-}13)$$

As we increase r_{xx} and r_{yy} there is an increase in r_{xy}. Of course, $r_{x_\infty y_\infty}$ remains unchanged. Equation (9-13) is plotted in Fig. 9-5, taking as an example r_{xy} as .20 when the initial reliability coefficients of both x and y are (a) .20, (b) .50, and (c) .80. We can see in the figure that as the reliability of measurement increases, the correlation between scores on the two tests increases, the increase being greater the lower are the initial reliabilities of the tests.

Let us now examine the limiting effects of reliability upon the correlation between tests. The highest possible correlation between two tests, of course, is represented by a coefficient of correlation of 1.00. Suppose that this is in fact the degree of relationship between two tests when both are measured with perfect reliability. We then write Eq. (9-13) as

$$r_{xy} = \sqrt{r_{xx}r_{yy}} \qquad (9\text{-}14)$$

The correlation between true scores on two tests is 1.00 or lower. In Eq. (9-14) we have taken it to be 1.00, the highest possible value. Therefore we can say that r_{xy} in Eq. (9-14) represents the highest possible correlation between two variables when their reliability coefficients are r_{xx} and r_{yy}.

TABLE 9-1.   The Maximum Value of the Coefficient of Correlation between Two Variables in Relation to Their Reliability Coefficients

r_{xx}	r_{yy}										
	.00	.10	.20	.30	.40	.50	.60	.70	.80	.90	1.00
.00	.00	.00	.00	.00	.00	.00	.00	.00	.00	.00	.00
.10	.00	.10	.14	.17	.20	.22	.24	.26	.28	.30	.32
.20	.00	.14	.20	.24	.28	.32	.35	.37	.40	.42	.45
.30	.00	.17	.24	.30	.35	.39	.42	.46	.49	.52	.55
.40	.00	.20	.28	.35	.40	.45	.49	.53	.57	.60	.63
.50	.00	.22	.32	.39	.45	.50	.55	.59	.63	.67	.71
.60	.00	.24	.35	.42	.49	.55	.60	.65	.69	.73	.77
.70	.00	.26	.37	.46	.53	.59	.65	.70	.75	.79	.84
.80	.00	.28	.40	.49	.57	.63	.69	.75	.80	.79	.89
.90	.00	.30	.42	.52	.60	.67	.73	.79	.85	.90	.90
1.00	.00	.32	.45	.55	.63	.71	.77	.84	.89	.95	1.00

Values computed from Eq. (9-14) are given in Table 9-1. This table shows that when the reliability of two tests is low, the highest possible coefficient of correlation between their scores is also low. On the other hand, when reliability is high, the highest possible coefficient of correlation between their scores also is high. From the table it also can be seen that the coefficient of correlation between scores on one test and those on another can be higher than the reliability coefficient of the first test provided the reliability coefficient of the second test is higher. It should be recalled that the values in Table 9-1 are upper limits. Thus the coefficient of correlation between two tests both of which have reliability coefficients of .80 might in fact be .00, but it could be no higher than .80.

THE NATURE AND EFFECTS OF UNSYSTEMATIC FACTORS

In Chap. 8 we made a broad classification of factors which affect test scores as systematic and unsystematic factors. We distinguished between the consistent trends in scores that are attributable to systematic factors and the random variations in scores that are attributable to unsystematic factors.

In order to develop our notions of reliability of measurement so that we can consider practical ways for measuring its extent, we shall have to examine in more detail the nature and effects of unsystematic factors. These factors can be classified into two types: those whose effects are different for the same individual on different occasions and are also different for different individuals on the same occasion, and those whose effects are different for the same individual on different occasions but are the same for all individuals on the same occasion. The difference between these two types of unsystematic factors lies in their effects in a single testing occasion. Hence we shall term the first type *varying unsystematic factors* and the second *constant unsystematic factors*.

VARYING UNSYSTEMATIC FACTORS

The effects of factors in this class are different on different occasions. Hence the score of an individual over a number of occasions sometimes is higher and sometimes is lower. In addition, the effects are different for different individuals on the same occasion, tending to increase the scores of some individuals on that occasion and to lower those of others. Some of these factors are in the testing situation itself and others are ascribed to the individual.

There are many different sources of unsystematic variation in a given testing situation. Some persons may be fortunate enough to sit in comfortable seats while they are taking a test, whereas others may find themselves in uncomfortable seats. Those near the window work under conditions of good illumination, whereas others may find themselves in the far corners, operating under the handicap of poor lighting. Because of their nearness to or distance from the test administrator, some hear the instructions clearly and others do not. When the measuring instrument is a rating procedure, differences among raters produce variations in scores.

The individual who happens to be rated by a lenient rater is likely to receive a higher rating than one who is rated by a strict rater.

Because the individual himself changes in unsystematic ways, he too is a source of random variation. His motivation, fatigue, nervousness, interest, and distractibility may be to one degree on one occasion and to another degree on another occasion. Different individuals taking a test at a given time also vary among themselves in these same respects. The motivation of some happens to be high at the time of testing, whereas that of others happens to be low; and some people happen to be rested, whereas others happen to be tired.

CONSTANT UNSYSTEMATIC FACTORS

There are a variety of other factors that are unsystematic in their general influence over a number of testing occasions and yet operate in the same fashion for all individuals at a given time. When these factors are operating, the scores of all individuals on one occasion may be higher or lower than their scores on another occasion. For example, we may have a speed test with a 10-min time interval. Sometimes through erroneous reading of the timing device the test administrator may shade the 10-min interval by several seconds, while on other occasions he may unknowingly be several seconds too generous in his timing. On any given occasion the time, though in error, is the same for all individuals being tested. Sometimes when a test is administered the lighting may be poor throughout the entire testing room, and on another occasion it may be excellent. While from one testing session to the next there are variations in quality of illumination, on any one occasion it is the same for all individuals. The foreman of a group of workers may feel friendly toward them because not too many months ago he was one of them, whereas the department head who never was a worker may regard them more "objectively." When the workers are rated by the foreman, there will be a different bias operating than when they are rated by the department head. When individuals are given a test in the morning, they may all be fresh and rested and consequently earn higher scores on it than when they take the test in the evening and are all tired.

Factors of this type may change each person's score by exactly the same absolute amount, or they may change each person's score by the same proportional amount. In each case the mean of the scores is different on the different testing occasions, and in the second there are differences not only in the means but also in the standard deviations of the scores.

Suppose the heights of individuals are measured by means of a ruler set against the wall. On one occasion the bottom of the ruler might sit exactly on the floor, whereas on another occasion a particle of dirt might happen to be on the floor where the ruler is set. On the second occasion, therefore, the height of each person would perhaps be $\frac{1}{16}$ in. less than his height on the first occasion. Hence the mean height would be different on the two occasions, but the range of individual differences would be the same since we have merely subtracted a constant from each person's score.

As another example, suppose that the time limit for a test is half an hour but the test administrator inadvertently lets people work for 31 min. Since all individuals have extra time, the mean score will be greater than when the test is administered with the correct time limits. Inasmuch as different individuals work at the task at different rates, the standard deviation of the scores also will be greater. A slow individual who answers one question per minute will increase his score by 1, whereas a fast individual who answers two questions per minute will increase his score by 2. There is, then, a differential effect whereby each person's score is increased in proportion to his speed of work. If the time limit of the test is erroneously shortened, each person's score will be reduced in proportion to his speed of work, and the standard deviation of the scores as well as the mean will be reduced.

UNSYSTEMATIC FACTORS AND RELIABILITY

We must now consider how unsystematic factors with constant effects bear upon the problem of reliability of measurement. First of all, we must ascertain how they can be discovered; then we should examine the nature of their effects in relation to different types of testing situations; and finally we must ask ourselves whether or not they should be included as one aspect of reliability of measurement.

CONSTANT UNSYSTEMATIC FACTORS VERSUS SYSTEMATIC FACTORS

From one occasion to another, unsystematic factors with constant effects operate in a random fashion for a given individual, but within any given occasion they operate exactly in the same manner for all individuals. On one occasion they have one influence upon the scores of all individuals, perhaps a facilitating effect, and on another occasion they have another influence upon the scores of all individuals, perhaps depressing them. Hence the means and sometimes the standard deviations of scores differ from one occasion to another.

We might conclude that constant factors should be classified with systematic rather than with unsystematic factors. However, they are different in that the constant unsystematic factors cause the scores of an individual, as well as the means and standard deviations of the scores of the total group, to vary in a random and unpredictable fashion from occasion to occasion, whereas systematic factors produce systematic changes.

DISTINCTION BETWEEN CONSTANT AND VARYING UNSYSTEMATIC FACTORS

It is clear that both types of unsystematic factors produce variations in an individual's scores on different occasions. Therefore if we administer a test to a single individual on many occasions, we cannot distinguish between the two types of factors on the basis of the scores alone. Suppose we administer a test to only one person at a time but to each person we administer the test a number of times. If we have n people and we administer the test k times to each person, we then have nk occasions on which the test has been administered. On each of these nk occasions the effects of varying factors are different and also the effects of constant unsystematic factors are different. Hence we could not distinguish their effects, and we could not ascertain which type of factor is determining variation among scores or whether both are at work. If the various testings of the subjects are randomly distributed among the k occasions, the constant factors operate in exactly the same manner as the varying factors, because they do not have the same constant effects upon all individuals. All individuals have equal likelihood of being tested under favorable and unfavorable conditions of constant factors as well as varying factors. Indeed, under these conditions it would be absurd even to attempt to differentiate between the two types of factors, since their effects are precisely the same.

As a matter of fact, the only way we can detect the operation of unsystematic factors with constant effects is to administer the test to a number of individuals on each occasion. In this fashion we can determine whether the factor is specific to the individual and to the occasion or only to the occasion. If we find that on every occasion the means and standard deviations of the scores are exactly the same, then it would appear that factors with constant effects are not operating. However, if the means and standard deviations do vary, and they vary among occasions in a random fashion, then we can say that constant factors are operating.

CONSTANT UNSYSTEMATIC FACTORS AND THE NATURE OF THE TEST AND MEASUREMENT SITUATION

There are some tests which can be administered simultaneously to a large number of individuals. Such tests, termed group tests, are used to measure a wide variety of aptitude, proficiency, and personality characteristics. With other tests and in some types of measurement situations it is possible to obtain scores on only one individual at a time. Such tests are called individual tests. For example, by its very nature the Stanford-Binet intelligence test can be administered to only one person on each testing occasion. Oral examinations, typing proficiency tests, and performance tests such as form boards and pegboards are other examples. Some tests could be administered to many individuals at a time, but circumstances prevent it. In the selection of employees, frequently applicants come in one at a time and therefore must be tested singly and on different occasions even though the test is of such a nature that it could be administered to many individuals at a time. If we wished to obtain ratings of the personality characteristics of a large group of individuals, it would be impossible to find one person who knows all of them, and therefore we might have to settle for having each subject evaluated by a different rater.

With these many individual tests and measurement situations we cannot detect the influence of constant unsystematic factors as we can with group tests and measurement situations. When we administer a test once to a number of individuals, we are holding constant or canceling out the effects of such factors because all are tested on the same given occasion. With a single application of an individual test to these same persons, however, we permit such factors to operate and to influence their scores.

RELIABILITY OF MEASUREMENT AND UNSYSTEMATIC FACTORS

Let us now consider the question of whether reliability of measurement should be conceived of as referring to the effects of only one type of unsystematic factors or to the effects of both types. Logically we could say that the decision is whether we should include only varying unsystematic factors, only constant unsystematic factors, or both types of factors. But in fact we are not faced with the second of these possibilities. If all individuals are tested on the same occasion or under the same circumstances, then only varying systematic factors can operate; but if each person is tested at a different time or under different circumstances, then both varying and constant unsystematic factors can operate. Consequently it is impossible to have circumstances wherein only constant unsystematic factors can operate.

Hence we might say that there are two types of reliability of measurement, the reliability of single-occasion tests and the reliability of multi-occasion tests. The ways we should use to determine these two types of reliability obviously would be different inasmuch as in the first case we are concerned only with varying unsystematic factors, whereas in the latter we are concerned with both varying and constant unsystematic factors.

While this distinction between two types of reliability of measurement makes a certain amount of sense inasmuch as it reflects an actual distinction between two different types of tests, it nevertheless still leaves some important problems. When we consider ways for determining the degree of reliability of measurement of tests, we shall see that we shall have to conclude that some methods give us overestimates of reliability and others underestimates, depending upon whether we consider reliability to refer to only varying unsystematic factors or to both varying and constant unsystematic factors.

EMPIRICAL METHODS FOR ESTIMATING THE RELIABILITY OF TESTS

There are four methods that are customarily used for estimating the reliability of tests. These ways are estimating reliability (1) from the coefficient of correlation between scores on repetitions of the same test, (2) from the coefficient of correlation between scores on parallel forms of a test, (3) from the coefficient of correlation between scores on comparable parts of the test, and (4) from the intercorrelations among the elements of a test. Let us now describe and evaluate each of these methods.

RELIABILITY DETERMINED FROM REPETITIONS OF THE SAME TEST

This first method for estimating the reliability of measurement is called the *test-retest* method. A given test is administered two or more times to the same group of individuals, and the intercorrelations among the scores on the various administrations are taken as the reliability coefficient. With tests of aptitude, personality, and achievement the test ordinarily is administered only twice so that only one estimate of the reliability coefficient is obtained. If the test is administered several times, the usual practice is to take the average of the intercorrelations among the scores obtained on the various occasions as the estimate of the reliability coefficient.

There are two main advantages with the test-retest method. Some other methods for estimating reliability require that more than one form of the test be available, but with the test-retest method nothing in addition to the test itself is required. A second advantage is that when this method is used the particular sample of items or stimulus situations is held constant. The individuals are tested with precisely the same instrument. Superficially, at least, it would seem that this tends to minimize the opportunity for actual measurement of traits other than those designed to be measured by the test.

The most serious disadvantages with the test-retest method lie in the variety of carry-over effects from one testing occasion to another. Sometimes there are practice effects so that on subsequent occasions scores increase in a systematic fashion. The individual may learn the specific content of the test or develop improved approaches or attitudes toward the material so that his scores increase. In some instances these practice effects are different for different individuals. Of two people who obtain precisely the same score on the first occasion, one may discover certain general principles that help answer the questions in the test or may even rehash or rehearse the material during the interval between the first and the second test. Therefore on the second testing occasion the score of one individual may be improved and that of the other may remain the same. If the correlation between the scores on the two occasions is low, we do not know whether the test is unreliable or whether differential systematic factors have been at work. On the other hand, if the coefficient between scores on the two occasions is high, then it would seem that factors having differential effects are not very important, and the correlation we obtain might be considered to be something like a lower limit of the reliability coefficient. This would be true, of course, only if we could rule out on the retest the effects of remembering the responses made on the first test.

In other instances there might be a specific carry-over effect in terms of remembering on one testing occasion the responses given on an earlier one and merely repeating these responses. The first time an individual takes a vocabulary test he might respond "true" to the item "Castigate means the same as throw out," and the second time he takes the test he remembers this and again answers "true." Similarly, in an attitude test, on the first testing occasion a person answers "indifferent" to the question "Do you approve of labor unions?" and remembering this on a second occasion, he again responds in the same fashion. Having assigned his subordinate Joe Smith the rating of "superior" in January, a factory foreman does so again in June when he is called upon to rate him, in order to demonstrate that he is consistent in his appraisals. These specific carry-overs from one occasion to another may not be deliberate on the part of the individual; indeed, he may be completely unaware of them. They are important because they introduce a false consistency in scores, a consistency which would not have occurred without them. Hence in some circumstances the test-retest method may give an overestimate of reliability.

Another carry-over problem with the test-retest method is the fact that taking a test may change the individual in some more or less permanent fashion. For example, if a test requires an individual to evaluate himself, the very process of self-evaluation may cause him to change his behavior. Changes of this sort might well be expected with certain kinds of personality measures. Therefore with some types of tests the test-retest method would have to be considered inapplicable.

One troublesome problem with the test-retest method has to do with the time interval between testing occasions. It is desirable to maximize the interval between testing occasions in order to minimize the effects of memory. But the longer the time interval between the two testing occasions, the greater the likelihood that the individual will change. Therefore the correlation between scores on two occasions reflects more than just reliability of measurement. Furthermore, increasing the time interval between testing occasions increases the administrative problem of getting the same group of individuals together on the second occasion. Consequently we expect lower and lower estimates of reliability as the time interval between the testing occasions increases.

If the test is administered on two or more different occasions, then those unsystematic factors we have termed constant unsystematic factors can affect test scores. On the other hand, if we administer the test two or more times on the same occasion, then there is far less opportunity for such factors to be effective in reducing the self-consistency of test scores. Therefore if the test is repeated on the same occasion, we expect a higher estimate of reliability than if it is administered on different occasions.

In terms of the theory of true and error scores and the eclectic concept of true scores and parallel tests, the test-retest method would seem to be eminently satisfactory. Indeed, if we forget the practical disadvantages discussed above, it would seem to be the very best because the individual can be measured a number of times with precisely the same instrument. However, it clearly is inapplicable in terms of the concept of domain sampling, since with this notion the reliability coefficient is not the correlation between two actual tests but rather the correlation between an actual test and an intellectual construct.

RELIABILITY DETERMINED FROM PARALLEL FORMS OF A TEST

Parallel forms of a test are a series of two or more tests which have the same content or nature. Two objective tests which have the same kind and number of items are parallel forms. An item in one parallel form of an arithmetic test might be "27 + 84 = _____," and an item in another form might be "48 + 72 = _____." An item in one form of an inventory designed to measure emotional stability might be "Do you sleep well at night?" and an item in another form might be "Do you have bad dreams at night?" In the rating of preschool children, nursery school teachers of the same age and experience might be considered parallel raters.

Parallel forms of a test should not be confused with parallel tests. Parallel forms of a test are tests similar in content and nature and designed to measure the same traits. Parallel tests are tests which meet certain statistical criteria. We considered these criteria in Chap. 8 when we discussed the three theoretical approaches to reliability. If a series of parallel forms of a test meet these criteria, they are also parallel tests; but if they do not, then even though they are parallel forms of a test they are not parallel tests.

Having available two or more parallel forms of a test, we take as an estimate of the reliability the intercorrelations among the scores on the parallel forms. If there are more than two forms available, the common practice is to take the average of the intercorrelations as the estimate of the reliability coefficient. In view of the fact that the various forms of a test do not contain precisely the same material, the possibility, if not the probability, exists that the various forms do not measure precisely the same traits. Therefore the intercorrelations among the tests reflect not only the degree of reliability of measurement but also the extent to which they measure different traits. Hence we might say that the method of determining reliability from the intercorrelations among parallel forms of a test gives estimates that are too low.

Because the content of parallel forms is not precisely the same, the carry-over effects from one test to another are minimized. In many instances there will be no specific carry-over effects at all, because there is no opportunity to utilize memory of specific responses made to an earlier form. However, there is still the possibility of general carry-over in terms of modes of response, attitudes toward the material, and the like. In the case of ratings where different raters are taken as "parallel forms" and make their ratings independently, there nonetheless may be contamination of the judgment of one rater by that of another if the raters have had an earlier opportunity to discuss the individuals being evaluated. For example, it is quite natural for nursery school teachers to discuss the various characteristics of their charges, so if they are called upon to rate the children their social intercourse will certainly affect their ratings even though these ratings are done independently.

One prime difficulty with the use of parallel forms as a means for estimating reliability is the labor required to develop them. If we are dealing with an objective test of 100 items, 200 are required for two forms, 300 for three forms, etc. In the construction of just one form of a test a great deal of time and effort is required. Thus while it might be possible to develop two forms, three or more forms frequently are just out of the question. In obtaining ratings of workers it usually is difficult enough to obtain ratings from two supervisors who are familiar with all members of a working group, and finding more than two is likely to be impossible.

Ordinarily when the method of parallel forms is used to estimate reliability of measurement, the various forms are administered on different occasions, though sometimes they are administered on the same occasion. It is apparent that if we consider reliability to refer only to the effects of varying unsystematic factors, the correlation between scores on parallel forms of a test administered on different occasions gives too low an estimate of reliability. Conversely, if we consider reliability to refer to the effects of both varying and constant unsystematic factors, the correlation between scores on parallel forms of a test administered on the same occasion gives too high an estimate.

In terms of the theory of true and error scores and the eclectic concept of true scores and parallel tests, the method of determining reliability from the correlation between parallel tests is quite satisfactory, provided, of course, the parallel forms meet the statistical criteria of parallel tests. In terms of the concept of domain sampling, the method is not pertinent inasmuch as reliability of measurement is taken as the relationship between scores on a test and a construct which is parallel to it, not the relationship between scores on two actual tests.

RELIABILITY DETERMINED FROM COMPARABLE PARTS OF A TEST

In many instances individuals cannot be measured on more than one occasion, and furthermore on that occasion it is possible to administer the test only once. Under such circumstances we can obtain an estimate of the reliability of measurement if we consider the test not as a single test but rather as the sum total of a number of parallel forms of a test.

Suppose, for example, we have an objective test comprised of 100 items all of which pertain to the same trait. Instead of saying that we have one test of 100 items we might say we have two tests each of 50 items or four tests each of 25 items. Having two or more parallel forms available, we can now proceed to estimate reliability by the method of the correlation between scores on parallel forms. Note that we do not have the reliability of a test of 100 items, but rather the reliability of a shorter test. If we have split the items in our test into two groups of 50 items each, we have the reliability of a 50-item test.

If, having split our test into shorter tests, we find the reliability of the shorter tests to be fully adequate, we can use the scores on any one part. However, we may not feel that the shorter tests adequately sample the trait we wish to measure, and since we have the total test we may as well use it and thereby gain in precision of measurement. We developed the Spearman-Brown formula as Eq. (9-4), which relates reliability of measurement to the number of measurements. We can apply this formula to the intercorrelations among the parts of the test and estimate the reliability of the total test. For this purpose $r_{JJ'}$ refers to the reliability coefficient of the total test, and r_{xx} to the reliability coefficient of the parts.

The common procedure is to divide a test into two parts and, from the correlation between the two parts, to estimate the reliability of a test twice as long—the total test—by means of the Spearman-Brown formula. For this split-half method of estimating reliability the Spearman-Brown formula becomes

$$r_{11} = \frac{2r_{\frac{1}{2}\frac{1}{2}}}{1 + r_{\frac{1}{2}\frac{1}{2}}} \tag{9-15}$$

where r_{11} refers to the reliability coefficient of the total test and $r_{\frac{1}{2}\frac{1}{2}}$ to the reliability coefficient of half the test. Thus if the correlation between scores on two halves of a test were .50, the reliability coefficient of the total test would be estimated to be

$$r_{11} = \frac{2(.50)}{1 + .50} = \frac{1.00}{1.50} = .67$$

If the total test is divided into more than two parts, then the average of the intercorrelations among the parts is used as the estimate of the reliability coefficient of the part tests and is used in Eq. (9-4). In this case k is the number of times that the total test is longer than the parts. If the total test has 100 items and we divide it into four parts of 25 items each, then k is 4. Suppose in this case the average of the intercorrelations among the four parts is .40. Then from Eq. (9-4) we estimate the reliability of the total test to be

$$r_{11} = \frac{4(.40)}{1 + (4 - 1)(.40)} = \frac{1.60}{2.20} = .76$$

It will be recalled that in the derivation of the Spearman-Brown formula (9-4), it was presumed that the tests are truly parallel tests having equal standard deviations and intercorrelations. Therefore, strictly speaking, the reliability of a test cannot be determined from comparable parts unless their standard deviations and intercorrelations are precisely the same. Since these conditions seldom if ever are satisfied in the real world of testing, the reliability coefficient determined by this method can be considered only as an estimate. It appears likely that variations among the part tests in terms of their standard deviations and intercorrelations will cause the obtained value of the reliability coefficient of the total test to be too low, though conceivably the value might be an overestimate.

The problem arises as to how to divide a total test into parts. With a 100-item test we could take the first 50 items as one half and the last 50 as the other half, or we could take the odd-numbered items as one half and the even-numbered ones as the other half. The second procedure, the odd-even method, is the one generally used, since it controls for any systematic factors operating during the testing period that change the performance from early in the testing session to later periods. An example of such a factor is fatigue. In order to maximize the probability that the two halves measure the same trait, sometimes the division is made on the basis of an analysis of the content of the items, making sure that both halves contain items of the same sort. So as to maximize the probability that the means and standard deviations of the two halves are equal, the items are assigned to the two halves so that for every item of a given level of difficulty in one half there is an item of similar difficulty in the other half. The important thing is to maximize the equality of the two halves so as to satisfy the requirements of the Spearman-Brown formula.

The prime advantage of the method of determining reliability from the intercorrelations among comparable parts of a test is its simplicity. A test need be given only once to a group of individuals. No repetition of the test or comparable forms is required. Obviously the method is not applicable to certain types of tests which are an integrated whole and cannot be divided into separate and equivalent parts, as is the case, for example, with speed tests. Commonly with aptitude tests there is a time limit and there are more items in the test than the individual can complete in the period allowed. The score is the number of questions correctly answered in the time allowed. Since an individual's score is a function of the rapidity with which he works, dividing up the items into two parts but having the individual take them not with independent timing but all within the same time limit does not give two or more independent determinations.

Inasmuch as with the method of comparable parts of a test the individual is tested on only one occasion, scores on group tests are not affected by what we have termed unsystematic factors. If we prefer to define reliability as pertaining only to varying unsystematic factors, then this method is a proper one. However, if we prefer to define reliability as pertaining to both varying and constant unsystematic factors, then this procedure gives an overestimate of reliability since it eliminates the effects of constant unsystematic factors. With individual tests whereby each person is tested on a different occasion, this method for determining reliability necessarily reflects the effects of both varying and constant unsystematic factors.

If we adhere either to the concept of true and error scores or to the eclectic concept of true scores and parallel tests, the method of determining reliability from the intercorrelations among comparable parts appears to be quite appropriate. We have parallel tests and ascertain the degree of relationship among them. However, together with the test-retest and parallel-forms methods, this method, too, is inappropriate in terms of the concept of domain sampling since reliability is taken as the relationship between two or more actual tests rather than the relationship between an actual test and a parallel construct.

The logical extreme of the method of determining reliability of measurement from the intercorrelations among comparable parts of a test is the division of a test into its smallest parts. If we have a test comprised of 100 items, instead of dividing it into two parts of 50 items each or four parts of 25 items each, we could divide it into 100 parts of one item each. As before, we use the intercorrelations among the parts as the estimate of the reliability of the part tests and estimate the reliability of the total test by means of the Spearman-Brown formula. The obvious advantage of this method lies in the fact that we avoid the troublesome problem of deciding how to divide the test into halves or quarters. As a simple example, if we have a test consisting of four items we could form the following halves:

$$1 + 2 \text{ and } 3 + 4 \qquad 1 + 3 \text{ and } 2 + 4 \qquad 1 + 4 \text{ and } 2 + 3$$

As the number of items increases, the number of possible divisions of the items into halves increases astronomically. Hence it would be impossible to determine the average of the correlations among all possible halves. The method of estimating reliability from the intercorrelations among the elements of a test avoids this difficulty. Inasmuch as this method is merely a logical extension of the method of estimating reliability from the correlation between comparable parts, it, too, cannot be used with tests which are integrated wholes, such as speed tests.

We can begin our derivation of the formula necessary for determining reliability by this method from Eq. (7-6), the variance of a composite. For present purposes we can write this formula as

$$\sigma_x{}^2 = \sigma_{x_1}{}^2 + \cdots + \sigma_{x_k}{}^2 + 2\sigma_{x_1}\sigma_{x_2}r_{x_1 x_2} + \cdots + 2\sigma_{x_{k-1}}\sigma_{x_k}r_{x_{k-1} x_k}$$

where x refers to the total test, and 1 to k, or i, refer to the elements of the test.

Since we are going to use the Spearman-Brown formula, we must presume that all the elements are parallel tests with equal intercorrelations and standard deviations so that

$$\sigma_{x_1} = \cdots = \sigma_{x_k} \qquad \text{and} \qquad r_{x_1 x_2} = \cdots = r_{x_{k-1} x_k}$$

We can therefore write the above formula as

$$\sigma_x{}^2 = k\sigma_{x_i}{}^2 + k(k-1)\sigma_{x_i}{}^2 r_{x_i x_i'}$$
$$= \sigma_{x_i}{}^2[k + k(k-1)r_{x_i x_i'}]$$
$$\frac{\sigma_x{}^2}{\sigma_{x_i}{}^2} = k + k(k-1)r_{x_i x_i'}$$
$$\frac{\sigma_x{}^2}{\sigma_{x_i}{}^2} - k = k(k-1)r_{x_i x_i'}$$
$$\frac{(\sigma_x{}^2/\sigma_{x_i}{}^2) - k}{k(k-1)} = r_{x_i x_i'}$$
$$\frac{\sigma_x{}^2}{k(k-1)\sigma_{x_i}{}^2} - \frac{1}{k-1} = r_{x_i x_i'} \tag{9-16}$$

The Spearman-Brown formula (9-4), applied to the intercorrelation among the elements of a test, $r_{x_i x_i'}$, to estimate the reliability of the total test, r_{xx}, would be

$$r_{xx} = \frac{k r_{x_i x_i'}}{1 + (k-1)r_{x_i x_i'}}$$

Substituting for $r_{x_i x_i'}$ from Eq. (9-16) in the Spearman-Brown formula, we have

$$
\begin{aligned}
r_{xx} &= \frac{k\{[\sigma_x{}^2/k(k-1)\sigma_{x_i}{}^2] - [1/(k-1)]\}}{1 + (k-1)\{[\sigma_x{}^2/k(k-1)\sigma_{x_i}{}^2] - [1/(k-1)]\}} \\
&= \frac{[k/(k-1)][(\sigma_x{}^2/k\sigma_{x_i}{}^2) - 1]}{1 + (\sigma_x{}^2/k\sigma_{x_i}{}^2) - 1} \\
&= \frac{k}{k-1}\frac{(\sigma_x{}^2 - k\sigma_{x_i}{}^2)/k\sigma_{x_i}{}^2}{\sigma_x{}^2/k\sigma_{x_i}{}^2} \\
&= \frac{k}{k-1}\frac{k\sigma_{x_i}{}^2}{\sigma_x{}^2}\frac{\sigma_x{}^2 - k\sigma_{x_i}{}^2}{k\sigma_{x_i}{}^2} \\
&= \frac{k}{k-1}\frac{\sigma_x{}^2 - k\sigma_{x_i}{}^2}{\sigma_x{}^2} \\
&= \frac{k}{k-1}\left(\frac{\sigma_x{}^2}{\sigma_x{}^2} - \frac{k\sigma_{x_i}{}^2}{\sigma_x{}^2}\right) \\
&= \frac{k}{k-1}\left(1 - \frac{k\sigma_{x_i}{}^2}{\sigma_x{}^2}\right) \tag{9-17}
\end{aligned}
$$

Seldom if ever do the elements of a test, such as the items in an objective test, have equal variances and intercorrelations; therefore they are not parallel tests. As a consequence, Eq. (9-17) is of little value for any practical purposes. As an approximation, sometimes the average of the variances of the elements, $\overline{\sigma_{x_i}{}^2}$, is used in place of $\sigma_{x_i}{}^2$. If this average value is used in Eq. (9-17), it is

$$r_{xx} = \frac{k}{k-1}\left(1 - \frac{k\overline{\sigma_{x_i}^2}}{\sigma_x^2}\right)$$

Since the number of cases times the mean of a variable is equal to the sum of that variable, we can write the formula as

$$r_{xx} = \frac{k}{k-1}\left(1 - \frac{\Sigma\sigma_{x_i}^2}{\sigma_x^2}\right) \tag{9-18}$$

If the elements of the test are dichotomous variables, as is usually the case with the items in an objective test, the formula is written as

$$r_{xx} = \frac{k}{k-1}\left(1 - \frac{\Sigma pq}{\sigma_x^2}\right) \tag{9-19}$$

where pq refers to the variances of the items [Eq. (3-18)] and σ_x^2 to the variance of total scores. Equations (9-17) to (9-19) are called the Kuder-Richardson formulae after the men who first derived them.

Equations (9-18) and (9-19) give only approximations of the reliability coefficient, and ordinarily these approximations are underestimates. But they are underestimates only if we hold either to the theory of true and error scores or to the eclectic concept of true scores and parallel tests which require the coefficient of correlation between parallel tests for determining reliability, the parallel tests being actual tests.

With the theory of domain sampling the situation is quite different. We developed Eq. (8-45), the reliability coefficient in terms of the theory of domain sampling, as the correlation between scores on a test and scores on a construct parallel to it. By definition we took the average of the covariances of the two parallel tests to be equal to each other, and both as equal to the average of the cross covariances. We can write Eq. (8-45) as

$$r_{xx} = \frac{k^2\overline{\sigma_{x_i}\sigma_{x_i}r_{x_ix_{i'}}}}{\sigma_x^2}$$

Equation (8-43), the variance of any parallel test in terms of the concept of domain sampling, can be written as

$$\sigma_x^2 = k\overline{\sigma_{x_i}^2} + k(k-1)\overline{\sigma_{x_i}\sigma_{x_i}r_{x_ix_{i'}}}$$

$$\sigma_x^2 - k\overline{\sigma_{x_i}^2} = k(k-1)\overline{\sigma_{x_i}\sigma_{x_i}r_{x_ix_{i'}}}$$

$$\frac{\sigma_x^2 - k\overline{\sigma_{x_i}^2}}{k(k-1)} = \overline{\sigma_{x_i}\sigma_{x_i}r_{x_ix_{i'}}}$$

Substituting this in the above formula for r_{xx}, we obtain the following:

$$r_{xx} = \frac{k^2\{(\sigma_x^2 - k\overline{\sigma_{x_i}^2})/[k(k-1)]\}}{\sigma_x^2}$$

$$= \frac{k}{k-1} \frac{\sigma_x^2 - k\overline{\sigma_{x_i}^2}}{\sigma_x^2}$$

$$= \frac{k}{k-1} \left(\frac{\sigma_x^2}{\sigma_x^2} - \frac{k\overline{\sigma_{x_i}^2}}{\sigma_x^2}\right)$$

$$= \frac{k}{k-1} \left(1 - \frac{\Sigma\sigma_{x_i}^2}{\sigma_x^2}\right) \tag{9-20}$$

It will be observed that this is precisely the same as Eq. (9-18), even though it was derived on an entirely different theoretical basis. It also, of course, has the form equivalent to Eq. (9-19) when the elements of the test are dichotomous variables.

Suppose we have each child in a class rated on the same scale of sociability by the same five teachers. For each child, then, we have the ratings by each of the five teachers (the elements) and the sum of the ratings by all teachers (total scores). Let us further suppose the variances of the ratings of the five teachers are 2, 3, 3, 4, and 6 respectively ($\Sigma = 18$), and the variance of total ratings is 45. Then by Eq. (9-20) we estimate the reliability coefficient of total ratings to be

$$r_{xx} = \frac{5}{5-1}\left(1 - \frac{18}{45}\right) = \frac{5}{4}(1 - .40) = (1.25)(.60) = .75$$

Suppose we have an objective test with 50 dichotomously scored items, the sum of the variances of the items being 7.00 and the variance of the total scores being 49.00. Then by Eq. (9-18) the reliability coefficient of the test is

$$r_{xx} = \frac{50}{50-1}\left(1 - \frac{7}{49}\right) = \frac{50}{49}(1 - .14) = (1.02)(.84) = .86$$

On the basis of the theory of domain sampling, Eq. (9-20) involves no presumptions at all concerning the nature of the elements of which a test is composed. Furthermore, it is not an approximation of the reliability coefficient; rather, it is the only correct way for determining it. From the point of view of the theory of true and error scores and the eclectic concept of true scores and parallel tests, estimating the reliability coefficient of a test from the intercorrelations of the parts as by means of the Kuder-Richardson formulae is a special case of the method of comparable parts of a test, and a poor estimate at that since the intercorrelations among the elements of a test and their standard deviations ordinarily differ widely. But from the point of view of the concept of domain sampling we obtain the precise and exact value of the reliability coefficient by this method.

IMPROVING RELIABILITY OF MEASUREMENT

It is apparent that the lack of reliability of measurement is an undesirable state of affairs. A test which gives a useful quantitative description is one which yields scores characteristic of an individual. Therefore in testing we wish to minimize the effects of unsystematic factors. Let us therefore consider ways for decreasing the effects of unsystematic factors and thereby increasing reliability of measurement.

IMPROVING RELIABILITY THROUGH INCREASING THE NUMBER OF MEASUREMENTS

We have seen that as the number of measurements increases, the reliability of measurement also increases. That is, if instead of using the scores on a single test we take the sum or average of the scores on two, three, or more parallel forms of the test, we increase reliability. We can accomplish this by increasing the number of items in an objective test, being sure that the new items have the same characteristics as the original items. If we are dealing with ratings, we can increase the reliability by increasing the number of raters, being sure that the new raters have the same characteristics as the original raters.

IMPROVING RELIABILITY THROUGH GOOD "HOUSEKEEPING" PROCEDURES

Another way of reducing the effects of unsystematic factors is by exercising good experimental controls when we obtain our measurements. Such controls can be effected in a variety of ways. For example, with speed tests we can utilize exact timing devices which automatically signal starting and stopping time rather than depend upon a fallible human reading a watch. We can take steps to ensure that the lighting is equal throughout the testing room and is the same for all occasions when the tests are being administered. We can train raters so that they all interpret the traits being rated in the same way and so that their personal biases are minimized. We can reduce variation among scores by the use of clear and consistent instructions. In other words, by means of a variety of "housekeeping" measures we can "clean up" our testing situation and thereby reduce the effects of unsystematic factors. This is not to imply that we can completely eliminate them; rather, we seek to minimize their effects.

IMPROVING RELIABILITY THROUGH SIMULTANEOUS TESTING
OF ALL INDIVIDUALS

There are, of course, many unsystematic factors at work whose effects we cannot detect or of whose existence we are completely unaware. Some of these are the type we have termed varying unsystematic factors, and some are of the type we have termed constant unsystematic factors. We cannot do much about the former type except to increase the number of measurements, keep ever on the alert, and use good housekeeping procedures. However, we can do something about the latter, the constant unsystematic factors. Even if we are not aware of their existence, we can control them very simply by merely administering the test to all individuals on the same occasion. All persons are tested at the same time and in the same place. Under these circumstances these constant factors will not produce differences among individuals; rather, they will have precisely the same constant effects upon all individuals.

Control of both types of unsystematic factors through good "housekeeping" procedures can and should always be maintained. However, control of constant unsystematic factors through the simultaneous testing of all individuals is not always practicable. With individual tests or with circumstances where tests must be administered individually, constant factors cannot be controlled by the method of simultaneous or group testing. This means that scores on repeated individual tests must necessarily be affected by constant factors that go undetected or are not eliminated by "housekeeping" procedures.

With the simultaneous testing of all individuals, constant unsystematic factors are controlled out. Since they do not have a differential effect upon individuals, they do not affect the order of individuals on a trait. However, they do affect the mean and sometimes the standard deviations of the scores. We have eliminated the effects of these constant factors upon individual differences by simultaneous testing, and now we must correct for their effects upon the distributional characteristics of the scores. This we can do very simply by expressing the scores of all individuals in terms of standard scores.

Suppose we wish to examine the possibility that several repetitions of the same test or several forms of the same test are in fact parallel. We should administer the test or its several forms on a number of occasions. Let us say we find there are unsystematic variations in the means and standard deviations. We can correct the scores for the effects of constant unsystematic factors by transmuting the scores on each occasion to standard scores. Statistically, then, we have eliminated the effects of constant unsystematic factors through simultaneous testing of all individuals. Not all tests are administered at the same time, nor are they necessarily administered under the same conditions. On each occasion, however, all individuals take one repetition or form of the test. If we find that the coefficients of correlation between all the tests are the same and all tests are correlated to the same degree with each of a series of other tests, we can say that they are parallel. They are parallel because we have canceled out the effects of certain unsystematic factors.

SIMULTANEOUS TESTING AS A CONTROL FOR SYSTEMATIC FACTORS

We have seen that when a test is administered on several occasions we can eliminate the effects of constant unsystematic factors by the simultaneous testing of all individuals on each occasion. We have seen that with constant unsystematic factors there are variations among the means and standard deviations of the scores from one occasion to another. The only difference between these constant unsystematic factors and systematic factors is that the means and standard deviations of the latter show a trend, whereas those of the former do not. Hence there seems to be no reason for not eliminating the effects of systematic factors in the same way we have eliminated the effects of the constant unsystematic factors.

Systematic factors work in either of two ways. From one occasion to another they may have the same effect upon the scores of all individuals, just as do the constant unsystematic factors; or they may have a differential effect upon individuals so that the order of individuals changes from occasion to occasion. The latter factors we could not partial out by transmuting the scores obtained on each occasion to standard scores. Hence when systematic factors are operating and we find the order of individuals changes in a systematic fashion from one occasion to another, we cannot eliminate the systematic factors by use of standard scores. However, if the correlations among the scores obtained on the various occasions remain the same, then we can eliminate the effects of the systematic factors by using standard scores just as we did with constant unsystematic factors.

Summary

It follows mathematically from all three theories about reliability of measurement—the theory of true and error scores, the eclectic theory of true scores and parallel tests, and the theory of domain sampling—that as the number of measurements entering into a score increases, so does the reliability of measurement. The formula which relates number of measurements and reliability is termed the Spearman-Brown formula. This formula assumes that the added measures are parallel to the original measures, having the same standard deviations and intercorrelations.

If we are willing to assume that the correlation between true and fallible scores is homoscedastic, then it is possible to develop a formula which shows the effects of reducing or increasing the range of fallible scores upon the reliability coefficient. Reducing the range reduces the magnitude of the reliability coefficient, and increasing the range increases it.

The reliability of measurement affects the range of differences among individuals in their fallible scores. As reliability increases, the standard deviation of fallible scores decreases.

The correlation between two variables is influenced by the reliability with which they are measured. As their reliability decreases, so does the correlation between their fallible scores. The formula which relates the correlation between two variables and the reliability with which they are measured, the correction for attenuation, follows mathematically from all three theories about reliability. This formula also shows the limiting effects of reliability upon correlation. The lower the reliability, the lower the maximum possible correlation between fallible scores.

There are two types of unsystematic factors which produce variations in scores, the varying unsystematic factors and the constant unsystematic factors. For both types the effects are different for the same individual on different occasions; but the effects of varying unsystematic factors are different for different individuals on the same occasion, whereas the effects of constant unsystematic factors are the same for all individuals on the same occasion. With group tests constant unsystematic factors do not affect reliability of measurement since all individuals are tested on the same occasion. But with individual tests they lower reliability because each person is tested on a different occasion.

The four common ways for estimating reliability of measurement are from the coefficient of correlation between scores on repetitions of the same test, from the coefficient of correlation between scores on parallel forms of a test, from the coefficient of correlation between scores on comparable parts of a test, and from the intercorrelations among the elements of a test.

Both the test-retest and parallel-forms methods require more than one test administration. Carry-over effects from one test administration to another are likely to distort the estimate of reliability given by the test-retest method. The method of parallel tests involves a good deal of labor in the development of the required forms. When a test is an integrated whole, its reliability cannot be estimated from the correlation between comparable parts of it nor from the intercorrelations among its elements. If constant systematic factors are taken to be part of reliability, then these two methods give overestimates of the reliability coefficient. If we hold to the theory of true and error scores or to the eclectic theory of true scores and parallel tests, then all methods for estimating reliability are appropriate, though the estimate obtained from the intercorrelations among the elements of the test is likely to be the poorest. But if we hold to the theory of domain sampling, then the estimation of reliability from the intercorrelations among the elements is the only appropriate method.

Reliability can be improved by increasing the number of measurements, and through good "housekeeping" procedures. The simultaneous testing of all individuals will minimize the variation in their scores over parallel tests, and at the same time control the effects of systematic factors.

Selected Readings

Cronbach, L. J.: Test "reliability": its meaning and determination, *Psychometrika*, **12**:1–16, 1947.

———: "Essentials of Psychological Testing," 2d ed., Harper, 1960.

Gulliksen, H.: "Theory of Mental Tests," Wiley, 1950.

Guttman, L.: A basis for analysing test-retest reliability, *Psychometrika*, **10**:225–282, 1945.

Jackson, R. W. B., and G. A. Ferguson: Studies on the reliability of tests, Department of Education, University of Toronto, Bulletin 12, 1941.

Kuder, G. F., and M. W. Richardson: The theory of estimation of test reliability, *Psychometrika*, **2**:151–166, 1937.

Lyerly, S. B.: The Kuder-Richardson formula (21) as a split-half coefficient, and some remarks on its basic assumption, *Psychometrika*, **23**:267–270, 1958.

Thorndike, R. L.: "Personnel Selection," Wiley, 1949.

Tryon, R. C.: Reliability and behavior domain validity: reformulation and historical critique, *Psychological Bull.*, **54**:229–249, 1957.

chapter 10   *The Differential*

Weighting of Components in

a Composite Variable

In Chap. 7 we saw that many variables dealt with in psychological measurement are composites formed of two or more component variables. We examined the mean, standard deviation, and correlations of composite variables. We did not, however, consider the relative importance of the components, that is, the weights they carry in a composite. In some circumstances we may wish to have all the components carry equal weight, whereas in others it is necessary or desirable to have some of the components carry greater weight than others in the composite. We consider the possibility of differentially weighting the components so as to make the composite more precise or reliable, more meaningful, or more predictive of some other variable.

Suppose we wish to have factory workers rated in terms of their job performance. We could obtain ratings of their performance from their foremen, the department heads, and the factory supervisor. In forming a composite of the three ratings assigned to each worker, we might wish to assign greatest weight to the foreman's ratings and least weight to the ratings by the factory supervisor, since the foremen are most intimately acquainted with the performance of the workers and the factory supervisor is the least acquainted.

We might measure the sociability of nursery school children by counting the number of times in a 3-hr play period each child approaches, speaks to, helps, comforts, plays with, or smiles at other children. We might find that the measurements of approaches and helpings are highly reliable, whereas those of comfortings and smilings are of low reliability. In making a composite measure of sociability we might prefer to give greater weight to the first two components and less weight to the last two. In these examples we see that we might be able to achieve a composite of greater precision or reliability if we differentially weighted the components.

The job proficiency of salesmen can be measured by their total volume of sales, the number of new accounts they develop, and the number of repeat sales they make to the same customers. The economics of a particular situation might suggest that total volume of sales is most important and the number of repeat sales least important. We should then wish to give greatest weight to the first index and least to the third.

Suppose we are measuring achievement in a course in psychological measurement. We may have questions concerning the application of principles, matters of fact, and the derivation of formulae. Because we believe that the objective of the course is to provide the student with principles he will apply and that derivations merely give him the logic underlying formulae, we may wish to weight the first type of question most and the last type least. By differentially weighting the components which form a composite, then, we may feel that we have a composite which is more meaningful in the sense that it more accurately reflects the definition of the trait we wish to measure.

If we are using tests of mechanical aptitude and intelligence to select students for a shop course, we may wish to give greater weight to the former than to the latter. The amount of abstract material to be learned in such a course is relatively small and has little influence on the grades the students earn in the course. On the other hand, if we were using these two tests to select students for an engineering college we might wish to weight the tests in just the reverse fashion, giving greater weight to the intelligence test because in engineering college the student does have to learn a great deal of abstract material. By differentially weighting the two tests in one way for the shop course and in another way for the engineering college, we hope to obtain better predictions of grades in both.

In the foregoing examples we have indicated cases wherein we desire to differentially weight the components that form a composite. But sometimes we may wish to have all the components carry equal weight. If we were measuring knowledge of American literature we might wish to have questions concerning novels, plays, essays, and poetry carry equal weight in determining total scores. Consequently it is also important in some cases to know that the components which form a composite are equally weighted.

In this chapter we shall consider the nature of weights and their effects upon composite scores. We shall examine the effects upon the composite mean and standard deviation and upon the order of individuals in composite scores. In addition, we shall observe the relationship between differentially weighted composite scores and scores on an outside variable and shall develop a way for maximizing this correlation.

THE NATURE AND PROCESS OF DIFFERENTIAL WEIGHTING OF COMPONENTS IN A COMPOSITE

Let us now examine the nature of weights and see how we go about applying differential weights to the components in obtaining a total weighted composite score.

THE DIFFERENTIAL WEIGHTING OF COMPONENT SCORES

When we differentially weight component scores we multiply each score by its appropriate weight, all scores in a given component being multiplied by the same value, and then we sum the products to obtain the composite score. Thus

$$X_{c_a} = W_1 X_{1_a} + \cdots + W_k X_{k_a}$$
$$\cdots\cdots\cdots\cdots\cdots\cdots\cdots\cdots$$
$$X_{c_n} = W_1 X_{1_n} + \cdots + W_k X_{k_n}$$

In these equations the weights are symbolized by W with the subscripts referring to the particular weight assigned to each component. Thus the scores of each of the a to n individuals on component 1 are multiplied by W_1, and each of their scores on component k is multiplied by W_k. After each component score of an individual is multiplied by its appropriate weight, the products are summed to form the total weighted composite score X_c.

The general formula representing the differential weighting of raw component scores in a composite is

$$X_{c_W} = W_1 X_1 + \cdots + W_k X_k \tag{10-1}$$

In deviation-score form this equation is

$$x_{c_W} = W_1 x_1 + \cdots + W_k x_k \tag{10-2}$$

Different sets of weights applied to the component scores of a given composite might not only give distributions of scores which differ in shape but also order the individuals in a different manner. To illustrate this, let us take a case where we have three component variables forming a composite. The raw scores for five individuals on each of the components

TABLE 10-1.   Illustration of the Effects of Two Different Sets of Differential Weights upon Composite Scores

Person	Raw component scores			Scores when: $W_1 = 1, W_2 = 2, W_3 = 3$				Scores when: $W_1 = 7, W_2 = 2, W_3 = 5$			
	X_1	X_2	X_3	X_1	X_2	X_3	X_c	X_1	X_2	X_3	X_c
a	4	3	2	4	6	6	16	28	6	10	44
b	11	5	1	11	10	3	24	77	10	5	92
c	6	7	4	6	14	12	32	42	14	20	76
d	7	10	3	7	20	9	36	49	20	15	84
e	9	8	6	9	16	18	43	63	16	30	109

are listed in Table 10-1, and in this table the scores have been treated with two different sets of weights. The weights in the first set are 1, 2, and 3, respectively, for the three components; and the weights in the second set are 7, 2, and 5, respectively. Figure 10-1 gives the distributions of composite scores when the two different sets of weights are applied to the

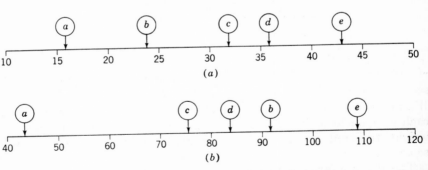

Figure 10-1   The effects of two different sets of differential weights on scores. Scores when (a) $W_1 = 1$, $W_2 = 2$, $W_3 = 3$; and (b) $W_1 = 7$, $W_2 = 2$, $W_3 = 5$.

component scores. We can see from this example that not only are the relative differences among individuals different, thereby giving distributions of scores of different shapes, but also the order of individuals is different.

WEIGHTS AS RELATIVE VALUES

In terms of their effects upon the relative differences among individuals, the shape of the distribution of composite scores, and the order of individuals in composite scores, it is not the absolute magnitude of the weights which is important; rather, it is their magnitudes relative to one another. It makes no difference, either in terms of the relative positions of individuals in composite scores or in terms of the shape of the distribution

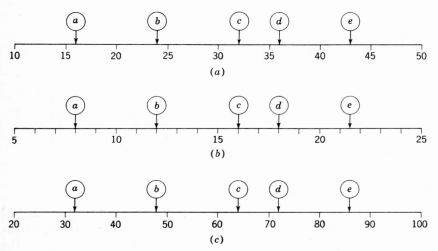

Figure 10-2 The effects of various sets of differential weights on composite scores when the weights maintain the same relative values to each other. Scores when (a) $W_1 = 1$, $W_2 = 2$, $W_3 = 3$; (b) $W_1 = 0.5$, $W_2 = 1.0$, $W_3 = 1.5$; and (c) $W_1 = 2$, $W_2 = 4$, $W_3 = 6$.

of composite scores, whether we multiply or divide all the weights by any given number.

To illustrate this, let us take the same case we have just considered of a composite made up of three components. Let us assign them respectively the weights of 1, 2, and 3. We could divide the weights, say, by their average, 2, which gives us the values 0.5, 1.0, and 1.5; or we could multiply them, say, by 2, which gives us the values 2, 4, and 6. Let us now apply all three sets of weights to the scores of the five individuals. The computations are given in Table 10-2, and the distribution of composite scores is shown in Fig. 10-2. This figure clearly shows that if we maintain the same relative values among the weights, even though we use different absolute values for them, the relative differences among individuals in composite scores are exactly maintained.

Sometimes we can use this property of weights to simplify the computation of composite scores. For example, if the weights we wish to assign to three components are 0.73, 2.19, and 2.92, respectively, we could just as well use the values 1, 3, and 4 and thereby save ourselves a great deal of computational labor.

TABLE 10-2.   Illustration of the Effects of Various Sets of Differential Weights upon Composite Scores when the Weights Maintain the Same Relative Values to Each Other

Person	Raw component scores			Scores when: $W_1 = 1$, $W_2 = 2$, $W_3 = 3$				Scores when: $W_1 = 0.5$, $W_2 = 1$, $W_3 = 1.5$				Scores when: $W_1 = 2$, $W_2 = 4$, $W_3 = 6$			
	X_1	X_2	X_3	X_1	X_2	X_3	X_c	X_1	X_2	X_3	X_c	X_1	X_2	X_3	X_c
a	4	3	2	4	6	6	16	2.0	3	3.0	8.0	8	12	12	32
b	11	5	1	11	10	3	24	5.5	5	1.5	12.0	22	20	6	48
c	6	7	4	6	14	12	32	3.0	7	6.0	16.0	12	28	24	64
d	7	10	3	7	20	9	36	3.5	10	4.5	18.0	14	40	18	72
e	9	8	6	9	16	18	43	4.5	8	9.0	21.5	18	32	36	86

NOMINAL AND EFFECTIVE WEIGHTS

We can differentiate two different kinds of weights: the *nominal* weights, which are those we deliberately assign to components; and the *effective* weights, which are those the components actually carry in the composite. The nominal and effective weights may or may not be the same. Suppose the nominal weights assigned to three component variables which form a composite are 5, 3, and 1, respectively. We then multiply the scores on the first component by 5, the scores on the second by 3, and the scores on the third by 1. If, unknown to us, the three components already carry weights of 1, 4, and 7, respectively, then after applying our nominal weights the total effective weights carried by the components are 5 (1 × 5) for the first component, 12 (3 × 4) for the second, and 7 (7 × 1) for the third. Clearly, this is a different pattern of weights than we had in mind. In order for the effective weights to correspond to the nominal weights, we have to be sure that the components carry equal weight to begin with.

As we shall see, in many situations it is doubtful whether we can actually determine the effective weights. As a consequence, when we assign nominal weights we cannot be sure that the weights the components actually carry in the composite are in fact those we wish them to carry. This is also a troublesome problem when we do not assign differential weights but expect all the components to carry equal weight.

THE RELATIVE CONTRIBUTION OF COMPONENTS TO COMPOSITE SCORES

Let us now attempt to determine the relative contribution of the components to total composite scores when we simply sum them together. It will be recalled that we are concerned with a simple additive composite wherein

$$X_c = X_1 + \cdots + X_k$$

THE CONTRIBUTION OF A COMPONENT TO THE MEAN OF COMPOSITE SCORES

In Eq. (7-4) we showed that the mean of composite scores is simply the sum of the means of the components. This formula is

$$\bar{X}_c = \bar{X}_1 + \cdots + \bar{X}_k$$

It is clear from this formula that the mean of composite scores is solely and entirely a function of the means of the components. Those components that have the higher means contribute more to the composite mean than do those with smaller means, and each component contributes to the mean in direct proportion to its magnitude. If a component is dropped, the mean of the composite is reduced exactly by the amount of the mean of that component.

In a simple summed composite, then, the effective weight of a component in determining the mean of composite scores is the magnitude of the mean of that component. If we wish to have all components carry equal effective weights in the composite, we simply divide the scores in each composite by its mean. All scores in component 1 are divided by $\bar{X}_1$, and all scores in component k are divided by $\bar{X}_k$. If now we assign nominal weights, we can be sure that they are also the effective weights.

THE CONTRIBUTION OF A COMPONENT TO THE VARIANCE OF COMPOSITE SCORES

In Eq. (7-7) we saw that the variance of composite scores is

$$\sigma_c^2 = \sigma_1^2 + \cdots + \sigma_k^2 + 2\sigma_1\sigma_2 r_{12} + \cdots + 2\sigma_{k-1}\sigma_k r_{(k-1)k} \quad (10\text{-}3)$$

This formula shows that the variance of composite scores is determined by the variances of the components and their covariances.

As in the case of the mean of composite scores, we should like to know the contribution of each component to the composite variance. Let us begin by taking a special case, one wherein all the components are independent, that is, a situation wherein the intercorrelations among the components are all zero. If we look at Eq. (10-3), we see that there is a whole series of covariance terms. Since we are taking all the coefficients of correlation to be zero, all these terms drop out. We are therefore left with the following:

$$\sigma_c{}^2 = \sigma_1{}^2 + \cdots + \sigma_k{}^2 \tag{10-4}$$

From this formula it is clear that when we are dealing with a composite of uncorrelated components, each component contributes to the variance of the composite in direct proportion to its own variance. To equalize the contribution of all components, we simply divide the scores in each component by its variance in the same fashion as we divided them by their means in order to equalize the contributions of the means.

However, it is very unlikely that all the components in a composite of psychological variables will ever be completely uncorrelated. For all practical purposes we can say that this situation will never occur, though it may be closely approximated. Therefore the case of independent components is only of theoretical interest.

To get at the problem of the contribution of the components to the composite, sometimes the terms in Eq. (10-3) are arranged as follows:

$$\begin{aligned}
\sigma_c{}^2 = \sigma_1{}^2 &+ \sigma_1\sigma_2 r_{12} + \cdots + \sigma_1\sigma_k r_{1k} \\
&+ \sigma_2{}^2 + \sigma_2\sigma_1 r_{21} + \cdots + \sigma_2\sigma_k r_{2k} \\
&\cdots\cdots\cdots\cdots\cdots\cdots\cdots\cdots\cdots \\
&+ \sigma_k{}^2 + \sigma_k\sigma_1 r_{k1} + \cdots + \sigma_k\sigma_{k-1} r_{k(k-1)}
\end{aligned} \tag{10-5}$$

In Eq. (10-5) we have a series of terms for each component which is comprised of its variance plus its covariances with all the other components. Now the question is, as is sometimes suggested, whether these terms are the contributions of the components to the variance of composite scores. Let us see what we have done in Eq. (10-5) with the terms in Eq. (10-3). In Eq. (10-3) there are two of each covariance term (for example, $2\sigma_1\sigma_2 r_{12}$). What we have done in Eq. (10-5) is to arbitrarily allocate one of each covariance term to one component and the other to its partner. What is the justification for this? Nothing, really, except that the division seems equitable and fair, and there are two like terms. Now it is all well and good, in order to be equitable and fair, for partners to divide their assets equally, but that is not our concern here. We are trying to discover the contribution of each component to the composite.

Let us draw a parallel. Suppose we have three men, Harry, George, and Wilberforce, whom we are going to put to work on a joint task, and we wish to determine the contribution of each to the total product. The first task is gathering seashells, with Harry at Waikiki, George at Malibu, and Wilberforce at Rye. Clearly the contribution of each man to the total product is independent of that of the other two, and is simply the number of shells he himself gathers. The situation is not unlike that represented in Eq. (10-4).

Now let us assign our three men another task, pulling weights by means of a rope. When each man pulls alone we find Harry pulls 100 lb, George 120 lb, and Wilberforce 140 lb, which makes a total of 360 lb. However, when all three men actually pull together on the same rope at the same time, they succeed in moving 390 lb. This situation is similar to that represented in Eq. (10-5). Now to whom shall we attribute this extra 30 lb? Shall we allocate one-third of it to each member of the team, saying that Harry contributed 110 lb of pull to the load, George 130 lb, and Wilberforce 150 lb? It is obvious that there has been an interaction among the three men, and it is to the interaction and not to the individual men that the extra 30 lb is to be attributed. Hence it is impossible to determine the contribution of each man to the group product—and it is equally impossible to determine the contribution of each component to the composite variance when the intercorrelations among the components are greater than zero.

TRANSMUTING COMPONENT SCORES TO STANDARD-SCORE FORM IN RELATION TO THEIR CONTRIBUTION TO COMPOSITE SCORES

In dealing with composite scores it is common practice to transmute the scores on the components to standard-score form in the belief that this procedure equalizes the weights carried by the components. Let us examine this proposition.

It will be recalled that we found the contribution of each component to the mean of composite scores to be directly proportional to the magnitude of its mean. Expressing Eq. (7-4), the formula for the mean of composite scores, in standard-score form, we have

$$\bar{X}_{c_z} = \bar{z}_1 + \cdots + \bar{z}_k \tag{10-6}$$

Since the mean of standard scores is zero, when all components are expressed in standard-score form they contribute equally to the mean of composite scores, which in this case also would be zero.

However, the situation is quite different with the variance of composite scores. The formula for the variance of composite scores when the scores on each of the components is expressed in standard-score form [Eq. (7-8)] is

$$\sigma_c^2 = k + 2r_{12} + \cdots + 2r_{(k-1)k} \tag{10-7}$$

This formula shows us that transmuting component scores to standard-score form does not eliminate the troublesome correlation terms. As we have seen, it is these terms which prevent us from separating out the contributions of the individual components. As pointed out in Chap. 7, what is accomplished by transmuting component scores to standard-score form is to render their scores comparable in terms of the performance of some specified norming group.

THE EFFECTS OF DIFFERENTIAL WEIGHTING OF THE COMPONENTS IN A COMPOSITE

Let us now see what effects the assignment of differential nominal weights has upon the mean and standard deviation of composite scores and upon the order of individuals in terms of composite scores. If we do not assign differential weights to the components, we are in effect assigning them each the nominal weight of 1. In examining the effects of differential weighting, then, we shall compare composite scores differentially weighted, the average of the weights being 1, with composite scores when all the components are assigned the same weight of 1.

THE EFFECTS OF DIFFERENTIAL WEIGHTING OF COMPONENTS UPON THE MEAN OF COMPOSITE SCORES

The mean of composite scores when the components are differentially weighted can be written from Eq. (10-1) as

$$
\begin{aligned}
\bar{X}_{c_W} &= \frac{\Sigma(W_1X_1 + \cdots + W_kX_k)}{n} \\
&= W_1\frac{\Sigma X_1}{n} + \cdots + W_k\frac{\Sigma X_k}{n} \\
&= W_1\bar{X}_1 + \cdots + W_k\bar{X}_k
\end{aligned}
\tag{10-8}
$$

Equation (10-8) shows us that the mean of composite scores when the components are differentially weighted is simply equal to the sum of the means of the components, each multiplied by its weight. Therefore it is apparent that the components which are assigned higher weights contribute proportionally more to the composite mean than do the components assigned lower weights.

THE EFFECTS OF DIFFERENTIAL WEIGHTING OF COMPONENTS UPON THE STANDARD DEVIATION OF COMPOSITE SCORES

When the components are differentially weighted, the variance of the composite scores can be written from Eq. (10-2) as

$$\sigma_{cw}{}^2 = \sigma^2_{W_1x_1+\cdots+W_kx_k} = \frac{\Sigma(W_1x_1 + \cdots + W_kx_k)^2}{n}$$

$$= \frac{W_1{}^2\Sigma x_1{}^2 + \cdots + W_k{}^2\Sigma x_k{}^2 + 2W_1W_2\Sigma x_1x_2 + \cdots + 2W_{k-1}W_k\Sigma x_{k-1}x_k}{n}$$

$$= W_1{}^2\frac{\Sigma x_1{}^2}{n} + \cdots + W_k{}^2\frac{\Sigma x_k{}^2}{n} + 2W_1W_2\frac{\Sigma x_1x_2}{n} + \cdots + 2W_{k-1}W_k\frac{\Sigma x_{k-1}x_k}{n}$$

$$= W_1{}^2\sigma_1{}^2 + \cdots + W_k{}^2\sigma_k{}^2 + 2W_1W_2\sigma_1\sigma_2r_{12} + \cdots + 2W_{k-1}W_k\sigma_{k-1}\sigma_k r_{(k-1)k} \tag{10-9}$$

$$\sigma_{cw} = \sqrt{W_1{}^2\sigma_1{}^2 + \cdots + W_k{}^2\sigma_k{}^2 + 2W_1W_2\sigma_1\sigma_2r_{12} + \cdots + 2W_{k-1}W_k\sigma_{k-1}\sigma_k r_{(k-1)k}} \tag{10-10}$$

An illustration of the computation of the variance of composite scores by means of Eq. (10-9) is given in Table 10-3.

TABLE 10-3. Illustration of the Computation of the Variance of Composite Scores from the Intercorrelations among the Components and Their Standard Deviations when the Components Are Differentially Weighted

	Components						
	1	2	3	4	σ	σ^2	W
1		.20	.40	.00	5	25	6
2			.30	.10	3	9	1
3				.50	6	36	2
4					4	16	7

$$\sigma_{cw}{}^2 = (36)(25) + (1)(9) + (4)(36) + (49)(16) + 2(6)(1)(5)(3)(.20)$$
$$+ 2(6)(2)(5)(6)(.40) + 2(6)(7)(5)(4)(.00) + 2(1)(2)(3)(6)(.30)$$
$$+ 2(1)(7)(3)(4)(.10) + 2(2)(7)(6)(4)(.50)$$
$$= 2,535.4$$

It is a little difficult to see in Eq. (10-9) the various factors that affect the magnitude of the composite variance when the components are differentially weighted. Therefore let us carry Eq. (10-9) a bit further, and for simplicity let us consider that all the components are given in standard scores and therefore have the value of 1 and that all the intercorrelations among the components are equal in magnitude so that

$$r_{12} = \cdots = r_{(k-1)k} = r$$

Then we can write Eq. (10-9) as

$$\sigma_{c_W}{}^2 = W_1{}^2 + \cdots + W_k{}^2 + 2W_1W_2r + \cdots + 2W_{k-1}W_kr$$
$$= \Sigma W^2 + rW_1(W_2 + \cdots + W_k) + \cdots$$
$$+ rW_k(W_1 + \cdots + W_{k-1})$$

From Eq. (3-13) we know that the variance of a set of values is equal to the mean of the squares of those values minus the square of their mean. Hence

$$\sigma_W{}^2 = \frac{\Sigma W^2}{k} - \bar{W}^2$$

and consequently

$$k\sigma_W{}^2 + k\bar{W}^2 = \frac{\Sigma W^2}{k}$$

Therefore

$$\sigma_{c_W}{}^2 = k\sigma_W{}^2 + k\bar{W}^2 + rW_1(\Sigma W - W_1) + \cdots + rW_k(\Sigma W - W_k)$$
$$= k\sigma_W{}^2 + k\bar{W}^2 + rW_1\Sigma W - rW_1{}^2 + \cdots + rW_k\Sigma W - rW_k{}^2$$

Rearranging terms gives

$$\sigma_{c_W}{}^2 = k\sigma_W{}^2 + k\bar{W}^2 + rW_1\Sigma W + \cdots + rW_k\Sigma W - rW_1{}^2 - \cdots - rW_k{}^2$$
$$= k\sigma_W{}^2 + k\bar{W}^2 + r\Sigma W(W_1 + \cdots + W_k) - r\Sigma W^2$$

Again substituting for $\Sigma W^2/k$ as we did above, we get

$$\sigma_{c_W}{}^2 = k\sigma_W{}^2 + k\bar{W}^2 + r\Sigma W\Sigma W - kr\sigma_W{}^2 - kr\bar{W}^2$$

Recall that the mean of a set of values is equal to their sum divided by their number. Hence

$$\bar{W} = \frac{\Sigma W}{k}$$

and consequently

$$k\bar{W} = \Sigma W$$

Therefore

$$\sigma_{c_W}{}^2 = k\sigma_W{}^2 + k\bar{W}^2 + k^2r\bar{W}^2 - kr\sigma_W{}^2 - kr\bar{W}^2$$
$$= k(\sigma_W{}^2 + \bar{W}^2 + kr\bar{W}^2 - r\sigma_W{}^2 - r\bar{W}^2)$$
$$= k[\sigma_W{}^2(1 - r) + r\bar{W}^2(k - 1) + \bar{W}^2] \qquad (10\text{-}11)$$
$$\sigma_{c_W} = \sqrt{k[\sigma_W{}^2(1 - r) + r\bar{W}^2(k - 1) + \bar{W}^2]} \qquad (10\text{-}12)$$

Let us look at the term σ_W in Eqs. (10-11) and (10-12). This is the standard deviation of the weights and is an index of the extent to which the weights differ among themselves in magnitude. If the weights differ greatly, then σ_W is large; and if they are very similar, then σ_W is small. In fact, if they are all of exactly the same magnitude, that is, if the components are all assigned the same weight (for example, the weight of 1), then σ_W is zero and Eq. (10-11) resolves to Eq. (7-9), the variance of a simple composite.

To show the effects of differentially weighting the components upon the standard deviation of composite scores, Eq. (10-12) is plotted as Fig. 10-3. Ordinarily the standard deviation of a set of values, all values being positive, is smaller in magnitude than the mean of those values.

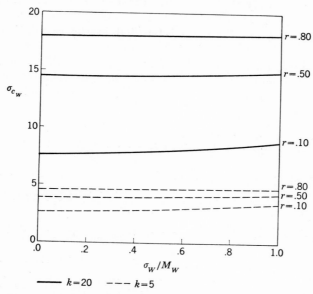

Figure 10-3 The effects on the standard deviation of composite scores (σ_{c_W}) of the relative variation among the weights assigned to the components (σ_W/M_W), the number of components (k), and the level of the intercorrelations among the components (r).

That is, usually $\sigma_x < \bar{X}$. When the standard deviation is equal to the mean, we have an extreme condition of variation. Therefore when $\sigma_W/\bar{W} = 1$ we have about as much variation among weights as we are ever likely to encounter. To facilitate comparisons, in Fig. 10-3 the standard deviation of differentially weighted composite scores is plotted against the relative variation of the weights. From this figure we can derive the following principles:

1. The larger the variation among the nominal weights, the larger the standard deviation of composite scores; but even when the variation among the weights is very large, the standard deviation of composite scores is not greatly increased.
2. The lower the intercorrelations among the scores of the components, the more pronounced the effect of differentially weighting the components.

THE EFFECTS OF DIFFERENTIALLY WEIGHTING COMPONENTS UPON
THE ORDER OF INDIVIDUALS IN COMPOSITE SCORES

Let us now examine the effects of differential weighting of components upon the order of individuals in composite scores. If differentially weighting the components does not greatly change the order of individuals in composite scores over that given by composite scores based upon components with equal nominal weights, then there is little point in assigning such weights. We are therefore interested in the correlation between differentially and equally weighted composite scores. It will be understood, of course, that we are speaking of nominal rather than effective weights. Consequently, when we speak of equally weighted components we merely mean that they all carry the same nominal weight of 1. The correlation we wish is

$$r_{cwc} = r_{(W_1x_1 + \cdots + W_kx_k)(x_1 + \cdots + x_k)}$$

$$= \frac{\Sigma(W_1x_1 + \cdots + W_kx_k)(x_1 + \cdots + x_k)}{n\sigma_{cw}\sigma_c}$$

$$= \frac{\Sigma(W_1x_1{}^2 + W_1x_1x_2 + \cdots + W_1x_1x_k + \cdots + W_kx_kx_1 + \cdots + W_kx_kx_{k-1} + W_kx_k{}^2)}{n\sigma_{cw}\sigma_c}$$

$$= \frac{W_1\dfrac{\Sigma x_1{}^2}{n} + W_1\dfrac{\Sigma x_1x_2}{n} + \cdots + W_1\dfrac{\Sigma x_1x_k}{n} + \cdots + W_k\dfrac{\Sigma x_kx_1}{n} + \cdots + W_k\dfrac{\Sigma x_kx_{k-1}}{n} + W_k\dfrac{\Sigma x_k{}^2}{n}}{\sigma_{cw}\sigma_c}$$

$$= \frac{W_1\sigma_1{}^2 + W_1\sigma_1\sigma_2r_{12} + \cdots + W_1\sigma_1\sigma_kr_{1k} + \cdots + W_k\sigma_k\sigma_1r_{k1} + \cdots + W_k\sigma_k\sigma_{k-1}r_{k(k-1)} + W_k\sigma_k{}^2}{\sigma_{cw}\sigma_c}$$

Rearranging terms gives

$$r_{cwc} = \frac{W_1\sigma_1{}^2 + \cdots + W_k\sigma_k{}^2 + (W_1\sigma_1\sigma_2r_{12} + \cdots + W_1\sigma_1\sigma_kr_{1k}) + \cdots + (W_k\sigma_k\sigma_1r_{k1} + \cdots + W_k\sigma_k\sigma_{k-1}r_{k(k-1)})}{\sigma_{cw}\sigma_c}$$

$$(10\text{-}13)$$

An illustration of the computation, by means of Eq. (10-13), of the coefficient of correlation between composite scores when the components are differentially weighted and when they are equally weighted is given in Table 10-4. For the denominator Eq. (10-10) is used for computing σ_{cw} and Eq. (7-6) for computing σ_c.

Note that in each set of parentheses in the numerator of Eq. (10-13) there are $k - 1$ terms. The terms within a set of parentheses are all the covariance terms for a given component with all the other components, each covariance being multiplied by the weight of that component. As we did for convenience in deriving the standard deviation of differentially weighted composite scores, for simplicity let us again take all the inter-

TABLE 10-4. Illustration of the Computation of the Coefficient of Correlation between Composite Scores when the Components Are Differentially Weighted and when They Are Equally Weighted

	Components						
	1	2	3	4	σ	σ^2	W
1		.20	.40	.00	5	25	6
2			.30	.10	3	9	1
3				.50	6	36	2
4					4	16	7

$\sigma_{cw}{}^2$ was computed in Table 10-3 and $\sigma_c{}^2$ in Table 7-2.

$$r_{cwc} = \frac{\begin{array}{c}(6)(25) + (1)(9) + (2)(36) + (7)(16) + (6)(5)(3)(.20) + (6)(5)(6)(.40) \\ + (6)(5)(4)(.00) + (1)(3)(5)(.20) + (1)(3)(6)(.30) \\ + (1)(3)(4)(.10) + (7)(4)(3)(.10) + (7)(4)(6)(.50)\end{array}}{\sqrt{2,535.4}\ \sqrt{1,517}}$$

$$= \frac{593.80}{(50.35)(38.95)} = .30$$

correlations among the components as being equal and the scores on all the components as being given in standard-score form. Then we can write Eq. (10-13) as

$$r_{cwc} = \frac{\begin{array}{c}W_1 + \cdots + W_k + (W_1 r + \cdots + W_1 r) \\ + \cdots + (W_k r + \cdots + W_k r)\end{array}}{\sigma_{cw}\sigma_c}$$

$$= \frac{\Sigma W + r[(k-1)W_1] + \cdots + r[(k-1)W_k]}{\sigma_{cw}\sigma_c}$$

$$= \frac{\Sigma W + r(k-1)(W_1 + \cdots + W_k)}{\sigma_{cw}\sigma_c}$$

$$= \frac{\Sigma W + r(k-1)\Sigma W}{\sigma_{cw}\sigma_c}$$

$$= \frac{\Sigma W[1 + r(k-1)]}{\sigma_{cw}\sigma_c}$$

Substituting for σ_{cw} from Eq. (10-12) and for σ_c from Eq. (7-9) gives

$$r_{cwc} = \frac{\Sigma W[1 + r(k-1)]}{\sqrt{k[\sigma_W{}^2(1-r) + r\bar{W}^2(k-1) + \bar{W}^2]}\ \sqrt{k + k(k-1)r}}$$

Dividing the numerator and denominator by k gives

r_{c_wc}

$$= \frac{(\Sigma W/k)[1 + (k - 1)r]}{\sqrt{1/k} \sqrt{k[\sigma_W{}^2(1 - r) + r\bar{W}^2(k - 1) + \bar{W}^2]} \sqrt{1/k} \sqrt{k + k(k - 1)r}}$$

$$= \frac{\bar{W}[1 + (k - 1)r]}{\sqrt{\sigma_W{}^2(1 - r) + r\bar{W}^2(k - 1) + \bar{W}^2} \sqrt{1 + (k - 1)r}}$$

Dividing the numerator and denominator by $\bar{W}$ gives

$$r_{c_wc} = \frac{(\bar{W}/\bar{W})[1 + (k - 1)r]}{(1/\bar{W}) \sqrt{\sigma_W{}^2(1 - r) + r\bar{W}^2(k - 1) + \bar{W}^2} \sqrt{1 + (k - 1)r}}$$

$$= \frac{1 + (k - 1)r}{\sqrt{(\sigma_W{}^2/\bar{W}^2)(1 - r) + (r\bar{W}^2/\bar{W}^2)(k - 1) + \bar{W}^2/\bar{W}^2} \sqrt{1 + (k - 1)r}}$$

Dividing the numerator and denominator by $\sqrt{1 + (k - 1)r}$ gives

$$r_{c_wc} = \frac{\sqrt{1 + (k - 1)r}}{\sqrt{(\sigma_W/\bar{W})^2(1 - r) + r(k - 1) + 1}}$$

$$= \sqrt{\frac{1 + (k - 1)r}{(\sigma_W/\bar{W})^2(1 - r) + 1 + (k - 1)r}} \tag{10-14}$$

Equation (10-14) is plotted in Fig. 10-4. From this figure we can derive

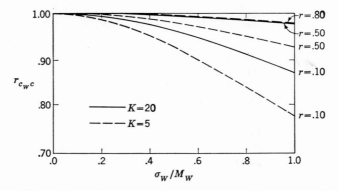

Figure 10-4 The effects of the relative variation of the weights (σ_W/M_W), the level of correlations among the components (r), and the number of components (k) on the correlation between composite scores when the components are differentially weighted and when they are equally weighted (r_{c_wc}).

the following principles:

1. The greater the relative variation among the nominal weights, the more the order of individuals in composite scores is changed.
2. The lower the intercorrelations among the components, the greater the effects of differential weighting upon the order of individuals in composite scores.
3. The fewer the number of components, the greater the effects of differential weighting upon the order of individuals in composite scores.

THE CORRELATION BETWEEN DIFFERENTIALLY WEIGHTED COMPOSITE SCORES AND SCORES ON AN OUTSIDE VARIABLE

In Chap. 7 we saw that the correlation between scores on a composite and scores on an outside variable is a function of the magnitude of the correlations between the components and the outside variable and the magnitude of the intercorrelations among the components (Fig. 7-2). Let us now examine the correlation between scores on a differentially weighted composite and scores on an outside variable. We shall see that with a differentially weighted composite the pattern of weights assigned the components also is a factor in the relationship between composite scores and scores on an outside variable.

THE COEFFICIENT OF CORRELATION BETWEEN DIFFERENTIALLY WEIGHTED COMPOSITE SCORES AND SCORES ON AN OUTSIDE VARIABLE

The correlation between differentially weighted composite scores and scores on an outside variable is

$$
\begin{aligned}
r_{0c_W} &= r_{x_0(W_1x_1 + \cdots + W_kx_k)} \\
&= \frac{\Sigma x_0(W_1x_1 + \cdots + W_kx_k)}{n\sigma_0\sigma_{c_W}} \\
&= \frac{\Sigma(W_1x_0x_1 + \cdots + W_kx_0x_k)}{n\sigma_0\sigma_{c_W}} \\
&= \frac{W_1(\Sigma x_0x_1/n) + \cdots + W_k(\Sigma x_0x_k/n)}{\sigma_0\sigma_{c_W}} \\
&= \frac{W_1\sigma_0\sigma_1 r_{01} + \cdots + W_k\sigma_0\sigma_k r_{0k}}{\sigma_0\sigma_{c_W}} \\
&= \frac{\sigma_0(W_1\sigma_1 r_{01} + \cdots + W_k\sigma_k r_{0k})}{\sigma_0\sigma_{c_W}} \\
&= \frac{W_1\sigma_1 r_{01} + \cdots + W_k\sigma_k r_{0k}}{\sigma_{c_W}} \quad (10\text{-}15)
\end{aligned}
$$

An illustration of the computation by means of Eq. (10-15) of the correlation between scores on an outside variable and scores on a differentially weighted composite is given in Table 10-5.

TABLE 10-5.   Illustration of the Computation of the Coefficient of Correlation between Differentially Weighted Composite Scores and Scores on an Outside Variable

	Components						
	0	1	2	3	4	σ	W
0		.40	.50	.00	.30	7	
1			.20	.40	.00	5	6
2				.30	.10	3	1
3					.50	6	2
4						4	7

Note that σ_0 does not enter into the computation of r_{0c_W}. $\sigma_{c_W}^2$ was computed in Table 10-3.

$$r_{0c_W} = \frac{(6)(5)(.40) + (1)(3)(.50) + (2)(6)(.00) + (7)(4)(.30)}{\sqrt{2,535.4}}$$

$$= \frac{21.90}{50.35} = .43$$

If scores on all components are given as standard scores, then Eq. (10-15) resolves to

$$r_{0c_{z,W}} = r_{0(W_1 z_1 + \cdots + W_k z_k)}$$
$$= \frac{W_1 r_{01} + \cdots + W_k r_{0k}}{\sqrt{W_1^2 + \cdots + W_k^2 + 2W_1 W_2 r_{12} + \cdots + 2W_{k-1} W_k r_{(k-1)k}}} \tag{10-16}$$

THE PATTERN OF WEIGHTS AND THE CORRELATION BETWEEN
DIFFERENTIALLY WEIGHTED COMPOSITE SCORES AND SCORES ON
AN OUTSIDE VARIABLE

By the term "pattern of weights" we refer to the relative magnitude of the nominal weights assigned to the components of a composite variable. For example, if we have a composite formed of four components, the weights assigned them might be respectively 1, -0.5, 3, and 15; or 2, 7, -11, and -3. Different patterns of weights assigned to the components would result in different orderings of individuals in terms of total weighted composite scores, and consequently the magnitude of the correlation between composite scores and scores on an outside variable might be expected to vary with the different patterns of weights.

By way of illustration, four examples are given in Fig. 10-5. Each of these composites consists of two components, and in each case there is a different pattern of correlations among the two components and the outside variable. In these examples the weight assigned to the first component is 1, and the weight assigned to the second component has been

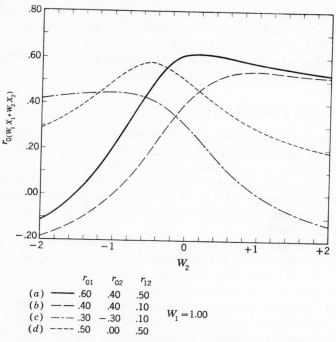

		r_{01}	r_{02}	r_{12}
(a)	——	.60	.40	.50
(b)	– –	.40	.40	.10
(c)	–·–	.30	–.30	.10
(d)	----	.50	.00	.50

$W_1 = 1.00$

Figure 10-5 The effects of different patterns of weights on the correlation between a composite variable and an outside variable.

varied from -2 to $+2$, thus providing widely varying patterns of differential weights. Applying Eq. (10-15) in each case, we can see in Fig. 10-5 that the magnitude of the correlation between a differentially weighted composite and an outside variable does in fact vary considerably with the pattern of weights assigned to the components.

In addition, we can see in Fig. 10-5 that there is in every case an optimal pattern of weights, optimal in the sense that the particular pattern of weights results in the highest possible correlation between differentially weighted composite scores and scores on the outside variable. If we are interested in predicting scores on an outside variable from scores on a composite, it would be helpful to know the optimal pattern of weights. For example, if we wished to predict college grades from a combination of high school grades and scores on an aptitude test, knowing the optimal pattern of weights would permit us to take advantage of the maximal possible correlation between the composite and the outside variable. We could, of course, use Eq. (10-15) or (10-16), inserting our standard deviations and intercorrelations as well as a number of different combinations of weights and discovering the optimal weights by means of a trial-and-error basis. However, this is an inefficient process and a laborious one, especially when there are many variables involved. Therefore it would be desirable to have a procedure which would give us precisely and directly the optimal set of weights. Multiple correlation provides such a procedure, and we shall discuss it in the following section.

MULTIPLE CORRELATION

Through the process termed multiple correlation we can obtain a set of optimal weights. When these optimal weights are applied to the components forming a composite, the correlation between differentially weighted composite scores and scores on an outside variable is at a maximum. The application of any other weights to the components would result in composite scores which bear a lower correlation with scores on the outside variable.

Multiple correlation is similar to simple correlation, which we discussed in Chaps. 5 and 6. Simple correlation tells us how well we can predict scores on one variable from scores on another, and multiple correlation tells how well we can predict scores on one variable from the optimally weighted composite of scores on several other variables. In simple correlation we deal with variation in one variable, holding constant variation in another; and in multiple correlation we are dealing with variation in one variable, simultaneously holding constant variation in a number of other variables. Just as we developed a regression equation for simple correlation, we shall develop a multiple regression equation; but the multiple regression equation is considerably more complicated than the regression equation in the case of the simple correlation between two variables. This multiple regression equation will give us the optimal pattern of weights we want. The multiple coefficient of correlation, symbolized as $R_{0.12\cdots k}$, where 0 is the outside variable and 1 to k the components forming the composite, will give us the magnitude of the correlation between the optimally weighted composite and the outside variable.

THE MULTIDIMENSIONAL SCATTER DIAGRAM

When we are dealing with a correlation between two variables, the scatter diagram is represented on a flat surface or plane as a large square, and the columns and rows form a series of small square or cells. The scatter diagram has two dimensions, x_0 and x_1, and for each person we have two scores, x_0 and x_1. We find the row representing his score on one variable and the column representing his score on the other and then plot his score in the cell at the intersection of the row and the column.

When we are dealing simultaneously with the relationships among a number of variables, our scatter diagram must have as many dimensions

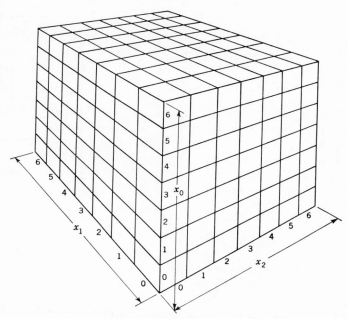

Figure 10-6   The three-dimensional scatter diagram.

as there are variables. If there are k variables there are k dimensions to our scatter diagram. If k is 3, our scatter diagram takes the form of a cube with the three dimensions x_0, x_1, and x_2. The cells now are little cubes in the big cube. A three-dimensional scatter diagram is shown in Fig. 10-6. For each person there are three scores, x_0, x_1, and x_2. When plotting an individual's scores we find the row representing his score on one variable, for example, x_1; and the column representing his score on another variable, for example, x_2. If we look at Fig. 10-6 we shall see that a "row" and a "column" are slices through the large cube. The intersection of these two slices or planes forms a vertical straight line. In Fig. 10-6 the intersection is a "tower" of cells or small blocks. Now we locate in this tower the cell representing the individual's score on the last variable, x_0. A tally in this cell represents the individual's scores on all three tests.

If we have more than three variables we cannot, of course, represent the scatter diagram in this simple graphic fashion. We can, however, represent these variables mathematically. Indeed, we have done this before. When we discussed composites we presented various formulae in which a number of different variables or dimensions are represented. The

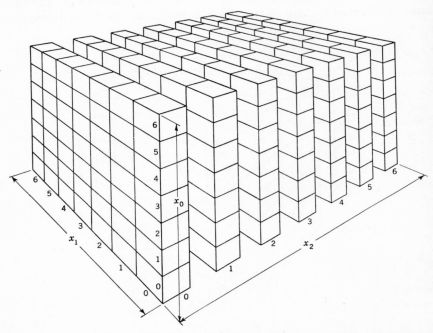

Figure 10-7 Slices through the three-dimensional scatter diagram to illustrate the correlation between variables x_0 and x_1 with x_2 held constant.

regression equation as given in Eq. (5-13) is a mathematical representation of the two dimensions in simple correlation. In deriving the multiple coefficient of correlation and formulae pertinent to it we shall deal with the three-variable problem so that easy reference can be made to the scatter diagram in Fig. 10-6; then we shall generalize these formulae to many dimensions.

CORRELATION BETWEEN TWO VARIABLES WITH VARIATION IN A
THIRD PARTIALED OUT

Suppose we take slices through the cube shown in Fig. 10-6, say through variable 2. This is shown in Fig. 10-7. Then in any given slice all individuals have the same x_2 score. For these individuals x_2 is constant, but they still differ among themselves in variables 0 and 1. Each slice is a scatter diagram of the correlation between variables 0 and 1 when the effects of variable 2 have been held constant or partialed out.

We could, of course, have taken slices through variable x_1. Then we should have had a series of scatter diagrams giving the relationship between x_0 and x_2 with the effects of x_1 held constant. Indeed, we could have taken horizontal slices through variable 0, and then we should have had a series of scatter diagrams giving the relationship between x_1 and x_2 with the effects of x_0 held constant.

MULTIPLE CORRELATION AND LINEARITY OF RELATIONSHIPS

When we dealt with the simple relationship between pairs of psychological variables, we found it desirable to consider only linear relationships. While it is true that curvilinear relationships do occur between psychological variables, linear relationships are the general rule. Furthermore, we saw that if we do not consider the scores given directly by the operations of measurement necessarily to be equal units on some scale, we may be able to justify using some function of them or normalizing the distribution of scores, which gives us transmuted scores which are linearly related to other variables. While it is possible to develop multiple correlation for use with curvilinear relationships, we shall nevertheless deal only with linear relationships in multiple correlation just as we did with simple correlation.

In dealing with simple correlation we saw that we could take linear relationships in either of two senses. First of all, we could take linear relationships to refer only to those situations wherein the means of the scores in the columns and the means of the scores in the rows all fall precisely on straight lines. However, we saw this to be very restrictive since such a situation seldom if ever occurs. Therefore we saw the desirability of taking linear correlation as a model, using as regression lines not lines drawn through the means of the columns and rows but rather straight lines which are the best-fitting lines in a least-squares sense. We take linearity as our model and use the best-fitting straight line as the specific description of our model.

As we did with simple correlation, let us first take linear correlation to refer to the case where the means of the columns and rows fall precisely on straight lines. We have seen that slices through x_2 (Fig. 10-7) give us a series of scatter diagrams representing the relationship between x_1 and x_0. In each scatter diagram, of course, x_2 is constant. Now if there is no relationship at all between x_1 and x_0, that is, if $r_{01} = .00$, then in each scatter diagram the means of the x_0 scores in all the columns (towers) will be equal. Hence the regression line running through the means of the columns (towers) will be a straight line parallel to the base line x_1.

Now suppose that, in addition, x_2 and x_0 are completely unrelated. Then in every slice through x_1, every slice being a scatter diagram of the relationship between x_2 and x_0 with x_1 held constant, a similar state of affairs will exist. That is, all the means of the x_0 scores in the columns (towers) of x_2 will be equal and the regression line running through them will be parallel to the base line x_2. Consequently, if both x_1 and x_2 are completely unrelated to x_0, that is, $r_{10} = r_{20} = .00$, then the means in all the towers in Fig. 10-6 will be precisely equal to each other. This being the case, we

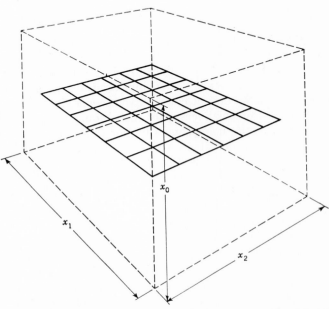

Figure 10-8 The regression lines and the regression plane in the three-dimensional scatter diagram when $r_{01} = r_{02} = .00$.

could pass a plane through these points and all points would fall precisely on the plane.

Just as in simple correlation the regression line running through the means of the columns describes the relationship between one variable and another, so in multiple correlation wherein we are dealing with the relationship between two variables simultaneously (x_1 and x_2) and another variable (x_0), the plane running through the means of the towers describes the relationship. This is shown graphically in Fig. 10-8. In this figure the regression lines in all the slices through x_1 and through x_2 are shown, and the intersections of these lines are the means of the x_0 scores in these columns.

Let us now consider the circumstance where x_2 and x_0 are unrelated

$(r_{20} = .00)$ but x_1 and x_0 are positively related. In every slice through x_2, which is a scatter diagram of the relationship between x_1 and x_0, the means of the x_0 scores in the columns (towers) fall on a straight line that runs diagonally across the slice. Recall, however, that since the relationship between x_2 and x_0 is zero in every slice through x_1, which is a scatter diagram of the relationship between x_2 and x_0, the means of the x_0 scores in all the columns (towers) are equal and the line running through them

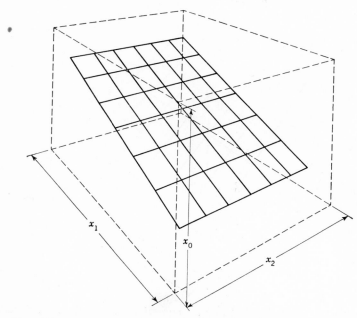

Figure 10-9 The regression lines and the regression plane in the three-dimensional scatter diagram when r_{01} is positive and $r_{02} = .00$.

is parallel to the base line x_2. However, these lines obviously are at different levels in the different slices through x_1, since x_1 and x_0 are positively related. This is shown in Fig. 10-9. Consequently, a plane running through the means of the towers would be tilted.

If both x_1 and x_2 are positively related to x_0, then the regression plane running through the means of the columns will be tilted in two dimensions as is shown in Fig. 10-10. In this case the correlation between variables 1 and 0 is higher than the relationship between variables 2 and 0; consequently the regression lines for x_1 and x_0 are steeper than those for x_2 and x_0. The regression plane therefore tilts more in one direction than in the other. If the relationship between either x_1 and x_2 with x_0 were negative, then the tilt of the plane would be in the opposite direction.

Now if we take the regression lines in simple correlation not as running through the means of the columns and rows but rather as the best-fitting straight lines in a least-squares sense, then it follows that the regression plane does not pass through the means of the towers but rather is the plane of best fit in a least-squares sense in the three-dimensional scatter diagram. If we passed any other plane through the three-dimensional

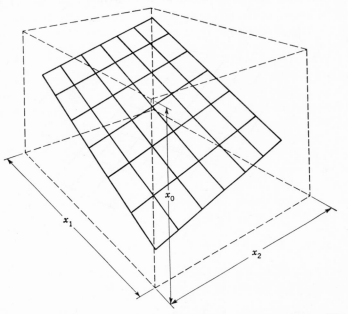

Figure 10-10   The regression lines and the regression plane in the three-dimensional scatter diagram when both r_{01} and r_{02} are positive.

scatter diagram, we should find that the sum or the mean of the squares of the deviations of x_0 from it would be greater. Of course in this case a curved or irregular surface of some sort that does pass precisely through the means of the towers would be the best-fitting surface. But if we wish the simplicity and comprehensibility that go along with linearity, we must take a plane surface as our model just as we take a straight line as our model in simple correlation.

VARIATION IN ONE VARIABLE HOLDING CONSTANT VARIATION IN A SECOND VARIABLE

Let us return to the two-variable problem and consider the relationship between x_0 and x_1. Our scatter diagram is represented in two dimensions on a plane surface and is composed of rows and columns. Consider any given row described by x_1. All individuals in this row have the same x_1 score, but they differ in their scores on x_0 (unless variables 0 and 1 are perfectly correlated). For individuals in this row the distribution of x_0 scores describes the extent of variation in scores on test 0 when scores on test 1 are held constant.

Now we compute the mean of the x_0 scores in this particular row. For each person who falls in this row let us subtract this mean $\bar{x}_{0_1}$ from his score x_0. This gives us deviation scores in variable 0 with the effects of variable 1 held constant and therefore eliminated. We could go through this process for every row, obtaining deviation scores for each person on variable 0 with the effects of variable 1 held constant.

It will be recalled that we are dealing with linear correlation. Therefore the means of the rows all fall on the same straight line, or the regression line is taken as the estimates of the means. These means are described by the regression equation, which, from Eq. (5-13), is

$$\bar{x}_{0_1} = b_{0.1} x_1 \qquad (10\text{-}17)$$

where
$$b_{0.1} = r_{01} \frac{\sigma_0}{\sigma_1} \qquad (10\text{-}18)$$

If we symbolize scores on variable 0 with the effects of variable 1 held constant as $x_{0.1}$, then we have

$$x_{0.1} = x_0 - \bar{x}_{0_1} = x_0 - b_{0.1} x_1 \qquad (10\text{-}19)$$

We have shown in Eq. (6-13) that the standard deviation of scores in one variable with the effects of a second one held constant is

$$\sigma_{0.1} = \sigma_0 \sqrt{1 - r_{01}^2} \qquad (10\text{-}20)$$

This value is the standard deviation of the distribution of our errors of prediction, the standard error of estimate.

VARIATION IN ONE VARIABLE SIMULTANEOUSLY HOLDING CONSTANT VARIATION IN SEVERAL OTHER VARIABLES

Let us now consider the effects upon the variation in one variable x_0 when the variation in two other variables x_1 and x_2 is held constant simultaneously. We are now dealing with a given tower of cells in the large cube shown in Fig. 10-6. All individuals who fall in any given tower have the same x_1 score and the same x_2 score and differ only in terms of their scores on x_0.

What is our regression equation, the equation for the prediction of variable 0 from the combination of variables 1 and 2? Whereas with the two-variable problem the regression equation describes a line, now we wish a regression equation that describes a plane. We can write the equation we wish by analogy from Eq. (10-17), the regression equation for the two-variable problem. If we look at Eq. (10-17), we shall see that we have a value b, the regression coefficient, which is the slope of the regression line. In the three-variable problem, however, we are dealing with a plane with two slopes, one as the plane cuts through x_1 and the other as it cuts through x_2. But note in Eq. (10-17) that b involves partialing out only one variable. Now for each regression coefficient we must partial out two variables. Thus by analogy we can write

$$\bar{x}_{0_1} = b_{0\cdot(1.2)}x_1 + b_{0\cdot(2.1)}x_2$$

or, in more common nomenclature,

$$\bar{x}_{0_1} = b_{01.2}x_1 + b_{02.1}x_2 \tag{10-21}$$

The regression coefficients in Eq. (10-21) can be thought of as weights applied to x_1 and x_2 to give us our best estimate of x_0. That is, $\bar{x}_0$ is our estimate of the score in variable 0 obtained by an individual knowing his scores in variables 1 and 2. $b_{01.2}$ is the constant by which we multiply scores in variable 1, and $b_{02.1}$ is the constant by which we multiply scores in variable 2 in making a weighted composite score which gives us the best prediction of variable 0.

By analogy with Eq. (10-19) we can write deviation scores in variable 0 with the effects of both variables 1 and 2 held constant as

$$\begin{aligned} x_{0.12} &= x_0 - \bar{x}_0 \\ &= x_0 - b_{01.2}x_1 - b_{02.1}x_2 \end{aligned} \tag{10-22}$$

We also want to write the formula for the regression coefficients and for the standard error of prediction. Reference to Eqs. (10-18) and (10-20) will show that we shall have to deal with the correlation between two variables when the effects of a third are held constant.

PARTIAL CORRELATION

As we have seen, if we take a slice anywhere through the cube representing the three-dimensional scatter diagram, we have a scatter diagram of the relationship between scores on two variables with scores on a third held constant. For example, Fig. 10-7 represents a series of scatter diagrams of the relationship between variables 0 and 1 with the effects of variable 2 held constant. We could compute the coefficient of correlation in each slice. We should like to have a single coefficient describing the relationships in all the slices, a summary value for the relationship between variables 0 and 1 with variable 2 constant. Such a coefficient is termed the *coefficient of partial correlation* and is symbolized as $r_{01.2}$.

In the case we are considering here, we wish to obtain the coefficient of correlation between scores on variable 0 and variable 1 with the effects of variable 2 held constant. From Eq. (10-19) we can write this formula as

$$r_{01.2} = r_{(x_0 - b_{0.2}x_2)(x_1 - b_{1.2}x_2)}$$
$$= \frac{\Sigma(x_0 - b_{0.2}x_2)(x_1 - b_{1.2}x_2)}{n\sigma_{x_0 - b_{0.2}x_2}\sigma_{x_1 - b_{1.2}x_2}}$$

Let us first consider the numerator divided by n:

$$\frac{\Sigma(x_0 - b_{0.2})(x_1 - b_{1.2}x_2)}{n} = \frac{\Sigma(x_0x_1 - b_{1.2}x_0x_2 - b_{0.2}x_1x_2 + b_{0.2}b_{1.2}x_2{}^2)}{n}$$

$$= \frac{\Sigma x_0x_1}{n} - b_{1.2}\frac{\Sigma x_0x_2}{n} - b_{0.2}\frac{\Sigma x_1x_2}{n} + b_{0.2}b_{1.2}\frac{\Sigma x_2{}^2}{n}$$

$$= \sigma_0\sigma_1 r_{01} - b_{1.2}\sigma_0\sigma_2 r_{02} - b_{0.2}\sigma_1\sigma_2 r_{12} + b_{0.2}b_{1.2}\sigma_2{}^2$$

From Eq. (10-18) we can substitute for the regression coefficients b their equivalents in terms of coefficients of correlation and standard deviations:

$$\frac{\Sigma(x_0 - b_{0.2})(x_1 - b_{1.2}x_2)}{n}$$

$$= \sigma_0\sigma_1 r_{01} - r_{12}\frac{\sigma_1}{\sigma_2}\sigma_0\sigma_2 r_{02} - r_{02}\frac{\sigma_0}{\sigma_2}\sigma_1\sigma_2 r_{12} + r_{02}\frac{\sigma_0}{\sigma_2}r_{12}\frac{\sigma_1}{\sigma_2}\sigma_2{}^2$$

$$= \sigma_0\sigma_1 r_{01} - \sigma_0\sigma_1 r_{02}r_{12} - \sigma_0\sigma_1 r_{02}r_{01} + \sigma_0\sigma_1 r_{02}r_{12}$$

$$= \sigma_0\sigma_1(r_{01} - r_{02}r_{12} - r_{02}r_{12} + r_{02}r_{12})$$

$$= \sigma_0\sigma_1(r_{01} - r_{02}r_{12})$$

Now we can turn to the denominator and derive the first standard deviation:

$$\sigma_{x_0 - b_{0.2}x_2}^2 = \frac{\Sigma(x_0 - b_{0.2}x_2)^2}{n}$$

$$= \frac{\Sigma(x_0{}^2 - 2b_{0.2}x_0x_2 + b_{0.2}^2x_2{}^2)}{n}$$

$$= \frac{\Sigma x_0{}^2}{n} - 2b_{0.2}\frac{\Sigma x_0x_2}{n} + b_{0.2}^2\frac{\Sigma x_2{}^2}{n}$$

Substituting from Eq. (10-18) the equivalents of the b terms, we have

$$\sigma_{x_0 - b_{0.2}x_2}^2 = \sigma_0{}^2 - 2r_{02}\frac{\sigma_0}{\sigma_2}\sigma_0\sigma_2 r_{02} + r_{02}{}^2\frac{\sigma_0{}^2}{\sigma_2{}^2}\sigma_2{}^2$$

$$= \sigma_0{}^2 - 2r_{02}{}^2\sigma_0{}^2 + r_{02}{}^2\sigma_0{}^2$$

$$= \sigma_0{}^2 - r_{02}{}^2\sigma_0{}^2$$

$$= \sigma_0{}^2(1 - r_{02}{}^2)$$

$$\sigma_{x_0 - b_{0.2}x_2} = \sigma_0\sqrt{1 - r_{02}{}^2}$$

By analogy, the other standard deviation in the denominator is

$$\sigma_{x_1 - b_{1.2}x_2} = \sigma_1\sqrt{1 - r_{12}{}^2}$$

Putting together the numerator and the denominator, we have

$$r_{01.2} = \frac{\sigma_0 \sigma_1 (r_{01} - r_{02} r_{12})}{\sigma_0 \sqrt{1 - r_{02}^2} \, \sigma_1 \sqrt{1 - r_{12}^2}}$$

$$= \frac{r_{01} - r_{02} r_{12}}{\sqrt{(1 - r_{02}^2)(1 - r_{12}^2)}} \tag{10-23}$$

This is the formula for partial correlation, the correlation between two variables when we wish to hold constant variation in a third variable. The general formula for partial correlation, the correlation between two variables when variation in a number of other variables is held constant, is

$$r_{01.23\ldots k} = \frac{r_{01.23\ldots (k-1)} - r_{0k\cdot23\ldots(k-1)} r_{1k\cdot23\ldots(k-1)}}{\sqrt{(1 - r_{0k\cdot23\ldots(k-1)}^2)(1 - r_{1k\cdot23\ldots(k-1)}^2)}} \tag{10-24}$$

The computation of the coefficient of partial correlation is illustrated in Table 10-6.

TABLE 10-6. Illustration of the Computation of the Coefficient of Partial Correlation

	Intercorrelations among three variables		
	0	1	2
0		.50	.30
1			.40
2			

$$r_{01.2} = \frac{r_{01} - r_{02} r_{12}}{\sqrt{(1 - r_{02}^2)(1 - r_{12}^2)}} = \frac{.50 - (.30)(.40)}{\sqrt{[1 - (.30)^2][1 - (.40)^2]}} = .4346$$

$$r_{02.1} = \frac{r_{02} - r_{01} r_{21}}{\sqrt{(1 - r_{01}^2)(1 - r_{21}^2)}} = \frac{.30 - (.50)(.40)}{\sqrt{[1 - (.50)^2][1 - (.40)^2]}} = .1259$$

$$r_{12.0} = \frac{r_{12} - r_{10} r_{20}}{\sqrt{(1 - r_{10}^2)(1 - r_{20}^2)}} = \frac{.40 - (.50)(.30)}{\sqrt{[1 - (.50)^2][1 - (.30)^2]}} = .3026$$

THE PARTIAL STANDARD DEVIATION

In Eq. (10-20) we presented the equation for the variation in one variable when variation is another is eliminated. This is the partial standard deviation. As we gave it in Eq. (10-20) it is the variation in variable 0 when variation in variable 1 is held constant. Now we wish to hold variation in variable 2 constant in addition to holding constant variation in variable 1.

Let us inspect Eq. (10-20). We can see that the value under the square-root sign is the important one. In the value $(1 - r_{01}^2)$ we have held constant that part of the variation in variable 0 that can be ascribed to the same factors that produce variation in variable 1. Now in addition we wish to hold constant that part of the variation in variable 0 that can be ascribed to the factors that produce variation in variable 2. But if variables 1 and 2 are correlated and we hold variable 2 constant as it stands, we are partialing out some of the effects of variable 1 which we already dealt with in $(1 - r_{01}^2)$. Therefore all we wish to partial out now from the variation in variable 0 is the variation in variable 2 which is not accounted for by variable 1. Hence by analogy with Eq. (10-20) we write

$$\sigma_{0.12} = \sigma_0 \sqrt{(1 - r_{01}{}^2)(1 - r_{02.1}^2)} \tag{10-25}$$

The general formula for the partial standard deviation is

$$\sigma_{0.12\ldots k} = \sigma_0 \sqrt{(1 - r_{01}{}^2)(1 - r_{02.1}^2)(1 - r_{03.12}^2) \cdots (1 - r_{0k \cdot 12 \ldots (k-1)}^2)} \tag{10-26}$$

The computation of the partial standard deviation is illustrated in Table 10-7.

TABLE 10-7.   Illustration of the Computation of the Partial Standard Deviation

Intercorrelations among and
standard deviations of three variables

	0	1	2	σ
0		.50	.30	10
1			.40	8
2				12

$$\sigma_{0.12} = \sigma_0 \sqrt{(1 - r_{01}{}^2)(1 - r_{02.1}^2)} = 10 \sqrt{[1 - (.50)^2][1 - (.1259)^2]} = 8.5910$$
$$\sigma_{1.02} = \sigma_1 \sqrt{(1 - r_{10}{}^2)(1 - r_{12.0}^2)} = 8 \sqrt{[1 - (.50)^2][1 - (.3026)^2]} = 6.6032$$
$$\sigma_{2.01} = \sigma_2 \sqrt{(1 - r_{20}{}^2)(1 - r_{21.0}^2)} = 12 \sqrt{[1 - (.30)^2][1 - (.4472)^2]} = 10.9116$$

The coefficients of partial correlation were computed in Table 10-6.

THE MULTIPLE REGRESSION EQUATION

In Eq. (10-21) we gave the multiple regression equation using the regression coefficients b. Knowing the formulae for the partial correlation and the partial standard deviation, we can by analogy with Eqs. (10-17) and (10-18) write the formulae for the multiple regression coefficients in terms of correlations and standard deviations as

$$b_{01.2} = r_{01.2} \frac{\sigma_{0.2}}{\sigma_{1.2}} \tag{10-27}$$

$$b_{02.1} = r_{02.1} \frac{\sigma_{0.1}}{\sigma_{2.1}} \tag{10-28}$$

The general formula is

$$b_{01.23\ldots k} = r_{01.23\ldots k} \frac{\sigma_{0.23\ldots k}}{\sigma_{1.23\ldots k}} \tag{10-29}$$

The multiple regression equation in raw-score form is

$$\bar{X}_{0_i} = b_{01.23\ldots k}X_1 + \cdots + b_{0k \cdot 12 \cdots (k-1)}X_k + \bar{X}_0$$
$$- b_{01.23\ldots k}\bar{X}_1 - \cdots - b_{0k \cdot 12 \cdots (k-1)}\bar{X}_k \tag{10-30}$$

When the component variables are given in standard-score form, the regression coefficients are indicated by the symbol β (beta). The multiple regression equation in standard-score form is

$$\bar{z}_{0_i} = \beta_{01.23\ldots k}z_1 + \cdots + \beta_{0k \cdot 12 \cdots (k-1)}z_k \tag{10-31}$$

The beta coefficients can be developed for the three-variable case as follows, parallel to Eqs. (10-27) and (10-28):

$$\beta_{01.2} = r_{01.2} \frac{\sigma_{0.2}}{\sigma_{1.2}}$$

Substituting for the coefficient of partial correlation from Eq. (10-23) and for the partial standard deviations from Eq. (10-20), we have

$$\beta_{01.2} = \frac{r_{01} - r_{02}r_{12}}{\sqrt{(1 - r_{02}^2)(1 - r_{12}^2)}} \frac{\sigma_0 \sqrt{1 - r_{02}^2}}{\sigma_1 \sqrt{1 - r_{12}^2}}$$

Since the scores are in standard-score form, all standard deviations have the value of 1. Hence

$$\beta_{01.2} = \frac{r_{01} - r_{02}r_{12}}{1 - r_{12}^2} \tag{10-32}$$

By a similar derivation we can show that the other beta coefficient is

$$\beta_{02.1} = \frac{r_{02} - r_{01}r_{12}}{1 - r_{12}^2} \tag{10-33}$$

From Eq. (10-29) and parallel to the above two equations, we can write the general formula as

$$\beta_{01.23\ldots k} = r_{01.23\ldots k} \frac{\sigma_{0.23\ldots k}}{\sigma_{1.23\ldots k}}$$
$$= \frac{\beta_{01.3\ldots k} - \beta_{02.3\ldots k}\beta_{21.3\ldots k}}{1 - \beta_{12.3\ldots k}\beta_{21.3\ldots k}} \tag{10-34}$$

The computations of the multiple regression coefficients and the multiple regression equations are illustrated in Table 10-8.

TABLE 10-8.   Illustration of the Computation of the Multiple Regression Coefficients and of the Multiple Regression Equations

	Intercorrelations among and means and standard deviations of three variables				
	0	1	2	$\bar{X}$	σ
0		.50	.30	50	10
1			.40	40	8
2				70	12

$$b_{01.2} = r_{01.2} \frac{\sigma_{0.2}}{\sigma_{1.2}} = .4346 \frac{9.539}{7.332} = .5654$$

$$\sigma_{0.2} = \sigma_0 \sqrt{1 - r_{02}{}^2} = 10 \sqrt{1 - (.30)^2} = 9.539$$
$$\sigma_{1.2} = \sigma_1 \sqrt{1 - r_{12}{}^2} = 8 \sqrt{1 - (.40)^2} = 7.332$$

$$b_{02.1} = r_{02.1} \frac{\sigma_{0.1}}{\sigma_{2.1}} = .1259 \frac{8.660}{10.998} = .0991$$

$$\sigma_{0.1} = \sigma_0 \sqrt{1 - r_{01}{}^2} = 10 \sqrt{1 - (.50)^2} = 8.660$$
$$\sigma_{2.1} = \sigma_2 \sqrt{1 - r_{21}{}^2} = 12 \sqrt{1 - (.40)^2} = 10.998$$

$$\bar{X}_{0_i} = b_{01.2}X_1 + b_{02.1}X_2 + \bar{X}_0 - b_{01.2}\bar{X}_1 - b_{02.1}\bar{X}_2$$
$$= .5654X_1 + .0991X_2 + 50 - (.5654)(40) - (.0991)(70)$$

$$\beta_{01.2} = \frac{r_{01} - r_{02}r_{12}}{1 - r_{12}{}^2} = \frac{.50 - (.30)(.40)}{1 - (.40)^2} = .4524$$

$$\beta_{02.1} = \frac{r_{02} - r_{01}r_{12}}{1 - r_{12}{}^2} = \frac{.30 - (.50)(.40)}{1 - (.40)^2} = .1190$$

$$\bar{z}_{0_i} = \beta_{01.2}z_1 + \beta_{02.1}z_2 = .4524z_1 + .1190z_2$$

The coefficients of partial correlation were computed in Table 10-6.

THE COEFFICIENT OF MULTIPLE CORRELATION

We are now in a position to consider the problem of the prediction of scores on one variable from the optimally weighted composite of scores on several others. The coefficient of correlation between scores on one variable and the optimally weighted composite of scores on several others is termed the *coefficient of multiple correlation*. To distinguish this coefficient from other coefficients of correlation it is symbolized as $R_{0.12\cdots k}$, where variable 0 is the variable being predicted and variables 1 to k are the predictor variables.

From the simple correlation between two variables [Eq. (5-7)], we know that

$$r_{01} = \sqrt{1 - \frac{\sigma_{0.1}^2}{\sigma_0{}^2}}$$

By analogy we can write the coefficient of multiple correlation for the three-variable case as

$$R_{0.12} = \sqrt{1 - \frac{\sigma_{0.12}^2}{\sigma_0^2}} \tag{10-35}$$

The general formula would be

$$R_{0.12\cdots k} = \sqrt{\frac{1 - \sigma_{0.12\cdots k}^2}{\sigma_0^2}} \tag{10-36}$$

Let us develop Eq. (10-35) further:

$$R_{0.12}^2 = 1 - \frac{\sigma_{0.12}^2}{\sigma_0^2}$$

Substituting for $\sigma_{0.12}^2$ from Eq. (10-25), we have

$$R_{0.12}^2 = 1 - \frac{\sigma_0^2(1 - r_{01}^2)(1 - r_{02.1}^2)}{\sigma_0^2}$$
$$= 1 - 1(1 - r_{01}^2)(1 - r_{02.1}^2)$$

Substituting for $r_{02.1}$ from Eq. (10-23) gives us

$$R_{0.12}^2 = 1 - (1 - r_{01}^2)\left\{1 - \left[\frac{r_{02} - r_{01}r_{12}}{\sqrt{(1 - r_{01}^2)(1 - r_{12}^2)}}\right]^2\right\}$$
$$= 1 - (1 - r_{01}^2)\left[1 - \frac{r_{02}^2 - 2r_{01}r_{02}r_{12} + r_{01}^2 r_{12}^2}{(1 - r_{01}^2)(1 - r_{12}^2)}\right]$$
$$= 1 - (1 - r_{01}^2)\left[\frac{(1 - r_{01}^2)(1 - r_{12}^2)}{(1 - r_{01}^2)(1 - r_{12}^2)} - \frac{r_{02}^2 - 2r_{01}r_{02}r_{12} + r_{01}^2 r_{12}^2}{(1 - r_{01}^2)(1 - r_{12}^2)}\right]$$
$$= 1 - \frac{(1 - r_{01}^2)^2(1 - r_{12}^2)}{(1 - r_{01}^2)(1 - r_{12}^2)} + \frac{(1 - r_{01}^2)(r_{02}^2 - 2r_{01}r_{02}r_{12} + r_{01}^2 r_{12}^2)}{(1 - r_{01}^2)(1 - r_{12}^2)}$$
$$= \frac{1 - r_{12}^2}{1 - r_{12}^2} - \frac{(1 - r_{01}^2)(1 - r_{12}^2)}{1 - r_{12}^2} + \frac{(r_{02}^2 - 2r_{01}r_{02}r_{12} + r_{01}^2 r_{12}^2)}{1 - r_{12}^2}$$
$$= \frac{(1 - r_{12}^2) - (1 - r_{01}^2)(1 - r_{12}^2) + (r_{02}^2 - 2r_{01}r_{02}r_{12} + r_{01}^2 r_{12}^2)}{1 - r_{12}^2}$$
$$= \frac{1 - r_{12}^2 - (1 - r_{12}^2 - r_{01}^2 + r_{01}^2 r_{12}^2) + r_{02}^2 - 2r_{01}r_{02}r_{12} + r_{01}^2 r_{12}^2}{1 - r_{12}^2}$$
$$= \frac{1 - r_{12}^2 - 1 + r_{12}^2 + r_{01}^2 - r_{01}^2 r_{12}^2 + r_{02}^2 - 2r_{01}r_{02}r_{12} + r_{01}^2 r_{12}^2}{1 - r_{12}^2}$$
$$= \frac{r_{01}^2 + r_{02}^2 - 2r_{01}r_{02}r_{12}}{1 - r_{12}^2} \tag{10-37}$$
$$R_{0.12} = \sqrt{\frac{r_{01}^2 + r_{02}^2 - 2r_{01}r_{02}r_{12}}{1 - r_{12}^2}} \tag{10-38}$$

Equation (10-38) is a computational formula for the coefficient of multiple correlation involving three variables.

We can rearrange the terms in the numerator of Eq. (10-37) as follows:

$$R_{0.12}^2 = \frac{r_{01}^2 - r_{01}r_{02}r_{12} + r_{02}^2 - r_{01}r_{02}r_{12}}{1 - r_{12}^2}$$

$$= \frac{r_{01} - r_{02}r_{12}}{1 - r_{12}^2} r_{01} + \frac{r_{02} - r_{01}r_{12}}{1 - r_{12}^2} r_{02}$$

Substituting from Eqs. (10-32) and (10-33) gives

$$R_{0.12}^2 = \beta_{01.2}r_{01} + \beta_{02.1}r_{02}$$
$$R_{0.12} = \sqrt{\beta_{01.2}r_{01} + \beta_{02.1}r_{02}} \tag{10-39}$$

In this form the formula for the general case is

$$R_{0.12 \cdots k} = \sqrt{\beta_{01.23 \cdots k}r_{01} + \cdots + \beta_{0k.12 \cdots (k-1)}r_{0k}} \tag{10-40}$$

Thus we can see that the coefficient of multiple correlation is the square root of the sum of the products of the regression coefficients and coefficients of correlation for each component and the outside variable.

The computation of the coefficient of multiple correlation is illustrated in Table 10-9.*

TABLE 10-9.   Illustration of the Computation of the Coefficient of Multiple Correlation

	Intercorrelations among three variables		
	0	1	2
0		.50	.30
1			.40
2			

$$R_{0.12} = \sqrt{1 - \frac{\sigma_{0.12}^2}{\sigma_0^2}} = \sqrt{1 - \frac{(8.5910)^2}{(10)^2}} = .5118$$

$$R_{0.12} = \sqrt{\frac{r_{01}^2 + r_{02}^2 - 2r_{01}r_{02}r_{12}}{1 - r_{12}^2}} = \sqrt{\frac{(.50)^2 + (.30)^2 - 2(.50)(.30)(.40)}{1 - (.40)^2}} = .5118$$

$$R_{0.12} = \sqrt{\beta_{01.2}r_{01} + \beta_{02.1}r_{02}} = \sqrt{(.4524)(.50) + (.1190)(.30)} = .5118$$

The partial standard deviation was computed in Table 10-7 and the multiple regression coefficients in Table 10-8.

* As can be seen from Tables 10-6 to 10-9, the computation of the multiple regression coefficients and the coefficient of multiple correlation "by hand" is by no means simple. With only three variables the computational task is not too bad, but with more variables it is so long and tedious, even with the aid of a table calculating machine, that it is almost impossible. Today with high-speed computers readily available there is no longer need to suffer through the seemingly endless arithmetic involved in complex problems. Therefore one who is confronted with a problem in multiple correlation is well advised not to attempt the computations himself but rather to have them done by a computer.

THE COEFFICIENT OF MULTIPLE CORRELATION IN RELATION TO THE STANDARD ERROR OF PREDICTION

Equation (10-20) relates the standard error of prediction and the coefficient of correlation as follows:

$$\sigma_{0.1} = \sigma_0 \sqrt{1 - r_{01}^2}$$

We can see that the coefficient of correlation is directly related to the extent of error in prediction as measured by $\sigma_{0.1}$. When the coefficient of correlation is high the error of prediction is small, and when the coefficient is low the error is large. When we are dealing with two variables, the distribution of scores in any column (or row, as the case may be) is the distribution of our errors. The combined distribution of errors in all columns is measured by $\sigma_{0.1}$.

We can write the relationship between the standard error of prediction and the coefficient of multiple correlation just as we did above for simple correlation:

$$\sigma_{0.12\cdots k} = \sigma_0 \sqrt{1 - R_{0.12\cdots k}^2} \tag{10-41}$$

The partial standard deviation describes our errors of predicting variable 0 from the weighted composite of the other variables. If we refer to Fig. 10-6, we can see that the distribution of scores in the towers is the distribution of our errors of prediction. The combined distribution of errors in all towers is the partial standard deviation. Therefore the coefficient of multiple correlation relates to the accuracy of prediction of scores on one variable from the optimally weighted combination of scores on several others.

COMPARISON OF THE REGRESSION COEFFICIENTS WITH OTHER POSSIBLE WEIGHTS

The best prediction of an individual's score in variable 0 is, of course, the mean of the 0 scores in the tower in which he falls. This mean is given or estimated by the multiple regression equation. Therefore it follows that if we were dealing with linear correlation, in a differentially weighted composite use of any values other than the regression coefficients would not give us the best prediction of an individual's score, since the value we obtained would not be the mean of the tower described by a particular x_1 score and a particular x_2 score.

Let us examine the validity of the proposition that the regression coefficients are the best weights in the formation of a differentially weighted composite for use in predicting scores on an outside variable. Figure 10-11 gives three illustrative cases involving the correlations among three variables. The figure gives for each case the coefficients of multiple correlation computed from Eq. (10-38) and the two beta coefficients computed from Eqs. (10-32) and (10-33).

Now let us assign various combinations of weights to variables 1 and 2 in each of the three cases and compute the coefficients of correlation between the weighted composite of 1 and 2 and 0 by means of Eq. (10-15),

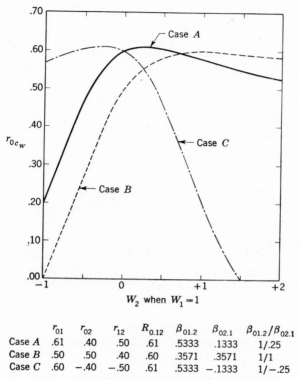

	r_{01}	r_{02}	r_{12}	$R_{0.12}$	$\beta_{01.2}$	$\beta_{02.1}$	$\beta_{01.2}/\beta_{02.1}$
Case A	.61	.40	.50	.61	.5333	.1333	1/.25
Case B	.50	.50	.40	.60	.3571	.3571	1/1
Case C	.60	−.40	−.50	.61	.5333	−.1333	1/−.25

Figure 10-11   The effects of various differential weights assigned the components of a composite on the correlation between the composite and an outside variable.

the coefficient of correlation between a weighted composite and an outside variable. To simplify the task, the weight of 1 is always assigned to variable 1 and the weight assigned to variable 2 is varied. Thus when we wish variable 2 to carry half the weight of variable 1, the weights of variable 1 and 2 respectively are 1 and 0.5. When we wish to assign half again as much weight to variable 2 as that assigned to variable 1, the weights of variables 1 and 2 respectively are 1 and 1.5. In addition, we can assign both positive and negative weights to variable 2.

The coefficients of correlation between the various weighted composites and the outside variable are shown in Fig. 10-11. In each of the three cases we can see that there is an optimal combination of weights which gives the highest correlation between the composite and the outside variable. Reading from the graphs, we can see that for case A the optimal weights for variables 1 and 2 respectively are 1 and 0.25, which yield a correlation between composite scores of .61; for case B the optimal weights are 1 and -0.25. In every case the optimal weights correspond precisely with the ratio of the beta coefficients, and the maximal coefficient of correlation between the weighted composite and the outside variable corresponds precisely with the coefficient of multiple correlation. Therefore the beta coefficients are the best weights. That is, when they are used as weights for the predictor variables the highest possible coefficient of correlation is obtained between the composite and the outside variable. Any other pattern of weights applied to the components necessarily results in lower correlations.

CONDITIONS THAT YIELD THE HIGHEST POSSIBLE MULTIPLE CORRELATIONS

As can be readily ascertained from the various formulae presented for multiple correlation, the magnitude of the coefficient of multiple correlation is a function of the intercorrelations that enter into it. If we know the conditions that yield high and low multiple correlations, then by judicious elimination of variables which do not add significantly to the multiple we can reduce the number of variables with which we are concerned and thereby reduce the labor of computation. The important conditions can be illustrated simply with the three-variable problem.

THE EFFECTS OF THE MAGNITUDE OF THE CORRELATION BETWEEN THE PREDICTED AND THE PREDICTOR VARIABLES UPON THE MULTIPLE CORRELATION

Let us take a simple case where r_{12} is equal to .50 and $r_{01} = r_{02}$. We shall vary the latter values and ascertain the effects upon the multiple correlation. Figure 10-12 shows the relationship between the magnitude of the correlation between the predicted and predictor variables and the coefficient of multiple correlation. It will be seen in this figure that as the magnitude of the correlation between the predicted and predictor variables increases, R increases. It is therefore apparent that, other things being equal, the multiple correlation increases as the coefficient of correlation between the predictor and predicted variables increases. Whenever a choice can be made, then, we should include variables that correlate high with the variable being predicted and eliminate those that have a low correlation.

THE EFFECTS OF THE MAGNITUDE OF THE INTERCORRELATIONS
AMONG THE PREDICTOR VARIABLES UPON MULTIPLE CORRELATION

Let us now examine a case where both r_{01} and r_{02} are .50 and we vary the magnitude of r_{12}. The effects of varying the magnitude of the intercorrelation between the two predictors upon the coefficient of multiple correlation are shown in Fig. 10-13. It will be observed in this figure that

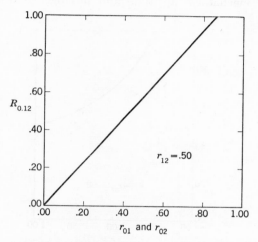

Figure 10-12 The effects on multiple correlation of the magnitude of the correlation between the predictor variables and the predicted variable.

when the correlation between the predictors is very high their joint prediction is little better than the prediction given by either the one or the other alone. As the correlation between the predictors falls in magnitude, their joint prediction increases and becomes quite significant when the correlation between them is high and negative. It is therefore apparent that, other things being equal, the multiple correlation increases as the coefficients of correlation among the predictors decrease or become negative. Whenever a choice can be made, then, we should include variables whose intercorrelations are low or negative.

THE EFFECTS OF SUPPRESSOR VARIABLES UPON
MULTIPLE CORRELATION

Occasionally a variable which is uncorrelated with the variable which is to be predicted will nonetheless contribute to the multiple correlation. Let us consider a case where $r_{01} = .50$ and $r_{02} = .00$, varying r_{12} and observing the effects upon the coefficient of multiple correlation. The

332 THEORY OF PSYCHOLOGICAL MEASUREMENT

relationship is shown in Fig. 10-14. In this figure we can see that when a variable is unrelated to the variable to be predicted, the net effect is to increase the multiple correlation. Such a variable is termed a *suppressor* variable since in effect it partials out or suppresses that part of the other predictor variable which is unrelated to the variable to be predicted.

Suppressor variables are rarely encountered in psychological measurement, but they are sometimes found. For example, scores on paper-and-pencil tests of mechanical aptitude and intelligence tests usually are

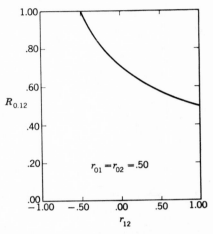

Figure 10-13 The effects on multiple correlation of the magnitude of the correlation among the predictors.

substantially related. In part this is because both tests involve verbal abilities. Mechanical aptitude tests usually show some relationship to measures of practical mechanical performance, but intelligence tests do not. In such a circumstance a combination of the mechanical aptitude test and the intelligence test gives a better prediction of practical mechanical performance than the mechanical aptitude test alone, because the intelligence test acts as a suppressor variable, partialing out from the mechanical aptitude test the verbal abilities which are unimportant in mechanical performance.

In a job interview situation an applicant may be rated in terms of the adequacy of his previous experience and his overall goodness as a person. Ratings on these two scales are likely to be highly correlated as a result of the halo effect. Sometimes it is found that the ratings of previous experience are predictive of later success on the job, but ratings of overall goodness have little predictive value. The two ratings together, then, would give better predictions than experience ratings alone, because the

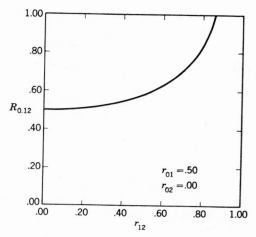

Figure 10-14 The effects on multiple correlation of the correlation between the predictor variables when one of them is uncorrelated with the predicted variable.

ratings of overall goodness would operate as a suppressor variable, partialing out from the experience ratings the effects of the interviewer's general impression, the halo effect.

Summary

When scores on the components forming a composite are deliberately weighted differentially, each score is multiplied by its appropriate weight. It is not the absolute magnitude of the weights which is important; rather, it is their relative magnitudes. Weights deliberately assigned to components are termed nominal, and those the components actually carry in the composite are termed effective.

The mean of composite scores is solely and entirely a function of the means of the components. When the intercorrelations among the components differ from zero, the contribution of the components to the standard deviation of composite scores cannot be determined.

When components are deliberately weighted differentially, those components which are assigned higher weights contribute more to the composite mean than do those which are assigned lower weights. The greater the variation among the nominal weights, the larger the standard deviation of composite scores, and this effect is more pronounced the lower are the intercorrelations among the components. When differential weights are applied to components, the order of individuals in composite scores is more and more changed the greater is the relative variation among the weights, the lower are the intercorrelations among the components, and the smaller is the number of components.

The correlation between a differentially weighted composite and an outside variable varies with the pattern of weights, the relative magnitudes of the nominal weights assigned to the components of the composite. For any given composite there is an optimal pattern of weights. This pattern is optimal in the sense that when the weights are applied to the components, the highest possible correlation between the composite and the outside variable results.

The optimal weights are given by the multiple regression equation, and the coefficient of correlation between the optimally weighted composite and the outside variable is termed the coefficient of multiple correlation. This coefficient is derived from partial correlation, the correlation between two variables when scores on other variables are held constant. It is parallel to the simple Pearsonian coefficient of correlation between two variables, and is interpreted in the same way with respect to linearity and homoscedasticity.

The coefficient of multiple correlation is higher the higher are the correlations between the components and the outside variable, and the lower are the inter-correlations among the components. In addition, a component which correlates low with the outside variable but is highly correlated with the other components adds to the multiple correlation. Variables of this sort are termed suppressors, since they suppress or hold constant that part of other components which is unrelated to the outside variable.

Selected Readings

Ezekiel, M.: "Methods of Correlation Analysis," Wiley, 1941.

Gulliksen, H.: "Theory of Mental Tests," Wiley, 1950.

Horst, A. P.: The prediction of personal adjustment, SSRC Bulletin 48, 1941.

————: Relations among m sets of measures, *Psychometrika*, 26:129–149, 1961.

Hotelling, H.: Relations between two sets of variates, *Biometrika*, 28:321–377, 1936.

Lubin, A.: Some formulae for use with suppressor variables, *Educational and Psychological Meas.*, 17:286–296, 1957.

Peel, E. A.: Prediction of a complex criterion and battery reliability, *Brit. J. Psychol.*, 1:84–94, 1948.

Wherry, R. J., and R. H. Gaylord: Test selection with integral score weights, *Psychometrika*, 11:173–183, 1946.

Wilks, S. S.: Weighting systems for linear functions of correlated variables when there is no dependent variable, *Psychometrika*, 3:23–40, 1938.

chapter II   Validity of

Measurement

When we set about measuring a trait, we first define it and then develop operations designed to yield quantitative descriptions of the extent to which individuals possess or manifest it. Inasmuch as the operations are developed directly from the definition, it might be presumed that they must necessarily measure the defined trait. Yet the definition is only a blueprint, as it were, which may or may not be exactly followed in developing the operations of measurement. Hence we may well wonder about the degree to which the properties measured by a set of operations in fact correspond to the defined trait. Before a set of operations is accepted, it may be necessary to obtain some indications that it measures what is intended.

Our knowledge about individuals and our theoretical conceptions may indicate the existence of some particular trait. However, the trait may not be of such a character that we can give a precise definition of it. This is particularly true when the trait is some abstract intellectual construct such as "intelligence" or "rigidity" rather than some readily observable trait such as "reaction time" or "nest-building behavior." In such a case the definition of the trait is not so much a detailed blueprint for the development of operations of measurement as it is a guidepost giving

335

general directions. Consequently we are unsure both of the nature of the trait with which we are concerned and of the traits which in fact are measured by the operations we develop from the definition.

As psychologists we are often interested in predicting or forecasting behavior. Thus in connection with counseling a high school pupil we may wish to predict from his intelligence-test score the level of academic success he is likely to attain if he goes to college. Similarly, in appraising applicants for a sales job we might wish to forecast their probable success as salesmen from the scores they earn on a test of sociability. In these circumstances we have some clearly specified type of behavior or a trait such as college grades earned or dollar value of merchandise sold measured by one set of operations, and we are concerned with the accuracy with which we can predict it from the traits measured by another set of operations.

It is from these and similar situations that the problem termed validity of measurement arises. It is apparent that validity pertains to the nature of the traits measured by a set of operations. But it should also be apparent that validity is a broad problem area. Indeed, it cannot be said that there is a high degree of agreement on what constitutes the problem of validity. Consequently there is no consensus on what constitutes proper validation, the procedure by means of which the validity of tests and of other operations of measurement is determined.

THE MEANINGS OF VALIDITY AND OF VALIDATION

As is the case with reliability of measurement, the term validity of measurement means different things to different people. However, whereas we saw that with reliability of measurement it is possible to formulate different definitions in reasonably precise ways, this is not always the case with validity of measurement.

When we recall the variety of purposes, both theoretical and practical, for which individuals are measured psychologically, it is not surprising to find different definitions of the term validity being offered. Each of these many purposes has led to somewhat different notions about what validity of measurement is and consequently to the development of different types of procedures for determining validity. These procedures in turn have led to a further examination of the concept of validity, with the consequence that there have been additional variations in the meaning given to the term validity. We cannot, therefore, define validity of measurement in any simple way. What we can do, as we did with the problem of reliability of measurement, is to describe the more or less modal points of view.

THE TYPES OF QUESTIONS ASKED IN CONNECTION WITH VALIDITY

Perhaps the commonest definition given for the term validity is that it refers to the extent to which a test or a set of operations measures what it is supposed to measure. Yet in some instances the definition of the trait may not be entirely clear. Therefore it would be difficult to ascertain the validity of a particular set of operations. In other instances, while it seems obvious that the operations well measure the traits included in the definition, it may appear that they also measure other properties which are not included in the definition. However, even if such circumstances exist, we should not necessarily conclude that the operations are entirely useless. Rather, it simply means that the properties measured are somewhat different from those anticipated. The operations may have less value than anticipated, or they may indeed have greater practical value because of the additional information they give. Therefore with respect to validity some prefer to ask the question "What traits are measured by the operations?" rather than the question "To what extent do the operations measure the traits they are supposed to measure?"

VARIETIES OF VALIDITY AND OF VALIDATION

By and large we can group the various points of view about validity of measurement into one of three categories and speak of the *predictive validity*, the *content validity*, or the *construct validity* of a particular set of operations. In addition to providing definitions of the term validity, they also indicate something of the ways in which validity is to be determined.

These three views about validity have somewhat different purposes and aims, and they arise from the kinds of questions asked in different situations where psychological measurement is used. Yet they cannot be considered to be entirely different logically, and, indeed, they overlap considerably in meaning and in their implications. In general, predictive and content validity are concerned with the question "To what extent do the operations measure the traits they are supposed to measure?" and construct validity with the question "What traits are measured by the operations?" Predictive and construct validity require knowledge of the empirical relationships between the scores given by the operations and scores on other variables, whereas content validity does not. The exercise of personal judgment is required in order to make statements about content and construct validity, and the description of validity is given in verbal terms; whereas statements about predictive validity are statistical descriptions of empirical relationships.

In the following sections we shall consider the nature of each of these types of validity and the processes of validation they involve. In addition, we shall consider a number of methodological and statistical problems connected with predictive validity.

PREDICTIVE VALIDITY

Predictive validity refers to the accuracy with which we can make guesses about one characteristic of an individual from another characteristic. That is, knowing the extent to which an individual manifests or possesses one property, how precisely can we estimate the extent to which he manifests or possesses some other property, the two properties being measured by different operations? With predictive validity we are concerned with the degree to which one set of operations can be substituted for another. The important feature of predictive validity is that there is a measure of the property which is taken to be perfect, the *criterion*, and we seek to estimate scores on it from scores on another measure, the *predictor*. The term prediction as used here does not imply that we are solely concerned with forecasting a future state of affairs, but merely that we are estimating what a given state of affairs is before we actually know. The state of affairs we predict may occur in the future, it may hold at the present time, or it may have held in the past.

DESCRIPTION OF PREDICTIVE VALIDITY

The predictive validity of a test is described in an objective and quantitative fashion by the degree of relationship between predictor scores and criterion scores. Thus the Pearsonian coefficient of correlation or its variants, such as the point biserial, biserial, phi, or tetrachoric coefficients, are commonly used to describe the degree of predictive validity. When these coefficients are used to indicate the degree of relationship between predictor and criterion scores, they are termed *validity coefficients*.

It is obvious that the relationship between two variables can be indicated by other ways than the coefficient of correlation. A scatter diagram or bivariate distribution graphically depicts the relationship between two variables. The difference between the means of the y scores of those individuals earning high and low x scores also tells us something about the relationship between the two variables. But the coefficient of correlation, the validity coefficient, is most commonly used because it gives the most precise description of the degree of relationship and gives it in the simplest and most convenient manner.

VARIETIES OF PREDICTIVE SITUATIONS

Predictive validity describes the accuracy with which we can estimate from the extent to which an individual manifests or possesses one property now the extent to which some other property will be manifested or possessed by him in the future, is now manifested or possessed by him, or was manifested or possessed by him in the past. All these three types of predictive situations involve the relationship between predictor and criterion scores. They differ only in terms of the time of occurrence of the criterion scores. In all three situations the higher the relationship between predictor and criterion scores, the higher the validity, that is, the more accurately can criterion scores be estimated from predictor scores.

Sometimes we are concerned with the precision with which we can predict from an individual's present characteristics what his behavior will be in a given situation if, in the future, he finds himself in that situation. When a high school pupil is counseled, it is helpful to be able to predict what his performance in college is likely to be. Consequently we should be interested in knowing the degree of validity of high school grades in predicting college grades. When applicants for a factory job are considered, it is helpful to know which applicants are most likely to perform well on it. Therefore we should like to know the validity with which scores on a test of manual dexterity administered at the time of hiring predict later performance on the job.

When tests are used in this manner to predict future performance, they are termed *aptitude* tests. Aptitude tests are used to estimate the level of proficiency an individual is likely to achieve in some occupation or his probable performance in some training or educational situation. Thus we say of one individual that he has low clerical aptitude, meaning that if he goes into office work his chances of success are small; and of another individual that his college aptitude is high, meaning that if he goes to college the probability is that he will earn high grades.

The term *prognostic* also is applied to certain tests of this general kind. Usually they are applied to tests which are used to predict behavior that has social or moral connotations or pertains to the individual's adjustment to life. Prognostic measures are used to indicate the probability that a prisoner will be successful if paroled. Tests which are used to indicate the likelihood that psychotherapy will be successful for a patient or which type will be most beneficial to him are termed prognostic.

Sometimes we are interested in the precision with which we can estimate the extent to which the individual now possesses a given trait or behaves in a particular way from the extent to which he possesses some other trait or behaves in some other way. We use scores on one variable, then, to estimate scores on another, both variables measuring present properties of the individual. It may be too difficult, expensive, or time-consuming to measure some property directly, and therefore we prefer to use some other way to obtain quantitative descriptions of that property. This type of validity is often called *concurrent* validity.

If we were interested in measuring proficiency in repairing automobiles, it would be necessary to measure the speed and accuracy with which the individual could rectify all the various possible automotive indispositions, from those of the carburetor to those of the differential gear. We should have to have a large number of cars manifesting all the sundry mechanical disorders. Each person would be required to do all the myriad repair tasks, and we should have to be sure that each was presented with exactly the same series of problems. Since undoubtedly it would take a number of days to measure the speed and accuracy of a single individual's performance, we should not want to do it very often. Consequently if we found that scores on a paper-and-pencil test of knowledge of automotive mechanics and repair were substantially related to performance scores, we should be delighted to use them as substitutes for the cumbersome performance measures.

Sometimes the direct measures of the trait in which we are interested are in error or are not comparable from one individual to another. For example, if we wished to measure the knowledge of high school mathematics, we might find that the grading systems vary markedly from school to school. Consequently, if two pupils from different schools earned the same grade in a mathematics course, we should not be willing to say that their achievement in mathematics is the same. We therefore might construct a standard test of knowledge of high school mathematics and use it in place of high school grades. If within each school the test scores were found to be substantially correlated with mathematics grades, we should probably be willing to use the score an individual made on the test in place of his course grades as a quantitative description of his knowledge of mathematics.

Some tests of this type are called *diagnostic* because they provide indications that certain unfavorable states of affairs exist. Thus tests used as aids in discovering the sources of maladjustment are termed diagnostic. Similarly, tests designed to discover the causes of a pupil's difficulty in learning to read are termed diagnostic.

Finally, sometimes we are interested in the accuracy with which we can estimate the extent to which an individual possessed a given trait in the past. In other words, we wish to estimate a criterion score which describes certain characteristics he manifested at an earlier time. It would appear that, rather than try to estimate them, we should get these criterion scores directly. Yet it may be too difficult, expensive, or time-consuming to do this, and furthermore such records may not be available for all individuals.

For example, suppose we wished to know whether an individual has ever been arrested for a traffic violation. We should have to make inquiries of the appropriate agencies in every state where he has driven a car. This would be quite time-consuming and probably not too easy. A much simpler and quicker thing to do would be to ask the individual the question "Have you ever been arrested for a traffic violation?" In responding to this question we might expect some falsification and errors of memory so that answers might not correspond exactly to past history. Nevertheless, if it were found that responses to the question were substantially related to past history, we might well be willing to substitute the question for the more time-consuming direct approach.

As another example, with patients who have received a brain damage it is often important to ascertain whether there has been any mental deterioration and, if so, to what extent. For some individuals, scores on intelligence tests administered before they suffered the cerebral insult are available. For such cases, scores on an intelligence test administered after the injury can be compared with the preinjury scores. However, these cases are likely to be rare, and so for most patients the extent of mental deterioration cannot be estimated. Suppose, however, that known preinjury scores were found to be substantially related to scores on some postinjury test. We could then with a known degree of accuracy use the postinjury test to estimate the previous intellectual level for the other individuals for whom no preinjury scores are available.

A given test may be used for more than one of these types of prediction. For example, an arithmetic test may have moderate validity in predicting success in clerical occupations, good validity in the diagnosis of failure in mathematics courses, and some but low validity in predicting whether or not the individual had formal schooling. Similarly, for any one given kind of prediction a given test may have differing validity. A test of ability to visualize spatial relations may have low validity in predicting success in clerical occupations, moderate validity in predicting success in engineering school, and good validity in predicting success in a machinist's apprentice training course.

CONTENT VALIDITY

The content validity of a set of operations refers to the degree to which those operations measure the traits which we wish to measure as *judged* from the characteristics or *content* of those operations. We examine a test or other measuring instrument and then, on the basis of our "insight" or "wisdom" as psychologists, judge its validity. The question asked is "To what extent do the operations measure what they are supposed to measure?" The answer is based entirely upon subjective or "professional" judgment, and the degree of validity is given in verbal terms such as "high," "moderate," or "low."

When we recall the many different situations in which we obtain quantitative descriptions of individuals on one trait or another, it would appear that content validity is the type of validity with which we are most concerned. Consider, for example, classroom examinations, thousands of which must be constructed and administered to students every week. They are taken to be valid measures of knowledge of school subjects, because the questions they contain all pertain to the subject matter and are drawn from the class discussions, the lectures, and the textbooks. In the psychological laboratory we use a wide variety of devices to measure different motor, perceptual, and cognitive abilities. These devices are taken to be inherently valid because the behavior they elicit seems so obviously to reflect the pertinent traits. What else could be measured by an aesthesiometer but touch sensitivity, by a stereoscope but binocular vision, by a maze but learning ability. Indeed, a very large proportion of the measuring devices we use seem by their very nature to measure the intended traits, so that we do not judge the validity of the operations in any systematic fashion but do it quite casually.

THE NATURE AND DETERMINATION OF CONTENT VALIDITY

The nature of content validity and the processes involved in determining it will be clearer if we consider a few examples. We might conclude that a test of simple reaction time is highly valid as a measure of simple reaction time, because from our analysis of the situation it is apparent that the individual is not required to make complex decisions, the intensity of the stimulus is considerably above threshold, and the response required is merely to depress a key with the forefinger. On the basis of our examination of the questions comprising a test of "knowledge of the history of the United States" we might conclude that the test has only moderate validity, because even though all the questions in it require knowledge of United States history, none of them deal with the Civil War period. We might say that a rating scale designed to measure "artistic creativity" is a very poor measure of this trait, since we find that the teachers using it base their ratings almost entirely upon the children's ability to draw realistic pictures.

From a study of the content or nature of the operations, then, we arrive at a judgment of the extent to which those operations measure the traits we intended them to measure. There are, in fact, two judgments involved: the extent to which each element or item of the test pertains to the trait as it is defined, and the extent to which the entire set of elements or items represents all aspects of the trait.

The grounds for judging the extent to which a test item measures the desired trait are not always entirely clear and could easily be incorrect. For example, consider the question "Would you rather read a book or go to a movie with a friend?" This might be included as a question in an inventory designed to measure the trait of "sociability," because it involves the choice between a solitary and a social activity. However, it may be that people respond to it on the basis of their interest in literature rather than on their gregariousness. Or it may be that in answering the question the tendency is to give the "sociable" response as a result of a need to conform and not as a result of a desire to be with others.

Nevertheless, in many instances the components of a test so manifestly reflect the trait which the test is intended to measure, and the situation in which the test is administered so clearly minimizes the effects of other factors, that the judgments about validity seem quite reasonable. Consider this question which might appear in a mathematics achievement test:

Solve the following equation for a:

$$\frac{a + b}{c} = d$$

To answer the question the individual must have studied the formal rules and procedures of algebra and have understood them. Knowledge of other subjects such as biology, art, economics, and literature clearly would be insufficient to permit him to answer the question correctly.

Similarly, to correctly answer the question in a vocabulary test

Which of the following words means the same as garish?
gaudy, tarnished, irregular, rude

the individual must understand the meaning of the key word and of the alternative words. Other types of knowledge would be of no value.

In these and many other instances there seems to be no doubt that the judgment of what traits the tests measure is correct. Therefore while in some instances there may be good and sufficient reason to question the validity of a test as judged by the nature and content of the operations, in others the traits measured seem so obvious that they can be agreed upon by all or almost all judges.

Not only do we want to know whether each of the components of a test reflects the trait being measured, but also we want to know whether they cover it in a representative fashion. Judgments of the validity of a test, then, must take into account the extent to which the elements or items which make it up cover all aspects and facets of the trait. For a test of arithmetic ability to be considered to have a high degree of validity it should contain questions involving not only addition, subtraction, and multiplication but also division. A test of knowledge of English literature obviously would not be representative of the subject if it did not have questions dealing with Shakespeare. The validity of a measure of proficiency in typing would be found wanting if individuals were evaluated only in terms of their speed and if accuracy of performance were ignored.

It is the function of the definition of a trait to provide a description of the nature and characteristics of that trait. We should establish the content validity of a test, then, by showing that its elements or items are a representative sample of all aspects and facets of the trait as prescribed by the definition. It is therefore apparent that the adequacy with which we can judge the validity of a test from its content is a function of the adequacy of the definition of the trait. The less detailed and complete the definition, the less well can we judge how representative its components are of the entire trait.

When we have a precise definition of a trait, we have a good idea of its limits and knowledge of the nature of its parts. Consequently we can make an accurate judgment of the extent to which the elements or items of a test are representative of all aspects and facets of the trait. Thus the trait of "eye-hand coordination" might be defined as "The ability to make quick and accurate movements guided solely by information obtained through vision. This ability involves moving an object by means of the hand to a fixed target or maintaining an object on a moving target. Eye-hand coordination is not just simple speed or accuracy of response or visual acuity but the combination of these two abilities in the performance of movements relative to a target." We may not like this particular definition, believing that it covers too much or not enough; but it is reasonably specific, indicating what is included in the trait and what is not, together with a description of the various areas covered by it.

On the basis of this definition we should know that a valid test of eye-hand coordination must involve movements of the hand relative to both stationary and moving targets. A test involving just one or the other type of target would not be representative. Similarly, the quantitative description of the individual's performance, his score, must reflect both the speed and the accuracy of his movements. Furthermore, if the test provides clues to the location of the target through sense modalities other than vision, its validity is impaired.

In some instances the trait is readily fractionated into aspects and phases so that it is easy to ascertain the extent to which the elements of the test are representative of the trait. For example, in measuring knowledge of a school subject such as history, the topic can be divided into natural parts such as time periods. If knowledge of history is measured by means of an objective test, we can count the number of items covering the events in each time period and determine whether all periods are equally represented. With a skill such as ability to perform simple arithmetic functions the trait is naturally divided into the four basic operations of addition, subtraction, multiplication, and division. If an arithmetic ability test contains many more problems of one sort at the expense of another, its representativeness may be challenged.

Nevertheless, even in seemingly clearcut cases such as these where the trait appears to be naturally fractionated into parts, areas, or phases, it cannot always be held that equal representativeness of all parts, areas, or phases in the test is sufficient for content validity. A historian may argue that the events in certain periods of time are of greater significance to the later course of history than are events in other periods of time. Thus it might be argued that the events that took place in American history from 1776 to 1780 shaped the course of the United States far more than those that took place from 1800 to 1840. Hence to be valid a test of knowledge of American history should have five times as many items dealing with the shorter early period than with the longer later period. In the same way, a mathematician might argue that since the process of division merely involves multiplication and subtraction in an arithmetic test, there should be far fewer division items than those of the other three types.

Unless the definition of the trait specifies the relative importance of the various aspects or phases of a trait, subjective judgment is required to determine whether in a test designed to measure that trait they should be equally represented or should have different weights. Subjective judgment, then, be it termed professional judgment, common sense, or "expertese," is involved in all phases of content validity and is its paramount characteristic.

HOMOGENEITY OF TEST ELEMENTS AND CONTENT VALIDITY

One approach to minimizing the effects of subjective judgment and at the same time giving a more precise statement of the degree of validity is to take the homogeneity of the parts of the test as the indication of validity. The argument is that if the component parts of the test do in fact measure the same trait, their scores should be positively correlated, and the higher their intercorrelations the more valid is the test.

Pursuant to this notion, the judgment of whether a particular item is valid or not is taken only as a first approximation of its validity. A test, then, is comprised of items which are considered to be valid "by and large." The judgment with respect to any given item is taken to be fallible and not to be entirely trusted. However, the total score over all the items, the pooled judgment as it were, is taken to have substantial validity. In other words, total scores are taken as the best available measure of the trait which the test is designed to measure. The next step is to eliminate those items which are unrelated to the total test score or have only a low relationship with it and to retain those items which have high correlations with the total score. An item analysis, such as that described in Chap. 7, is performed in which the correlations between scores on the items and total scores are computed. Sometimes the intercorrelations among the items are computed and those which are not related to other items are discarded.

By this process we develop a test which has greater homogeneity than the original test because the relationships among the items are higher. In addition to the judgmental process by means of which the original test elements were selected or developed, we add homogeneity as a basis for gauging validity.

This is a somewhat different notion from the basic concept of content validity, and has theoretical implications akin to those of the concept of domain sampling described in Chap. 8. Content validity in and of itself depends upon subjective judgment alone. Nevertheless, even if we consider homogeneity of the elements of a test as an "aid" to judgment and without any theoretical implications, it pertains only to that aspect of content validity which is concerned with the extent to which each element of the test measures the trait defined. It does not deal with the problem of the extent to which the elements of a test cover all aspects and phases of the trait. Indeed, by discarding those elements of a test which are uncorrelated with the large proportion of the elements, we may eliminate an important aspect or phase of the trait. For example, suppose mechanical aptitude is defined as knowledge of mechanical principles, ability to perceive spatial relationships, and manual dexterity. It is likely that those test elements pertaining to the first two aspects of mechanical aptitude would be positively related to a substantial degree, while those pertaining to the last aspect would be unrelated to the other two. If on these grounds the manual-dexterity elements were eliminated, an important aspect of mechanical aptitude as defined would not be measured.

Discarding parts of a test to ensure that the remaining elements are homogeneous, then, may result in a new test of lower validity—lower validity in the sense that it does not measure the trait as defined as well as the original heterogeneous test. What we have now is a test which measures only certain aspects or phases of the trait. This new test may be more useful and perhaps will give us new and fruitful ideas about the nature of human abilities, but it does not measure the trait as it was originally defined.

CONSTRUCT VALIDITY

In the study of behavior we are often interested in quite specific and concrete traits. Thus our concern may be with the speed of response to a particular stimulus or with success in a particular mechanics training course. In both instances we can measure the traits in which we are interested in a complete and unambiguous fashion, in the one case by simple reaction time and in the other by whether or not the individual graduates. The traits are measured directly and entirely by these operations, and the operations themselves completely define the traits.

In many other instances we are interested in much more general and intangible traits. These traits stem from our formal theories about behavior or from informal theorizing resulting from our observations of behavior. Thus in connection with a concept we have about the functioning of the central nervous system we may postulate a trait of vigilance, a general alertness, readiness to respond, or sensitivity to stimulation. Similarly, from our observation of the behavior of men using tools and equipment we may be led to postulate a trait of mechanical aptitude, a capacity to deal effectively with mechanical contrivances to some constructive ends.

We can describe these traits in verbal terms, and from their definitions we may be able to devise operations to measure them. But to ascertain the validity of these operations is not a simple proposition. Our traits are intellectual constructs rather than concrete tangible behaviors. Consequently, other than the very operations we have devised to measure the traits, there are no alternative operations which completely or precisely measure them. The fact that simple reaction time is related to scores on our test of vigilance, or that graduation from the mechanics course is related to scores on our test of mechanical aptitude, is not sufficient proof of validity. To be sure, because vigilance implies quickness of response and mechanical aptitude implies the ability to profit from training in a mechanical course, these relationships would be expected, and indeed must hold if our tests are to be considered valid measures of our constructs. Nevertheless, in and of themselves the relationships are not enough evidence of validity. Our theoretical conceptions of the traits necessarily lead us *in addition* to expect other types of relationships also to hold. For example, we should expect from our theory of vigilance that scores on the vigilance test will be reduced when a depressant drug is taken, and from our theory of mechanical aptitude that engineering students on the average will obtain higher scores on the mechanical aptitude test than will those majoring in history.

The theoretical notions we have about the traits, the intellectual constructs, by their very nature lead us to postulate various types and degrees of relationships between the traits and other specified variables. To demonstrate that the operations we devise do in fact measure the traits, we must show that *all* these relationships do in fact hold. It is in this fashion that construct validity is shown.

THE LIMITED ROLE OF PREDICTIVE VALIDITY

When we concern ourselves with predictive validity we are in effect saying that we have no real interest as such in the operations which form the predictor, but only in the criterion. Criterion scores are precisely what we want, but because of force of circumstances we cannot obtain them directly. Therefore we seek some other operations which we can use to obtain estimates of criterion scores.

However, as psychologists it is only infrequently that we wish to predict some specific behavior, our interest being entirely in the criterion. In general, this occurs only in those limited practical situations where we wish to forecast some future behavior such as success in school or in a job. More often our interests are broader. For theoretical purposes we are concerned with the relationships among psychological traits which are intellectual constructs and with the effects of various conditions upon such traits. To be sure, we may be interested in the predictive value of the traits, asking such questions as the extent to which measures of intelligence forecast later success in school. However, in these instances our interest clearly is in the operations we use as predictors and not in the criterion.

In many instances, while predictive validity may seem to be indicated, in fact it is not. For example, we say that we wish to establish the validity of a test of scholastic aptitude and therefore should do it by ascertaining the correlation between test scores and grades earned in college. But what college, what major, and for what period of time? The power of a test to predict grades differs from one college to another, from one major to another within the same college, and from one time period to another. We explain away these variations in relationship by saying that grades in some colleges are more reliable than in others and hence more predictable, and in some colleges grades are based less on academic achievement than on other factors. We say that some college majors depend more heavily upon ability factors than do other majors; and in some, performance is more reliably measured than in others. We say that in the past almost any high school student was admitted to college, whereas now there is a considerable restriction in range of ability of those who are admitted; and the high school preparation of students in the past was better or poorer than that at the present time.

In other words, we are taking the point of view that our test measures significant traits but that there is never a single satisfactory criterion available for the evaluation of validity. The traits measured by the operations from which we predict, then, are our primary concern. To put it another way, we are saying that there is a trait of scholastic aptitude which is measured by our test, and we offer as evidence of this the fact that test scores are positively related to success in a variety of different academic situations. Because these correlations are not perfect we conclude that academic success is determined by factors other than scholastic aptitude. Indeed, we may be able to demonstrate this by showing that among individuals with the same scholastic aptitude, that is, with the same score on our test, those who are highly motivated earn higher grades than do those who are less motivated.

This is not to deny any role whatsoever to predictive validity. Indeed, when we discussed it we saw many instances wherein it is of primary concern. Rather, the point is that in many circumstances predictive validity does not serve our ends.

THE NATURE AND DETERMINATION OF CONSTRUCT VALIDITY

We have seen that as a result of some theory we have about the nature and determinants of behavior we often are led to postulate some particular trait. The trait is an intellectual construct, fabricated of ideas, rather than being some objectively and directly observable behavior. The trait does not stand alone, as it were, but rather in its theoretical framework is conceived of as being related to various degrees and in various ways with other characteristics, having certain effects upon behavior, and being modified and changed by various sorts of treatments. These correlates, effects, and modifications may be either explicit or implicit in the theory; and the more complete and elaborated is the theory, the more enumerated and explicit they are in the definition of the trait. Consequently, to be considered a valid index of the constructed trait, any operations we devise to measure it must necessarily provide scores which have the posited relationships and effects and must yield to the modifying influences in the expected ways. The greater the congruence between the posited and obtained relationships, effects, and modifications, and the more of them which are demonstrated, the more valid can the operations be considered to be.

However, seldom if ever is our theory sufficiently developed so that all significant correlates, effects, and modifications can be spelled out completely and in detail beforehand. In order to obtain a more complete picture of the nature and characteristics of the construct we should necessarily have to investigate other possible pertinent relationships, effects, and modifications. These observed relationships, effects, and modifications further specify the construct, indicating with broader scope the nature and characteristics of the traits involved. The determination of construct validity, then, is not so much a process as it is a program. It is a dynamic and continuous process which more and more specifies the traits being measured by the operations and perhaps leads us to change some of our notions about them.

Obviously evidence pertaining to construct validity must come from a variety of sources. No single relationship can demonstrate it, as in the case of predictive validity, nor can an analysis of the nature and content of the operations provide all the needed evidence. Nevertheless, information of the kind given by both predictive and content validity is pertinent. In addition, experimental and other types of systematic investigations would be indicated to ascertain whether the postulated effects and modifications occur. The evidence from all these sources is weighed and integrated so that a final judgment can be made with respect to the traits measured by the operations. Therefore, though largely based upon objective and quantitative data, construct validity is determined and evaluated by a subjective process of judgment; and the degree of validity cannot be expressed by any single quantitative index such as a validity coefficient but must be given in verbal terms.

As an example, suppose we define the trait of finger dexterity as the ability to manipulate small objects quickly and accurately by movements of the fingers. On the basis of this definition we might develop a test wherein the individual with his fingers picks up small pins two at a time from a bin and successively places the pairs of pins in a series of holes in a board. When we examine the nature and content of the performance required by the test, we observe that people do follow the instructions, using the fingers of one hand to grasp and to manipulate the pins.

We should posit that if the test does in fact measure our construct of finger dexterity, its scores should be related to performance on jobs wherein the trait is important, with scores showing higher predictive validity on those jobs requiring higher levels of the trait. We might expect positive correlations between test scores and performance both on the job of package wrapper and on the job of instrument assembler, with the relationship for the latter job being the greater since in its performance finger dexterity is more of a key factor. Our construct does not involve the higher mental processes, so there should be no correlation between scores on our test and those on an intelligence test.

We might well anticipate that the degree of finger dexterity an individual possesses has certain effects upon other aspects of his behavior. Consequently, we should expect that people who are superior in finger dexterity would be more likely than others to seek entry into occupations where they can use this talent. Therefore dentists should score higher on the test than lawyers.

Certain treatments should affect our test scores. Thus exercises designed to make the fingers nimble should increase scores. Similarly, drugs that reduce the stiffness in the fingers of arthritic patients should enable them to earn higher test scores.

In defining our trait we dealt only with motor aspects, but there may well be some other features of it we have not recognized. Consequently, we should examine the relationships between scores on our test and scores on other types of tests such as measures of spatial judgment and touch sensitivity. The relationships we find here, be they high or low, help us to further specify and clarify the nature of the trait of finger dexterity.

SOME METHODOLOGICAL AND STATISTICAL PROBLEMS IN PREDICTIVE VALIDITY

There are a number of methodological and statistical problems that arise in connection with predictive validity. Because predictive validity plays a part in the determination of construct validity, these matters are also pertinent to it. In this section we shall discuss the prediction of criterion scores, the composition of a predictor and its validity, reliability of measurement in relation to validity, prediction when there are multiple criteria, and validity in relation to the range of individual differences.

ESTIMATING CRITERION SCORES FROM PREDICTOR SCORES

In our discussion of correlation in Chaps. 5 and 6 we saw that knowing nothing about an individual but his predictor score X, our best estimate of his criterion score is the average of the criterion scores, $\bar{Y}_i$, of those individuals who have the same predictor score as his. If we take the relationship between predictor and criterion scores to be linear, then we express the degree of relationship by means of the Pearsonian coefficient. It will be recalled from Chap. 5 that in this event we use the regression equation to give us a value we take as representative of the Y scores of individuals all of whom earn the same X score. We adopt either of two points of view. We consider the values of Y as given by the regression equation to be more accurate descriptions than the actual means of the columns, or we take those values as estimates of the actual means. That is, when we have a single predictor we use the regression line (the straight line of best fit in a least-squares sense), and when we have several predictors we use the regression plane (the plane of best fit in a least-squares sense) to make our predictions from X to Y. So it is by means of the regression equations [(6-4) to (6-9) when the predictor is a single variable and (10-30) and (10-31) when the predictor is a composite variable] that we predict an individual's criterion score from his predictor score.

The accuracy with which these predictions are made is described by the standard error of estimate or prediction [Eqs. (6-13) to (6-15) when the predictor is a single variable and Eqs. (10-25) and (10-26) when it is a composite variable]. The standard error of estimate is the standard deviation of the criterion scores of those individuals all of whom have the same predictor score. It should be recalled from our discussion in Chaps. 5, 6, and 10 that when the relationship is taken as being linear and is described by the Pearsonian coefficient, the deviations on which the standard error are based are deviations from the regression lines or regression plane and not from the means of the Y scores in the columns or towers, unless those means happen to fall on the regression line or plane. The standard error of estimate or prediction, then, describes the accuracy with which individual predictions are made by the regression equation. It will be remembered that we must adopt either of two points of view about the standard error of estimate. If we are willing to presume the relationship is homoscedastic, then we can take the standard error as descriptive of the accuracy of predictions at all levels of predictor scores. If we are not willing to do this, we must take the standard error as a weighted average of the errors of prediction [Eq. (5-1)].

THE COMPOSITION OF A PREDICTOR AND ITS VALIDITY

As we have seen, most of the devices we use for the measurement of psychological traits yield scores which are composites made up of the sum or average of the scores on a series of components. Aptitude and achievement tests, together with personality inventories, commonly are composed of a series of items or subtests; rating procedures are likely to involve the addition or averaging of ratings on several rating scales or of several raters; and measures of performance such as reaction time ordinarily involve the averaging of a number of different determinations of the behavior. In Chap. 7 we saw that the composition of a measuring device, that is, the nature of the intercorrelations among the components, is an important factor in its correlation with a variable outside the composite, in the present case the criterion. Equation (7-16) and Fig. 7-2 indicate that a predictor will have higher validity the lower are the intercorrelations among its components.

When we have a choice, then, we should form a predictor of components that have low intercorrelations. That is, we should prefer to have a predictor which is heterogeneous in composition rather than one which is homogeneous. If we are unable to choose among possible predictors but must use the ones we have, then in order to obtain the best possible prediction of the criterion we should weight them in terms of their multiple regression coefficients as given by Eq. (10-34). The important conclusion, then, is that the optimal condition for predictive validity is given by a heterogeneous predictor.

RELIABILITY AND PREDICTIVE VALIDITY

Equation (9-13) shows the effects of the reliability with which two variables are measured upon the correlation between them. This formula is

$$r_{xy} = r_{x_\infty y_\infty} \sqrt{r_{xx} r_{yy}}$$

That is, given $r_{x_\infty y_\infty}$ (the correlation between true predictor and true criterion scores), we find that as r_{xx} (the reliability of the predictor) and r_{yy} (the reliability of the criterion) change, so does the empirically determined validity coefficient r_{xy}. When this equation is plotted as in Fig. 9-5, we can see that as the reliability of either the predictor or the criterion becomes lower and lower, the validity becomes lower and lower. Indeed, as we saw in Table 9-1, if either the predictor or the criterion is completely unreliable, then fallible scores on the two variables will be completely uncorrelated and the validity will be zero. Hence we can say that reliability limits validity and that for optimal prediction both the predictor and the criterion should be measured with as high reliability as possible so that r_{xy} approaches $r_{x_\infty y_\infty}$, the highest possible validity.

PREDICTION WITH MULTIPLE CRITERIA

We have been discussing predictive validity as if the criterion always is a single variable. However, as is the case with other measures of psychological characteristics, the criterion often is a composite variable. The criterion of leadership might be a series of rating scales designed to measure various facets of the trait. The criterion of success for a particular sales job might involve the total dollar volume of sales, the number of new accounts developed, and the number of repeat sales to the same customers. In cases such as these, when we have multiple criteria we must somehow combine them in order to compute the coefficient of correlation between criterion and predictor scores so as to describe predictive validity.

In combining criteria, all of them can be taken to be of equal importance or they can be differentially weighted. Criteria can be taken to be of equal importance either in the sense that the units of measurement in which each is expressed are equivalent, so that they can be summed or averaged, or in the sense that they contribute equally to the variation in composite scores. If we wish to have the various component criteria contribute differently to the composite, they can be assigned differential nominal weights based on personal judgment about their relative importance, their reliability, or their correlation with a hypothetical trait which underlies all the component criteria. Finally, critical points may be set on each criterion and individuals placed into either of two classes, those whose criterion scores all fall above the critical points and those for whom one or more criterion scores fall below such points.

TAKING ALL THE MULTIPLE CRITERIA AS BEING EQUALLY IMPORTANT

In many instances the scales on which the different criteria are expressed are assumed to be equivalent, and scores on all component criteria are assumed to be comparable and therefore simply summed or averaged. Thus when academic success in college is measured by grades received in different courses, all these various grades are taken as being scores on comparable scales and are averaged to obtain a total criterion score. This is also likely to be done with ratings where ratings on a series of scales designed to measure different facets of a trait are merely summed or averaged. In some cases it is possible to change the units in which the various scales are expressed to other units which are equivalent. For example, suppose the success of factory workers is gauged both by the number of items of work they produce and by the number of accidents in which they are involved. If the value of an item of work is known, production can be expressed in terms of dollars. Similarly, if the cost of an accident is known, it too can be expressed in terms of dollars. The composite criterion score of a worker, then, would be the dollar value of his production minus the dollar cost of his accidents. The net value would be his contribution to his job.

If we wish to consider the various criteria as being of equal importance in the sense that they contribute equally to the variation in composite scores, the common procedure is to transmute the scores on each of the component criteria to standard or standardized scores. However, as we saw in connection with Eqs. (10-3) to (10-5), this ignores the intercorrelations among the criteria, and these intercorrelations also contribute to the variation in total scores. Therefore transmuting scores on each component criterion to standard or standardized scores does not result in a situation wherein each contributes equally to the variation in composite scores, though this result may be approximated thereby. But as we saw in Chap. 4, the use of standard or standardized scores does in a sense make the units comparable.

DIFFERENTIAL WEIGHTING OF COMPONENT CRITERIA

When it is believed that the various component criteria should be differentially weighted, nominal weights are assigned as in Eq. (10-1), and differentially weighted composite scores are obtained. The mean of these composite scores is given by Eq. (10-8) and the standard deviation by Eq. (10-10). Ordinarily differential weights are applied to component criterion scores after the scales have been made comparable, as through the use of standard or standardized scores. Either we can use weights which in our personal judgment best describe the relative importance of the component criteria, or we can differentially weight them in terms of their reliability or their correlations with a hypothetical trait which we assume underlies all of them.

Perhaps the most common method of developing differential weights is through personal judgment. On the basis of our theoretical notions about the characteristic being measured, our analysis of the characteristic, our values, or similar considerations, we make decisions about the relative importance of the various component criteria. Thus in measuring academic success in high school it might be felt that grades in "solids" are twice as important as those in other courses. In this event the weights of 2 and 1, respectively, would be assigned to grades in the two types of courses. In gauging the performance of salesclerks, the management of the department store might believe that dollar volume of sales is twice as important as number of absences and four times as important as accuracy in making change. Then the weights of 4, 2, and 1, respectively, would be assigned to the three component criteria.

Sometimes it makes sense to weight the various component criteria in terms of their reliability. It can be argued that less reliable criteria should not be given so much weight as more reliable ones since scores on them are largely determined by unsystematic factors. Equations (8-16) and (8-28) showed us that the extent to which variation in fallible scores reflects variation in true scores is given directly by the reliability coefficient. In these formulae the extent of variation among scores is measured by the variance. If we wish to measure variation by the standard deviation, we use the square root of the reliability coefficient as the appropriate index. It will be recalled that the square root of the reliability coefficient is also the correlation between true and fallible scores [Eqs. (8-23) and (8-29)]. So if we wish to assign nominal weights to the components so that the more reliable ones carry higher weights and the less reliable lower weights, we use as nominal weights the square roots of the reliability coefficients, that is, the correlation between fallible and true scores.

When we have a number of criteria, we can think of them as all measuring the same trait. Indeed, it can be argued that is why we chose them. While no one component criterion is a perfect measure of the trait, they all may be thought of as reflecting it to greater or lesser degrees. This underlying trait is, of course, an intellectual construct and presumably could just as well be measured by operations other than the particular ones we happen to have. Scores on this underlying trait would be conceived of as true criterion scores, and scores on each of the component criteria as fallible measures of it. We cannot, of course, directly obtain an individual's score on this intellectually constructed trait, but we can obtain an estimate of it by averaging his scores on the component criteria. The coefficient of correlation between the scores on a single variable and scores on an average composite as given by Eq. (7-20) is

$$r_{z_1 c_z} = \frac{1 + (k-1)\overline{r_{1i}}}{\sqrt{k + k(k-1)\overline{r_{ii'}}}}$$

where $\overline{r_{1i}}$ is the average of the correlations between scores of a given component criterion 1 and those on the other components, $\overline{r_{ii'}}$ is the average of the intercorrelations among the component criteria, and k is the number of them. Dividing the numerator and denominator by k, we have

$$r_{z_1 c_z} = \frac{\dfrac{1}{k} + \dfrac{k-1}{k}\,\overline{r_{1i}}}{\sqrt{\dfrac{1}{k} + \dfrac{k-1}{k}\,\overline{r_{ii'}}}}$$

This is the correlation between scores on one component criterion and scores on the k component criteria we happen to have. Since the underlying trait is an intellectual construct and conceivably could be measured by an infinite number of different specific operations, $k = \infty$. If we have chosen our criteria wisely, the k components we have represent well the infinite number in terms of their average intercorrelations. Consequently, $1/k$ closely approximates 0, and $(k-1)/k$ closely approximates 1. Therefore the above equation can be written as the correlation between scores on any one fallible component criterion j and true criterion scores and resolves to

$$r_{z_j z_\infty} = \frac{\overline{r_{ji}}}{\sqrt{\overline{r_{ii'}}}} \tag{11-1}$$

As we did when we wished to weight component criteria in terms of their reliability of measurement, we should again weight the component criteria in terms of their correlations with true scores. In this case we should be weighting them so as to get the best possible measure of some hypothetical general trait which underlies them.

USING CRITICAL CUTOFF POINTS ON THE MULTIPLE CRITERIA

In some situations where the criterion has many different facets each of which is measured by a different component criterion, it may seem that a simple or weighted summation of standard or standardized scores on them is not appropriate. For example, an airplane pilot whose takeoffs are smooth and whose cross-country flights are precise, but who is unable to land the aircraft without serious consequences, could not be considered to be a successful pilot. Similarly, a child who is well mannered at home and in adult groups and whose behavior in the classroom is excellent, but who in play situations is forever hitting, biting, and kicking other children, cannot be considered to be making a satisfactory social adjustment. In these instances as in many others it appears that critical points can be set on the component criteria, cutoff points below which any score automatically marks the individual as being low on the characteristic the total criterion is designed to measure. A low score on any one component is not taken as being compensated for by high scores on the others as is the case when we average the scores on the component criteria. On the other hand, an individual will be categorized as successful if his scores on all criteria fall above the critical points, even though they exceed them by very small amounts. Individuals, then, are placed in one or the other of two categories, those who are successful or high on the criterion and those who are unsuccessful or low on it. Consequently, we have a discontinuous dichotomous criterion, and validity coefficients are most appropriately expressed by the point biserial or phi coefficient.

The critical points might well be set at different points on the different component criteria, depending upon what we consider critical performance on each to be. In this sense this multiple cutoff procedure does provide a system of differential weights for the component criteria, but because each component is given a complete "veto" power, in another sense they are all equally important.

VALIDITY AND THE RANGE OF INDIVIDUAL DIFFERENCES

Sometimes we find ourselves in the position of being unable to determine the validity of a predictor for the entire range of scores. The only data available to us are the predictor and criterion scores for a restricted range of individuals. As is the case with the reliability coefficient, the magnitude of the validity coefficient is affected by the range of individual differences. Consequently, a description of the validity of the predictor based upon the scores of the restricted range could not be considered satisfactory.

There are two common situations where this circumstance occurs, one involving two variables and the other three variables. In the first situation a restriction of range results from a selection of individuals on the basis of their predictor scores. Criterion (X) and predictor (Y) scores are available only for individuals whose predictor scores are above some certain critical point, and we can estimate the validity of the predictor from their scores alone. There is, then, a *direct* or *explicit* restriction of the range of individual differences on the basis of X scores, and consequently the standard deviation of X scores is reduced. Any effects of this restriction on the extent of variation of Y scores are *indirect* or *incidental*. In the second situation the explicit selection is made on the basis of another variable, Z. Criterion (Y) and predictor (X) scores are available only for individuals whose Z scores fall above a certain critical point, and we can estimate the validity of the predictor from their scores alone. There is, then, explicit restriction on the basis of Z scores, and consequently the standard deviation of Z scores is reduced. Any effects of this restriction on the extent of variation of Y and X scores are incidental.

As an example of the first situation, suppose a company uses scores on a clerical test to select office workers. All those whose scores fall above a given critical point are offered employment, and all those whose scores fall below this point are rejected. As a consequence, test and criterion scores are available only for those persons whose test scores fall above the critical point. Therefore the coefficient of correlation between the test and the criterion of job success describes the accuracy of prediction only for this restricted range of persons and not for the entire range of applicants. Obviously it would be very helpful if we could estimate the validity of the test for the entire range of applicants from that of the restricted range of those who are selected.

As an example of the second situation, let us say that students have been admitted to college on the basis of their high school grades, with only those whose grades are above a given point being admitted. Suppose a scholastic aptitude test is being considered as a substitute admission procedure. To determine the validity of the test in predicting college grades, it might be administered to entering freshmen. However, these individuals have already been selected on the basis of their high school grades, and as a consequence the correlation between their test scores and college grades would describe the accuracy of prediction only for a restricted range and not for the entire range of applicants. Again it would be helpful if the validity of the test for the entire range could be estimated from its validity for the restricted range.

In the two foregoing examples we have illustrated the restriction of range by the selection of high-scoring individuals. In the following developments, however, no presumptions at all will be made about the zone where the scores of the selected individuals fall, but only that their scores do not cover the entire range. It might be that only low-scoring individuals are selected, or those in the middle of the distribution so that individuals at both extremes are excluded.

THE EFFECTS OF RESTRICTION OF RANGE ON VALIDITY—THE TWO-VARIABLE SITUATION

Let us symbolize the characteristics of the distributions of predictor and criterion scores and their relationships for the restricted and for the total range as follows:

	Total range	Restricted range
Standard deviation of predictor scores........	σ_x	σ_x'
Standard deviation of criterion scores.........	σ_y	σ_y'
Validity coefficient........................	r_{xy}	r_{xy}'
Regression coefficient.....................	$b_{y \cdot x}$	$b_{y \cdot x}'$
Standard error of estimate or prediction.......	$\sigma_{y \cdot x}$	$\sigma_{y \cdot x}'$

We are concerned with the effects of deliberate or explicit restriction of range of predictor scores upon the validity coefficient. The ratio σ_x'/σ_x describes the amount of explicit restriction on predictor scores, and the ratio σ_y'/σ_y the resulting amount of incidental restriction of criterion scores. In each case the amount of restriction is expressed as the ratio of the variation in scores of the restricted group to the variation in scores of the total group.

To proceed with our development it is necessary to make two assumptions. First we must assume that the slope of the regression line through the Y scores in the columns is the same both for the restricted and for the total range of X scores. That is, we assume

$$b_{y \cdot x}' = b_{y \cdot x} \qquad (11\text{-}2)$$

Second, we must assume that the standard error of estimate or the standard deviation of the Y scores in the columns is the same both for the restricted and for the total range of X scores. That is, we assume

$$\sigma_{y \cdot x}' = \sigma_{y \cdot x} \qquad (11\text{-}3)$$

What we are assuming is that the characteristics of that portion of the bivariate distribution of scatter diagram we do have are those of the total bivariate distribution. If the amount of restriction is small, so that σ_x' is almost as large as σ_x and the ratio σ_x'/σ_x approaches 1, the chances are greater that the characteristics of the portion of the bivariate distribution will be the same as those of the total distribution.

We could assume that the relationship between test and criterion scores is linear in the sense that all the means of the Y scores in the columns fall precisely on the same straight line and that all the standard deviations of the Y scores in the columns are equal, so that homoscedasticity holds. However, it is not necessary to make these restrictive assumptions. In Chap. 5 we saw that the regression coefficient describes the slope of the straight line of best fit in a least-squares sense [Eqs. (5-19) to (5-21)]. All we need to assume, therefore, is that the best-fitting straight line through that portion of the bivariate distribution we do have is also the best-fitting straight line through the remaining portion. In Eq. (5-1) we saw that $\sigma_{y \cdot x}^2$ can be thought of as the weighted means of the variances of the Y scores in the columns. So it is only necessary for us to assume that the weighted mean of the variances of the Y scores in the columns of that portion of the bivariate distribution we do have is equal to the weighted mean of the variances of the Y scores in the columns of the remaining portion.

From Eq. (5-15) we can write the regression coefficient as

$$b_{y \cdot x} = \frac{\Sigma xy}{n \sigma_x^2}$$

Since $r_{xy} = \Sigma xy/n\sigma_x\sigma_y$, we can write $r_{xy}\sigma_y = \Sigma xy/n\sigma_x$. Consequently,

$$b_{y\cdot x} = r_{xy}\frac{\sigma_y}{\sigma_x}$$

and, similarly,

$$b'_{y\cdot x} = r'_{xy}\frac{\sigma'_y}{\sigma'_x}$$

Since, by assumption in Eq. (11-2), $b'_{y\cdot x} = b_{y\cdot x}$,

$$r'_{xy}\frac{\sigma'_y}{\sigma'_x} = r_{xy}\frac{\sigma_y}{\sigma_x} \tag{11-4}$$

Solving for σ'_y, we have

$$\sigma'_y = \frac{r_{xy}\sigma_y\sigma'_x}{r'_{xy}\sigma_x} \tag{11-5}$$

By assumption in Eq. (11-3) $\sigma'_{y\cdot x} = \sigma_{y\cdot x}$, so substituting from Eq. (6-13), the standard error of estimate, we have

$$\sigma'_y\sqrt{1 - r'^2_{xy}} = \sigma_y\sqrt{1 - r_{xy}^2} \tag{11-6}$$

Squaring Eq. (11-6) and substituting for σ'_y from Eq. (11-5) gives

$$\frac{r_{xy}^2\sigma_y^2\sigma'^2_x}{r'^2_{xy}\sigma_x^2}(1 - r'^2_{xy}) = \sigma_y^2(1 - r_{xy}^2)$$

Dividing both sides of the equation by σ_y^2 gives

$$\frac{r_{xy}^2\sigma'^2_x}{r'^2_{xy}\sigma_x^2}(1 - r'^2_{xy}) = 1 - r_{xy}^2 \tag{11-7}$$

Multiplying both sides of the equation by $\sigma_x^2/r_{xy}^2\sigma'^2_x$ gives

$$\frac{\sigma_x^2}{r_{xy}^2\sigma'^2_x}\frac{r_{xy}^2\sigma'^2_x}{r'^2_{xy}\sigma_x^2}(1 - r'^2_{xy}) = \frac{\sigma_x^2}{r_{xy}^2\sigma'^2_x}(1 - r_{xy}^2)$$

$$\frac{1 - r'^2_{xy}}{r'^2_{xy}} = \frac{\sigma_x^2(1 - r_{xy}^2)}{r_{xy}^2\sigma'^2_x}$$

$$\frac{1}{r'^2_{xy}} - \frac{r'^2_{xy}}{r'^2_{xy}} = \frac{\sigma_x^2(1 - r_{xy}^2)}{r_{xy}^2\sigma'^2_x}$$

$$\frac{1}{r'^2_{xy}} - 1 = \frac{\sigma_x^2(1 - r_{xy}^2)}{r_{xy}^2\sigma'^2_x}$$

$$\frac{1}{r'^2_{xy}} = 1 + \frac{\sigma_x^2(1 - r_{xy}^2)}{r_{xy}^2\sigma'^2_x}$$

$$= \frac{r_{xy}^2\sigma'^2_x}{r_{xy}^2\sigma'^2_x} + \frac{\sigma_x^2(1 - r_{xy}^2)}{r_{xy}^2\sigma'^2_x}$$

$$= \frac{r_{xy}^2\sigma'^2_x + \sigma_x^2(1 - r_{xy}^2)}{r_{xy}^2\sigma'^2_x}$$

Inverting gives

$$\frac{r_{xy}'^2}{1} = \frac{r_{xy}^2 \sigma_x'^2}{r_{xy}^2 \sigma_x'^2 + \sigma_x^2 (1 - r_{xy}^2)}$$

Dividing the numerator and denominator of the fraction on the right-hand side of the equation by σ_x^2 gives

$$r_{xy}'^2 = \frac{r_{xy}^2 (\sigma_x'^2 / \sigma_x^2)}{r_{xy}^2 (\sigma_x'^2 / \sigma_x^2) + (\sigma_x^2 / \sigma_x^2)(1 - r_{xy}^2)}$$

$$= \frac{r_{xy}^2 (\sigma_x'^2 / \sigma_x^2)}{r_{xy}^2 (\sigma_x'^2 / \sigma_x^2) + 1 - r_{xy}^2}$$

$$r_{xy}' = \frac{r_{xy}(\sigma_x' / \sigma_x)}{\sqrt{1 - r_{xy}^2 + r_{xy}^2 (\sigma_x'^2 / \sigma_x^2)}} \tag{11-8}$$

Equation (11-8) shows what the validity of a predictor, r_{xy}', would be if we deliberately reduced the variation in X scores from σ_x to σ_x'. To show these effects, Eq. (11-8) is plotted in Fig. 11-1. In this figure we can see

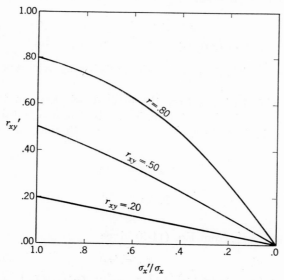

Figure 11-1 The effects of deliberate or explicit restriction of range of predictor (X) scores on the validity of the predictor (r_{xy}').

that as the variation in predictor scores is decreased, that is, as σ_x'/σ_x becomes smaller, the validity of the test, r_{xy}', also becomes smaller. It is therefore apparent that if a test is validated on a group whose predictor scores do not represent the total range, the validity coefficient will be reduced.

Equation (11-8) shows that the validity coefficient will be reduced when the range of predictor scores is reduced. Ordinarily we have data on a group with a restricted range and wish to estimate what the validity coefficient would be if we had the total range. That is, we wish r_{xy} rather than r'_{xy}. To obtain this value we start with Eq. (11-7), solving for r_{xy}. The solution is parallel to that for r'_{xy}, so equivalent to Eq. (11-8) we can write

$$r_{xy} = \frac{r'_{xy}(\sigma_x/\sigma'_x)}{\sqrt{1 - r'^2_{xy} + r'^2_{xy}(\sigma_x{}^2/\sigma'^2_x)}} \tag{11-9}$$

Suppose that workers are selected for an office job on the basis of their scores on a clerical aptitude test, the standard deviation of the scores of all the applicants being 10 and the standard deviation of those selected being 5. For those persons who are hired we find the coefficient of correlation between test and criterion scores to be .30. From Eq. (11-9) we can estimate the validity the test would have if all persons had been hired and there was no restriction in range. Placing the appropriate values in Eq. (11-9), we have

$$r_{xy} = \frac{(.30)^{10}\!/\!_5}{\sqrt{1 - (.30)^2 + (.30)^2[(10)^2/(5)^2]}} = \frac{.60}{1.13} = .53$$

Clearly, the coefficient of .30 considerably underestimates the validity of the test.

We might wish to know how the explicit selection on the predictor affects the variation in the criterion. The extent of incidental variation in the criterion is indicated by σ'_y/σ_y. Dividing both sides of Eq. (11-5) by σ_y gives us

$$\begin{aligned}\frac{\sigma'_y}{\sigma_y} &= \frac{r_{xy}\sigma'_y}{r'_{xy}\sigma_x} \\ &= \frac{r_{xy}(\sigma'_x/\sigma_x)}{r'_{xy}}\end{aligned} \tag{11-10}$$

Substituting for r'_{xy} from Eq. (11-8) gives

$$\begin{aligned}\frac{\sigma'_y}{\sigma_y} &= \frac{r_{xy}(\sigma'_x/\sigma_x)}{r_{xy}(\sigma'_x/\sigma_x)/\sqrt{1 - r_{xy}{}^2 + r_{xy}{}^2(\sigma'^2_x/\sigma_x{}^2)}} \\ &= \sqrt{1 - r_{xy}{}^2 + r_{xy}{}^2\frac{\sigma'^2_x}{\sigma_x{}^2}}\end{aligned} \tag{11-11}$$

To show the incidental effects on the variation of criterion scores of the explicit restriction of range of the predictor scores, Eq. (11-11) is plotted in Fig. 11-2. In this figure we can see that the greater is the deliberate restriction on the predictor, the greater is the incidental restriction on the criterion.

If we wished to express the incidental restriction on y in terms of r'_{xy} rather than r_{xy} as we did in Eq. (11-11), we should substitute for r_{xy} from

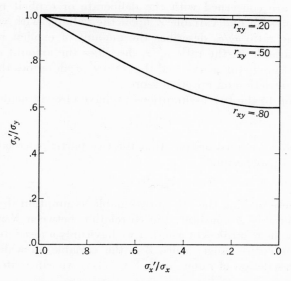

Figure 11-2 The incidental effects of deliberate or explicit restriction of range of predictor (X) scores on the variation in criterion (y) scores.

Eq. (11-9) in Eq. (11-10). Then

$$\frac{\sigma'_y}{\sigma_y} = \frac{\dfrac{r'_{xy}(\sigma_x/\sigma'_x)}{\sqrt{1 - r'^2_{xy} + r'^2_{xy}(\sigma_x^2/\sigma'^2_x)}} \dfrac{\sigma'_x}{\sigma_x}}{r'_{xy}}$$

$$= \frac{1}{\sqrt{1 - r'^2_{xy} + r'^2_{xy}(\sigma_x^2/\sigma'^2_x)}} \tag{11-12}$$

$$\sigma_y = \sigma'_y \sqrt{1 - r'^2_{xy} + r'^2_{xy}\frac{\sigma_x^2}{\sigma'^2_x}}$$

In the foregoing example of the selection of office workers let us say that the standard deviation of the criterion scores of those persons who were hired is 8. Variation in criterion scores has been subjected to incidental restriction. We estimate the standard deviation of criterion scores had all applicants been hired from the above formula as follows:

$$\sigma_y = 8\sqrt{1 - (.30)^2 + (.30)^2\frac{(10)^2}{(5)^2}} = 8\sqrt{1.27} = 9.04$$

THE EFFECTS OF RESTRICTION OF RANGE ON VALIDITY—THE THREE-VARIABLE SITUATION

Here we are concerned with the deliberate or explicit restriction of range of scores on one variable Z upon the validity with which X predicts Y. The ratio σ'_z/σ_z describes the amount of explicit restriction of scores on variable Z, the ratio σ'_x/σ_x describes the amount of incidental restriction of predictor scores, and the ratio σ'_y/σ_y describes the amount of incidental restriction on criterion scores.

In addition to the two assumptions we have already made that

$$b'_{y\cdot x} = b_{y\cdot x}$$

and $\sigma'_{y\cdot x} = \sigma_{y\cdot x}$, we must assume that the two partial correlations are the same. That is, we assume

$$r'_{xy\cdot z} = r_{xy\cdot z} \tag{11-13}$$

We are here making the not unreasonable assumption that if we hold scores of variable Z constant, the correlation between X and Y scores will be the same regardless of whether we have only a restricted range of Z scores or the entire range. Since Z is the variable on which there is a deliberate restriction of range, from Eq. (11-4) we can write

$$r'_{zx}\frac{\sigma'_x}{\sigma'_z} = r_{zx}\frac{\sigma_x}{\sigma_z} \tag{11-14}$$

and

$$r'_{zy}\frac{\sigma'_y}{\sigma'_z} = r_{zy}\frac{\sigma_y}{\sigma_z} \tag{11-15}$$

Solving these two equations for r'_{zx} and r'_{zy}, we have

$$r'_{zx} = r_{zx}\frac{\sigma_x\sigma'_z}{\sigma'_x\sigma_z} \tag{11-16}$$

and

$$r'_{zy} = r_{zy}\frac{\sigma_y\sigma'_z}{\sigma'_y\sigma_z} \tag{11-17}$$

Since Z is the variable on which there is deliberate restriction of range, from Eq. (11-6) we can write

$$\sigma'_x\sqrt{1 - r'^2_{zx}} = \sigma_x\sqrt{1 - r_{zx}{}^2}$$

and

$$\sigma'_y\sqrt{1 - r'^2_{zy}} = \sigma_y\sqrt{1 - r_{zy}{}^2}$$

Dividing both sides of the first of these two equations by σ'_x and both sides of the second equation by σ'_y gives us

$$\sqrt{1 - r'^2_{zx}} = \frac{\sigma_x}{\sigma'_x}\sqrt{1 - r_{zx}{}^2} \tag{11-18}$$

and

$$\sqrt{1 - r'^2_{zy}} = \frac{\sigma_y}{\sigma'_y}\sqrt{1 - r_{zy}{}^2} \tag{11-19}$$

Since by assumption in Eq. (11-13) $r'_{xy \cdot z} = r_{xy \cdot z}$, from Eq. (10-23) we can write the equality of these two partial coefficients of correlation as

$$\frac{r'_{xy} - r'_{zx}r'_{zy}}{\sqrt{(1 - r'^2_{zx})(1 - r'^2_{zy})}} = \frac{r_{xy} - r_{zx}r_{zy}}{\sqrt{(1 - r_{zx}^2)(1 - r_{zy}^2)}}$$

In this equation we can substitute for $\sqrt{1 - r'^2_{zx}}$ from Eq. (11-18) and for $\sqrt{1 - r'^2_{zy}}$ from Eq. (11-19):

$$\frac{r'_{xy} - r'_{zx}r'_{zy}}{(\sigma_x/\sigma'_x)\sqrt{1 - r_{zx}^2}\,(\sigma_y/\sigma'_y)\sqrt{1 - r_{zy}^2}} = \frac{r_{xy} - r_{zx}r_{zy}}{\sqrt{(1 - r_{zx}^2)(1 - r_{zy}^2)}}$$

Multiplying both sides of the equation by $\sqrt{(1 - r_{zx}^2)(1 - r_{zy}^2)}$ gives

$$\frac{r'_{xy} - r'_{zx}r'_{zy}}{\sigma_x \sigma_y / \sigma'_x \sigma'_y} = r_{xy} - r_{zx}r_{zy}$$

$$r'_{xy} - r'_{zx}r'_{zy} = (r_{xy} - r_{zx}r_{zy})\frac{\sigma_x \sigma_y}{\sigma'_x \sigma'_y}$$

$$r'_{xy} = (r_{xy} - r_{zx}r_{zy})\frac{\sigma_x \sigma_y}{\sigma'_x \sigma'_y} + r'_{zx}r'_{zy}$$

Substituting for r'_{zx} and r'_{zy} from Eqs. (11-16) and (11-17) gives

$$r'_{xy} = (r_{xy} - r_{zx}r_{zy})\frac{\sigma_x \sigma_y}{\sigma'_x \sigma'_y} + r_{zx}\frac{\sigma_x \sigma'_z}{\sigma'_x \sigma_z}r_{zy}\frac{\sigma_y \sigma'_z}{\sigma'_y \sigma_z}$$

$$= (r_{xy} - r_{zx}r_{zy})\frac{\sigma_x \sigma_y}{\sigma'_x \sigma'_y} + r_{zx}r_{zy}\frac{\sigma_x \sigma_y}{\sigma'_x \sigma'_y}\frac{\sigma'^2_z}{\sigma_z^2}$$

$$= \frac{\sigma_x \sigma_y}{\sigma'_x \sigma'_y}\left(r_{xy} - r_{zx}r_{zy} + r_{zx}r_{zy}\frac{\sigma'^2_z}{\sigma_z^2}\right) \tag{11-20}$$

Recalling that the explicit restriction is on variable Z and the incidental restriction is on both variables X and Y, from Eq. (11-11) we can write

$$\frac{\sigma'_z}{\sigma_x} = \sqrt{1 - r_{zx}^2 + r_{zx}^2\frac{\sigma'^2_z}{\sigma_z^2}}$$

and

$$\frac{\sigma'_y}{\sigma_y} = \sqrt{1 - r_{zy}^2 + r_{zy}^2\frac{\sigma'^2_z}{\sigma_z^2}}$$

Therefore

$$\frac{\sigma_x \sigma_y}{\sigma'_x \sigma'_y} = \frac{1}{\sqrt{[1 - r_{zx}^2 + r_{zx}^2(\sigma'^2_z/\sigma_z^2)][1 - r_{zy}^2 + r_{zy}^2(\sigma'^2_z/\sigma_z^2)]}} \tag{11-21}$$

Substituting for $\sigma_x \sigma_y / \sigma'_x \sigma'_y$ from Eq. (11-21) in Eq. (11-20) gives us

$$r'_{xy} = \frac{r_{xy} - r_{zx}r_{zy} + r_{zx}r_{zy}(\sigma'^2_z/\sigma_z^2)}{\sqrt{[1 - r_{zx}^2 + r_{zx}^2(\sigma'^2_z/\sigma_z^2)][1 - r_{zy}^2 + r_{zy}^2(\sigma'^2_z/\sigma_z^2)]}} \tag{11-22}$$

Equation (11-22) shows us what the validity of a predictor, r'_{xy}, would be if we deliberately reduced variation in scores on variable Z from σ_z to σ'_z. To show these effects Eq. (11-22) is plotted in Fig. 11-3. In this figure we can see that as the variation in Z scores is reduced, that is, as σ'_z/σ_z

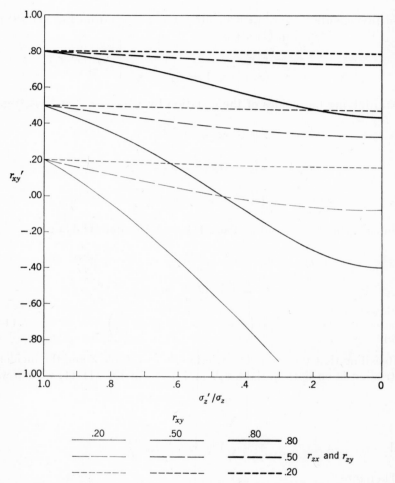

Figure 11-3 The effects of deliberate or explicit restriction of range of scores on variable Z upon the validity coefficient (r_{xy}).

becomes smaller, the validity of the test, r'_{xy}, also becomes smaller. It will also be seen that the lower is the correlation between the restricting variable Z and the predictor (X) and the criterion (Y), the less will be the effect of restriction of range on the validity coefficient. In some extreme cases where the correlation between the restricting variable and both the predictor and the criterion is higher than the correlation between the predictor and the criterion, restriction of range may even change a positive relationship to a negative one. It is therefore obvious that if a test is validated on a group whose scores are restricted on another variable, a variable related to both the predictor and the criterion, the validity coefficient will be underestimated.

Equation (11-22) shows that the validity coefficient will be reduced as the variation in scores on variable Z is reduced. Ordinarily we have data on a group with restricted range and wish to estimate what the validity coefficient would be if we had the total range. That is, we wish r_{xy} rather than r'_{xy}. To obtain this value, we start with Eqs. (11-14) and (11-15), solving for r_{zx} and r_{zy}. The solution is parallel to that for r'_{xy}, so that equivalent to Eq. (11-22) we can write

$$r_{xy} = \frac{r'_{xy} - r'_{zx}r'_{zy} + r'_{zx}r'_{zy}(\sigma_z{}^2/\sigma_z'^2)}{\sqrt{[1 - r_{zx}'^2 + r_{zx}'^2(\sigma_z{}^2/\sigma_z'^2)][1 - r_{zy}'^2 + r_{zy}'^2(\sigma_z{}^2/\sigma_z'^2)]}} \qquad (11\text{-}23)$$

Equation (11-23) permits us to estimate the validity with which scores on variable X predict those on variable Y for the total range when there has been a deliberate restriction on another variable Z. Suppose that students are admitted to college on the basis of their high school grade average, the standard deviation of the grade average of all applicants being .50 and that for those who are accepted being .25. Let us say that we wish to determine the validity of a scholastic aptitude test and administer it to entering freshmen, the high school graduates who have acceptable grades. Suppose we find with this selected group that the validity of high school grade average, Z, in predicting college grades is .30 (r'_{zy}), the validity of the scholastic aptitude test is .40 (r'_{xy}), and the correlation between high school grade average and scores on the scholastic aptitude test is .20 (r'_{zx}). We can estimate the validity for the entire range of applicants (r_{xy}) from Eq. (11-23) as follows:

$$r_{xy} =$$

$$\frac{.40 - (.20)(.30) + (.20)(.30)[(.50)^2/(.25)^2]}{\sqrt{\{1 - (.20)^2 + (.20)^2[(.50)^2/(.25)^2]\}\{1 - (.30)^2 + (.30)^2[(.50)^2/(.25)^2]\}}}$$

$$= \frac{.60}{\sqrt{1.42}} = .50$$

Summary

Validity of measurement pertains to the nature of the traits measured by a set of operations. Because it is a broad problem area, validity has been given somewhat different definitions. Sometimes validity refers to the degree to which a set of operations measures the traits it is supposed to measure, and sometimes it refers to the determination of the traits actually measured by a set of operations. Some definitions of validity require statistical descriptions of the degree of relationship between variables, and others involve judgment about the nature of the traits being measured. It is possible to differentiate three meanings of the term validity—namely, predictive validity, content validity, and construct validity.

Predictive validity refers to the accuracy with which it is possible to estimate the extent to which an individual possesses one property from the extent to which he possesses another, that is, how well we can guess, from the score an individual earns on a predictor variable, the score he earns on a criterion variable. The variable to be predicted may be a property the individual possessed in the past, a property he possesses now (concurrent validity), or a property he will possess in the future. Sometimes tests used in connection with concurrent validity are termed diagnostic tests, and those used in connection with forecasting future behavior are termed aptitude or prognostic tests.

When the Pearsonian coefficient, or its equivalents, is used to describe the relationship between predictor and criterion scores, it is termed a validity coefficient. The magnitude of the validity coefficient is limited by the reliability with which the predictor and criterion are measured. The magnitude of the validity coefficient is reduced when there is a restriction in the range of individual differences. It is possible to estimate the validity coefficient for the entire range of individuals if the extent to which the range has been restricted on the predictor or on some other variable related to it is known. When there are many criteria, they can be combined into a single composite criterion. By assigning differential weights to the component criteria, the composite can be made more reliable or meaningful.

The content validity of a set of operations refers to the degree to which those operations are, on the basis of their nature or content, judged to measure the traits we wish to measure by them. It is necessary to judge not only whether each component of the test measures the desired trait but also whether the entire set of components covers this trait in a representative fashion. To minimize the effects of personal judgment, sometimes the homogeneity of the components of a test is taken as an indication of validity. But homogeneity does not tell whether the components are a representative sample of the entire trait.

The notion of construct validity arises out of the fact that as psychologists we are often interested in traits that are complex and intangible. These traits stem from the theories we develop in our attempt to understand and explain behavior, and therefore the traits are intellectual constructs. From our theoretical conceptions about the nature of the trait, we expect that certain relationships should hold between scores on a test measuring it and scores on other variables, and that certain conditions or circumstances should affect scores in prescribed ways. A validity coefficient tells us something about the nature of the traits actually measured by our test, and so does an examination of the nature and context of the test itself. But our theory leads us to expect a wide variety of relationships and consequences. Evidence from many sources must be weighed and integrated before a final judgment can be made with respect to the traits measured by a test. If the expected relationships do not hold, then we modify our construct, redefining the trait measured by our operations. This redefinition leads us to posit a new set of relationships between test scores and other variables. The determination of validity, then, is not so much a process as it is a program. The measurement of the psychological properties of individuals is a complicated affair, to be accomplished laboriously, and seldom, if ever, with the degree of precision desired.

Selected Readings

Anastasi, A.: The concept of validity in the interpretation of test scores, *Educational and Psychological Meas.*, **10**:67–78, 1950.

Bechtoldt, H. P.: Construct validity: a critique, *Am. Psychologist*, **14**:619–629, 1959.

Cronbach, L. J., and P. E. Meehl: Construct validity in psychological tests, *Psychological Bull.*, **52**:281–302, 1955.

Ebel, L.: Must all psychological tests be valid? *Am. Psychologist*, **10**:640–647, 1961.

Gulliksen, H.: Intrinsic validity, *Am. Psychologist*, **5**:511–517, 1950.

Jenkins, J. G.: Validity for what? *J. Consulting Psychol.*, **10**:93–98, 1946.

Loevinger, J.: Objective tests as instruments of psychological theory, *Psychological Repts.*, *Monograph Suppl.* 9, **3**:635–694, 1957.

Thorndike, R. L.: "Personnel Selection," Wiley, 1949.

Exercises

The data given in Table E-1 will be used in the following exercises, which are designed to give some direct experience with the problems of measurement discussed in the text.

TABLE E-1. The Scores of 25 Subjects on Three Tests, *A*, *B*, and *C*, with Their Responses (+ Correct, 0 Incorrect) to Each of the 10 Items Comprising Test *A* and Each of the 10 Items Comprising Test *B*

Subject	Test A										Test B										Test C
	1	2	3	4	5	6	7	8	9	10	1	2	3	4	5	6	7	8	9	10	
1	+	+	0	0	+	+	0	+	+	0	+	+	+	+	+	+	0	0	0	+	17
2	+	+	0	0	0	+	0	0	0	0	+	+	+	+	+	+	+	0	0	0	5
3	+	+	+	+	+	+	+	+	0	+	+	+	+	+	+	+	+	+	+	+	11
4	0	0	+	+	+	0	0	+	0	0	+	+	+	+	0	+	0	+	+	0	6
5	0	+	+	+	+	0	+	0	0	0	+	+	+	+	0	0	+	+	0	+	10
6	+	0	0	0	0	0	0	0	0	0	0	0	0	+	0	0	0	0	0	0	1
7	+	+	+	+	+	0	+	+	0	0	+	+	+	+	+	+	+	0	0	0	15
8	+	0	0	+	+	+	+	0	0	0	+	0	+	0	+	+	+	+	+	+	8
9	+	0	0	+	0	0	0	0	0	0	0	+	+	+	+	0	+	0	0	0	3
10	+	+	+	+	+	+	+	+	+	+	+	+	+	+	+	+	0	0	+	+	19
11	+	+	0	+	+	0	0	+	0	+	0	0	+	+	+	+	0	0	0	0	9
12	+	+	+	+	+	+	0	0	+	+	+	+	0	+	+	0	+	0	0	+	20
13	0	0	0	0	0	0	0	0	0	0	0	+	+	0	0	0	0	0	0	0	12
14	+	0	+	+	0	+	+	+	0	+	+	+	+	+	+	+	+	+	0	0	7
15	+	+	+	+	+	+	+	+	+	0	+	+	+	+	+	+	+	+	0	+	14
16	+	+	+	+	0	+	0	+	0	+	+	+	+	+	+	+	+	+	+	0	18
17	+	+	+	+	+	0	0	0	0	0	+	+	+	+	+	0	0	+	+	0	16
18	+	+	0	0	0	+	+	0	0	0	+	+	+	0	0	+	+	+	+	0	8
19	+	+	0	0	0	0	0	0	+	0	+	+	0	0	0	0	0	+	0	0	0
20	0	+	0	0	0	0	0	0	0	0	0	0	0	0	0	0	0	0	0	0	4
21	+	+	+	+	0	+	+	0	+	0	+	+	0	+	+	0	+	+	+	+	21
22	+	+	+	+	0	+	0	0	0	0	+	0	0	+	+	+	0	+	+	0	11
23	0	+	+	0	0	0	0	0	0	0	0	+	+	0	+	+	+	+	0	0	2
24	+	+	+	0	0	+	0	0	+	+	+	+	+	0	0	+	0	0	0	+	17
25	0	0	+	+	0	0	+	0	0	+	+	+	+	0	+	+	0	0	0	+	13

Chapter 3

3-1. From the correct (+) responses to the items comprising tests A and B, compute the total test scores on each test for every subject. On the same graph draw the frequency distributions of the scores on tests A and B. How would you describe the two frequency distributions in terms of their general level, variation, skewness, and kurtosis?

3-2. For scores on tests A and B, compute the means, variances, standard deviations, and the indices of skewness and kurtosis. Compare these quantitative descriptions with the characteristics of the frequency distributions you observed in Exercise 3-1. Do the various statistical indices seem to give reasonable descriptions when you compare the two frequency distributions?

3-3. For each subject, compute his deviation scores on both test A and test B. Compute the means of the deviation scores. They should, of course, be precisely 0. If they are not, how do you explain the discrepancy?

3-4. Compute the means, variances, and standard deviations of the scores on each of the 10 items of test A.

Chapter 4

4-1. Determine the percentiles for the raw scores on tests A and B. Use the graphic method for determining percentiles. Do you believe the cumulative frequency curves should be smoothed? If so, why; and if not, why not?

4-2. Compute the standard scores for each person on tests A and B. You have already computed their deviation scores in Exercise 3-3 and the standard deviations in Exercise 3-2, so you only need to divide the deviation scores on each test by its standard deviation. Compute the mean and the standard deviations of both sets of standard scores. The means, of course, should be 0 and the standard deviation 1. If they are not, how do you explain the discrepancies?

4-3. For each of the 25 individuals, add together his scores on all three tests, A, B, and C. Rank the 25 individuals in terms of these total or composite scores, and by the ranking method determine the normalized standardized score (Z) of each person. For standardized scores use a mean of 50 and a standard deviation of 10. Make a frequency distribution of these scores. Does it appear to be normal? If not, how do you explain the discrepancy?

4-4. Using the composite scores or the ranks developed in Exercise 4-3, prepare stanine scores for all individuals. How feasible is it to obtain stanine scores with the precise frequencies required? What difficulties did you encounter in developing the stanine scores?

4-5. By the method of unequal base-line intervals, determine the normalized standard (z) scores of each person on tests A and B. Compute the indices of skewness and of kurtosis for both sets of normalized scores. Was the transformation effective in producing scores that are normally distributed? How do the skewness and kurtosis of these transformed scores compare with the skewness and kurtosis of the raw scores (Exercise 3-2)?

4-6. Percentile ranks were established for scores on a speed test using a group of subjects who were quite representative of a particular population. After the test had been used for some time, it was decided to increase the time limit. The test was administered to a group of 84 subjects both under the old and under the new time limits. These subjects, however, were not representative of the population but rather tended to make lower scores than the original group. Nevertheless, it was desired to estimate the population norms for the new time limit. This can be done from the distributions of the percentile ranks on the original test and the raw scores under the new conditions. These two distributions for the 84 subjects are given in Table E-2. By the method described in Chap. 4, estimate the population percentile ranks of the new scores.

TABLE E-2

Percentile ranks on original test	Number of cases	Raw scores on revised test	Number of cases
77	1	133	1
69	1	132	
60	2	131	1
50	4	130	
40	8	129	1
31	9	128	1
23	18	127	2
16	7	126	2
11	12	125	4
7	8	124	4
4	6	123	4
2	3	122	5
1	3	121	10
0	2	120	8
		119	4
		118	3
		117	6
		116	6
		115	4
		114	4
		113	3
		112	3
		111	2
		110	1
		109	1
		108	2
		107	1
		106	1

Chapter 5

5-1.   On graph paper make a chart similar to Fig. 5-3 representing the relationship between the deviation scores (computed in Exercise 3-3) on tests A
and B, representing each pair of scores as a dot. Use test A as the ordinate y,
and test B as the abscissa x. Would you describe the relationship as linear?
Homoscedastic?

5-2.   Make a similar chart representing the relationship between normalized
standard scores (computed in Exercise 4-2) on tests A and B. Does the
relationship between normalized scores appear to more closely approximate
a linear relationship and to more closely approximate homoscedasticity?
Should it? If so, why; and if not, why not?

5-3.   Compute the regression coefficients $b_{y \cdot x}$ and $b_{x \cdot y}$ for the deviation scores on
tests A and B. Do the two regression coefficients differ in magnitude?
Would you expect them to? If so, why; and if not, why not?

5-4.   Using the two regression coefficients just computed, plot the two regression
lines on the chart you developed in Exercise 5-1. Remember that for devia-
tion scores, $a_{y \cdot x}$ and $a_{x \cdot y}$ are 0, and both regression lines cross at the point
$x = 0$ and $y = 0$. Do the regression lines, the straight lines of best fit in a
least-square sense, give a good representation of the points in the scatter
diagram?

5-5.   Similarly, compute the two regression coefficients for the normalized standard scores on tests A and B. Do these coefficients differ in magnitude?
Would you expect them to? If so, why; and if not, why not?

5-6.   Using the two regression coefficients just computed, plot the regression line
on the chart developed in Exercise 5-2. Remember that standard scores are
merely deviation scores which happen to have a standard deviation of 1. Do
these regression lines give a better fit? If so, why; and if not, why not?

5-7.   Determine the deviation $(y \cdot x)$ of each y (test A) score from the regression
line described by $b_{y \cdot x}$ and the deviation $(x \cdot y)$ of each x (test A) score from
the line described by $b_{x \cdot y}$. This can be done by reading the distances of the
points from the two regression lines in the chart prepared in Exercise 5-1.
Compute the standard deviation of the $y \cdot x$ scores and the standard deviation of the $x \cdot y$ scores. These are the partial standard deviations $\sigma_{y \cdot x}$ and
$\sigma_{x \cdot y}$. Are they smaller than their corresponding standard deviations? If so,
why; and if not, why not?

Chapter 6

6-1.   Compute the Pearsonian coefficient of correlation between scores on test A
and test B by each of the five formulae below. You have computed the
standard scores on these tests in Exercise 4-2, and the deviation scores in
Exercise 3-3. The means and standard deviations were computed in Exercise 3-2, and the partial standard deviations in Exercise 5-7.

(a) $r_{xy} = \dfrac{\Sigma z_x z_y}{n}$

(b) $r_{xy} = \dfrac{\Sigma xy}{n \sigma_x \sigma_y}$

$(c)\ r_{xy} = \dfrac{\Sigma XY/n - \bar{X}\bar{Y}}{n\sigma_x\sigma_y}$

$(d)\ r_{xy} = \sqrt{1 - \dfrac{\sigma_{y\cdot x}^2}{\sigma_y{}^2}}$

$(e)\ r_{xy} = \sqrt{1 - \dfrac{\sigma_{x\cdot y}^2}{\sigma_x{}^2}}$

Are all the five values for the Pearsonian coefficient of correlation between test A and B the same? Should they be? Why? If they are not the same, how do you explain the differences?

6-2. Compute the coefficient of correlation between the normalized standardized scores on tests A and B. You developed these scores in Exercise 4-5. Also note that in Exercise 5-5 you computed the regression coefficients for normalized standard scores. Therefore, do you have to compute the coefficient required here? If so, why; and if not, why not? Is this coefficient greater or smaller than that computed in Exercise 6-1a? Which should it be? Why?

6-3. Using the Pearsonian coefficient of correlation between raw scores on test A and test B computed in Exercise 6-1c, compute the two partial standard deviations by the following formulae:

$$\sigma_{y\cdot x} = \sigma_y \sqrt{1 - r_{xy}{}^2}$$
$$\sigma_{x\cdot y} = \sigma_x \sqrt{1 - r_{xy}{}^2}$$

How do these values compare with those you determined in Exercise 5-7? If they are different, how do you explain the differences?

6-4. For each of the 10 items of test A, determine both the point biserial and the biserial coefficients of correlation between scores on the individual items and total scores on test A. Which type of coefficient tends to be higher? Which type would you expect to be higher? Why?

6-5. Determine all the phi coefficients and the tetrachoric coefficients of correlation among the scores on the 10 items of test A. Which type of coefficient tends to be higher? Which type would you expect to be higher? Why?

Chapter 7

7-1. In Exercise 4-3 you computed the composite score of each subject on all three tests, A, B, and C. Compute the mean and variance of these composite scores. Now compute their mean and variance by Eqs. (7-4) and (7-6), the formulae for determining the mean and variance of composite scores from the characteristics of the components. You have already computed the means and standard deviations of tests A and B in Exercise 3-2 and their correlation in Exercise 6-1c. You will have to compute the mean, standard deviation, and intercorrelations for test C in order to solve Eqs. (7-4) and (7-6). Obviously the two determinations of the mean and variance of composite scores should be the same. Are they? If not, how do you explain the differences?

7-2.   Add together the raw scores on test B and test C. Compute the coefficient of correlation between these composite scores and scores on test A. We now have the coefficient of correlation between a composite variable and an outside variable. Compute the coefficient of correlation between this composite (test B plus test C) and the outside variable (test A) by Eq. (7-14), the formula for determining the correlation between a composite and an outside variable from the characteristics of the components. The two determinations of the coefficient of correlation between the composite variable and the outside variable should be the same. Are they? If they are not, how do you explain the difference?

7-3.   In Exercise 6-5 you computed the phi coefficients among the items of test A. As an indication of the homogeneity of the test, average these coefficients. In Exercise 6-4 you computed the point biserial coefficients between each of the items and total test scores. On the basis of these point-biserial coefficients, eliminate the two items which have the lowest correlations with total scores. Now compute the average of the intercorrelations among the remaining eight items. Repeat the process, eliminating the next two items with the lowest correlations with total scores. Does the homogeneity of the test increase as items with the lowest correlations with total scores are eliminated? If so, why; and if not, why not?

Chapter 8

8-1.   Examine the means, standard deviations, and intercorrelations among tests A, B, and C. Can they be considered to be parallel tests? If so, why; and if not, why not?

8-2.   Examine the means, standard deviations, and intercorrelations among the items of test A. Can any of these items be considered to be parallel tests? If so, why; and if not, why not?

Chapter 9

9-1.   Suppose we take the items of test A as being a series of parallel tests even if they do not satisfy the criteria of parallelism. As an estimate of the reliability of single tests, we can take the average of the intercorrelations among the items. This value you already computed in Exercise 7-3. Apply this estimate of the reliability in the Spearman-Brown formula and predict what the reliability coefficient ought to be if the number of measurements were increased five times. Now let us actually increase the number of measurements five times. To do this, determine for each person his score on the five odd-numbered items and his score on the five even-numbered items. Compute the coefficient of correlation between these two scores. This is an empirical estimate of the reliability of measurement when the number of measurements is increased five times. Does increasing the number of measurements increase the reliability of measurement? Should it? Do the theoretical and empirical estimates of the reliability coefficient when the number of measurements is increased agree? If not, why not?

9-2.   In Exercise 9-1 you computed the coefficient of correlation between scores on the odd- and even-numbered items of test A. Using this coefficient in the Spearman-Brown formula, estimate the reliability coefficient of the total 10-item test (the method of comparable halves of a test). By this odd-even method, also estimate the reliability coefficient of test B. How would you describe the reliability with which these two tests measure individual differences?

9-3. Using the two reliability coefficients just determined, estimate for each test how many items would be necessary to achieve a reliability coefficient of .95.

9-4. Suppose both tests are administered to a group of individuals whose scores are restricted in range so that the standard deviation is only half as great as that of the original group. Estimate the reliability coefficients of tests A and B for this new group, using the reliability coefficients computed in Exercise 9-2. Are the reliability coefficients increased or decreased in magnitude? Which would you expect? Why?

9-5. Using the reliability coefficients for tests A and B computed in Exercise 9-2, apply the correction for attenuation to the coefficient of correlation between tests A and B (computed in Exercise 6-1c). Is this coefficient, the correlation between true scores on both tests, higher or lower than the correlation between fallible scores? Which should it be? Why?

9-6. By the Kuder-Richardson formula, compute the reliability coefficients of both tests. How do these coefficients compare with those computed in Exercise 9-2? Which do you think are the better estimates? Why?

Chapter 10

10-1. We wish to examine the effects upon the correlation between a composite and an outside variable of the pattern of weights assigned to the components of the composite. Scores on tests B and C will be taken as forming the composite, and scores on test A will be taken as the outside variable. Test B will always be weighted $+1$, and scores on test C will be weighted -1, 0, $+0.5$, $+1$, $+1.2$, $+1.4$, and $+2$. Scores on all variables will be taken as being standard scores. Therefore the necessary coefficients of correlation can be computed by Eq. (10-16). By this formula, compute the coefficients between the seven weighted composites of tests B and C with test A ($r_{X_A[(+1)X_B+(-1)X_C]}$, $r_{X_A[(+1)X_B+(0)X_C]}$, etc.). To solve Eq. (10-16) you need only the intercorrelations among the three tests. These you have computed in Exercises 6-1 and 7-1. Now make a chart like Fig. 10-5, plotting $r_{W_BX_B+X_CX_C}$ against W_B. Does the correlation between the weighted composites of tests B and C and test A vary with the pattern of weights? Is there one particular pattern of weights which gives a higher correlation between the composite and the outside variable? If so, estimate the weights and the correlation from your chart.

10-2. By means of Eq. (10-28), compute the coefficient of multiple correlation between test A and the combination of tests B and C. Is this coefficient higher than r_{AB} and r_{AC}? Should it be? If so, why; and if not, why not?

10-3. By means of Eqs. (10-32) and (10-33), compute the multiple regression weights for tests B and C in their relationship with test A. Compute the relative weights of the two tests in the multiple. That is, taking the weight of test B as 1, the relative weight of test C would be its multiple regression weight divided by the multiple regression weight of test B. Do this pattern of optimal weights and the coefficient of multiple correlation computed in Exercise 10-2 agree with the findings on the chart you developed in Exercise 10-1? Should they? If so, why; and if not, why not?

Chapter 11

11-1. Eliminate all cases whose scores on test A are 4 or below. Now for the remaining cases compute the coefficient of correlation between scores on test A and test B. Using Eq. (11-9), estimate the coefficient of correlation between scores on test A and test B for the entire range. Recall that you computed the variance of scores on test A for the entire range in Exercise 3-2. How does this estimate compare with the actual coefficient of correlation between scores on tests A and B for all cases you computed in Exercise 6-1? If there is a difference, how do you explain it?

11-2. Using the coefficient of correlation for the restricted range computed in Exercise 11-1, estimate by means of Eq. (11-11) the amount of incidental restriction in range on test B. Compare this with the actual amount of restriction, recalling that in order to compute the coefficient of correlation in Exercise 11-1 you had to compute the standard deviation of test B scores of the restricted group, and in Exercise 3-2 you computed the standard deviation of test B scores for all cases.

11-3. Eliminate all cases whose scores on test C are 7 or below. Now for the remaining cases compute the coefficient of correlation among scores on tests A, B, and C. In Exercise 7-1 you computed the standard deviation of scores for all cases on test C. Using Eq. (11-23), estimate the coefficient of correlation between scores on test A and test B for the entire range. How does this estimate compare with the actual coefficient of correlation between scores on tests A and B for all cases? If there is a difference, how do you explain it?

Appendix

STANDARD AND STANDARDIZED SCORE EQUIVALENTS OF
PERCENTILE RANKS IN A NORMAL DISTRIBUTION

(a)   % of cases earning lower scores
(b)   Standard scores
(c)   Standardized scores with a mean of 50 and a standard deviation of 10
(d)   Standardized scores with a mean of 100 and a standard deviation of 20

SQUARES AND SQUARE ROOTS OF NUMBERS FROM 1 TO
1,000

(a)	(b)	(c)	(d)	(a)	(b)	(c)	(d)
99.9	3.09	81	162	95.6	1.71	67	134
99.8	2.88	79	158	95.5	1.70	67	134
99.7	2.75	78	155	95.4	1.68	67	134
99.6	2.65	77	153	95.3	1.67	67	133
99.5	2.58	76	152	95.2	1.66	67	133
99.4	2.51	75	150	95.1	1.65	67	133
99.3	2.46	75	149	95.0	1.64	66	133
99.2	2.41	74	148	94.9	1.64	66	133
99.1	2.37	74	147	94.8	1.63	66	133
99.0	2.33	73	147	94.7	1.62	66	132
98.9	2.29	73	146	94.6	1.61	66	132
98.8	2.26	73	145	94.5	1.60	66	132
98.7	2.22	72	145	94.4	1.59	66	132
98.6	2.20	72	144	94.3	1.58	66	132
98.5	2.17	72	143	94.2	1.57	66	131
98.4	2.14	71	143	94.1	1.56	66	131
98.3	2.12	71	142	94.0	1.55	66	131
98.2	2.10	71	142	93.9	1.55	66	131
98.1	2.07	71	141	93.8	1.54	65	131
98.0	2.05	71	141	93.7	1.53	65	131
97.9	2.03	70	141	93.6	1.52	65	130
97.8	2.01	70	140	93.5	1.51	65	130
97.7	2.00	70	140	93.4	1.50	65	130
97.6	1.98	70	140	93.3	1.50	65	130
97.5	1.96	70	139	93.2	1.49	65	130
97.4	1.94	69	139	93.1	1.48	65	130
97.3	1.93	69	139	93.0	1.48	65	130
97.2	1.91	69	138	92.9	1.47	65	129
97.1	1.90	69	138	92.8	1.46	65	129
97.0	1.88	69	138	92.7	1.45	65	129
96.9	1.87	69	137	92.6	1.45	65	129
96.8	1.85	69	137	92.5	1.44	64	129
96.7	1.84	68	137	92.4	1.43	64	129
96.6	1.83	68	137	92.3	1.43	64	129
96.5	1.81	68	136	92.2	1.42	64	128
96.4	1.80	68	136	92.1	1.41	64	128
96.3	1.79	68	136	92.0	1.41	64	128
96.2	1.77	68	135	91.9	1.40	64	128
96.1	1.76	68	135	91.8	1.39	64	128
96.0	1.75	68	135	91.7	1.38	64	128
95.9	1.74	67	135	91.6	1.38	64	128
95.8	1.73	67	135	91.5	1.37	64	127
95.7	1.72	67	134	91.4	1.37	64	127

(a)	(b)	(c)	(d)	(a)	(b)	(c)	(d)
91.3	1.36	64	127	87.0	1.13	61	123
91.2	1.35	64	127	86.9	1.12	61	122
91.1	1.35	64	127	86.8	1.12	61	122
91.0	1.34	63	127	86.7	1.11	61	122
90.9	1.33	63	127	86.6	1.11	61	122
90.8	1.33	63	127	86.5	1.10	61	122
90.7	1.32	63	126	86.4	1.10	61	122
90.6	1.32	63	126	86.3	1.09	61	122
90.5	1.31	63	126	86.2	1.09	61	122
90.4	1.30	63	126	86.1	1.08	61	122
90.3	1.30	63	126	86.0	1.08	61	122
90.2	1.29	63	126	85.9	1.08	61	122
90.1	1.29	63	126	85.8	1.07	61	121
90.0	1.28	63	126	85.7	1.07	61	121
89.9	1.28	63	126	85.6	1.06	61	121
89.8	1.27	63	125	85.5	1.06	61	121
89.7	1.26	63	125	85.4	1.05	61	121
89.6	1.26	63	125	85.3	1.05	61	121
89.5	1.25	63	125	85.2	1.05	61	121
89.4	1.25	63	125	85.1	1.04	60	121
89.3	1.24	62	125	85.0	1.04	60	121
89.2	1.23	62	125	84.9	1.03	60	121
89.1	1.23	62	125	84.8	1.03	60	121
89.0	1.22	62	124	84.7	1.02	60	120
88.9	1.22	62	124	84.6	1.02	60	120
88.8	1.22	62	124	84.5	1.01	60	120
88.7	1.21	62	124	84.4	1.01	60	120
88.6	1.21	62	124	84.3	1.00	60	120
88.5	1.20	62	124	84.2	1.00	60	120
88.4	1.20	62	124	84.1	1.00	60	120
88.3	1.19	62	124	84.0	0.99	60	120
88.2	1.19	62	124	83.9	0.99	60	120
88.1	1.18	62	124	83.8	0.99	60	120
88.0	1.18	62	124	83.7	0.98	60	120
87.9	1.17	62	123	83.6	0.98	60	120
87.8	1.17	62	123	83.5	0.97	60	119
87.7	1.16	62	123	83.4	0.97	60	119
87.6	1.16	62	123	83.3	0.97	60	119
87.5	1.15	62	123	83.2	0.96	60	119
87.4	1.15	62	123	83.1	0.96	60	119
87.3	1.14	61	123	83.0	0.95	60	119
87.2	1.14	61	123	82.9	0.95	60	119
87.1	1.13	61	123	82.8	0.95	60	119

(a)	(b)	(c)	(d)	(a)	(b)	(c)	(d)
82.7	0.94	59	119	78.4	0.78	58	116
82.6	0.94	59	119	78.3	0.78	58	116
82.5	0.93	59	119	78.2	0.78	58	116
82.4	0.93	59	119	78.1	0.77	58	115
82.3	0.93	59	119	78.0	0.77	58	115
82.2	0.92	59	118	77.9	0.77	58	115
82.1	0.92	59	118	77.8	0.77	58	115
82.0	0.91	59	118	77.7	0.76	58	115
81.9	0.91	59	118	77.6	0.76	58	115
81.8	0.91	59	118	77.5	0.76	58	115
81.7	0.90	59	118	77.4	0.75	58	115
81.6	0.90	59	118	77.3	0.75	58	115
81.5	0.90	59	118	77.2	0.75	58	115
81.4	0.89	59	118	77.1	0.74	57	115
81.3	0.89	59	118	77.0	0.74	57	115
81.2	0.89	59	118	76.9	0.74	57	115
81.1	0.88	59	118	76.8	0.73	57	115
81.0	0.88	59	118	76.7	0.73	57	115
80.9	0.87	59	117	76.6	0.73	57	115
80.8	0.87	59	117	76.5	0.72	57	114
80.7	0.87	59	117	76.4	0.72	57	114
80.6	0.86	59	117	76.3	0.72	57	114
80.5	0.86	59	117	76.2	0.71	57	114
80.4	0.86	59	117	76.1	0.71	57	114
80.3	0.85	59	117	76.0	0.71	57	114
80.2	0.85	59	117	75.9	0.70	57	114
80.1	0.84	58	117	75.8	0.70	57	114
80.0	0.84	58	117	75.7	0.70	57	114
79.9	0.84	58	117	75.6	0.69	57	114
79.8	0.83	58	117	75.5	0.69	57	114
79.7	0.83	58	117	75.4	0.69	57	114
79.6	0.83	58	117	75.3	0.68	57	114
79.5	0.82	58	116	75.2	0.68	57	114
79.4	0.82	58	116	75.1	0.68	57	114
79.3	0.82	58	116	75.0	0.67	57	113
79.2	0.81	58	116	74.9	0.67	57	113
79.1	0.81	58	116	74.8	0.67	57	113
79.0	0.80	58	116	74.7	0.66	57	113
78.9	0.80	58	116	74.6	0.66	57	113
78.8	0.80	58	116	74.5	0.66	57	113
78.7	0.79	58	116	74.4	0.66	57	113
78.6	0.79	58	116	74.3	0.65	57	113
78.5	0.79	58	116	74.2	0.65	57	113

(a)	(b)	(c)	(d)	(a)	(b)	(c)	(d)
74.1	0.65	57	113	69.8	0.52	55	110
74.0	0.64	56	113	69.7	0.52	55	110
73.9	0.64	56	113	69.6	0.51	55	110
73.8	0.64	56	113	69.5	0.51	55	110
73.7	0.63	56	113	69.4	0.51	55	110
73.6	0.63	56	113	69.3	0.50	55	110
73.5	0.63	56	113	69.2	0.50	55	110
73.4	0.62	56	113	69.1	0.50	55	110
73.3	0.62	56	112	69.0	0.49	55	110
73.2	0.62	56	112	68.9	0.49	55	110
73.1	0.61	56	112	68.8	0.49	55	110
73.0	0.61	56	112	68.7	0.49	55	110
72.9	0.61	56	112	68.6	0.48	55	110
72.8	0.61	56	112	68.5	0.48	55	110
72.7	0.60	56	112	68.4	0.48	55	110
72.6	0.60	56	112	68.3	0.48	55	110
72.5	0.60	56	112	68.2	0.47	55	109
72.4	0.59	56	112	68.1	0.47	55	109
72.3	0.59	56	112	68.0	0.47	55	109
72.2	0.59	56	112	67.9	0.47	55	109
72.1	0.59	56	112	67.8	0.46	55	109
72.0	0.58	56	112	67.7	0.46	55	109
71.9	0.58	56	112	67.6	0.46	55	109
71.8	0.58	56	112	67.5	0.45	55	109
71.7	0.57	56	111	67.4	0.45	55	109
71.6	0.57	56	111	67.3	0.45	55	109
71.5	0.57	56	111	67.2	0.44	54	109
71.4	0.56	56	111	67.1	0.44	54	109
71.3	0.56	56	111	67.0	0.44	54	109
71.2	0.56	56	111	66.9	0.44	54	109
71.1	0.55	56	111	66.8	0.43	54	109
71.0	0.55	56	111	66.7	0.43	54	109
70.9	0.55	56	111	66.6	0.43	54	109
70.8	0.55	56	111	66.5	0.43	54	109
70.7	0.54	55	111	66.4	0.42	54	108
70.6	0.54	55	111	66.3	0.42	54	108
70.5	0.54	55	111	66.2	0.42	54	108
70.4	0.54	55	111	66.1	0.41	54	108
70.3	0.53	55	111	66.0	0.41	54	108
70.2	0.53	55	111	65.9	0.41	54	108
70.1	0.53	55	111	65.8	0.41	54	108
70.0	0.52	55	110	65.7	0.40	54	108
69.9	0.52	55	110	65.6	0.40	54	108

(a)	(b)	(c)	(d)	(a)	(b)	(c)	(d)
65.5	0.40	54	108	61.2	0.28	53	106
65.4	0.40	54	108	61.1	0.28	53	106
65.3	0.39	54	108	61.0	0.28	53	106
65.2	0.39	54	108	60.9	0.28	53	106
65.1	0.39	54	108	60.8	0.27	53	105
65.0	0.39	54	108	60.7	0.27	53	105
64.9	0.38	54	108	60.6	0.27	53	105
64.8	0.38	54	108	60.5	0.27	53	105
64.7	0.38	54	108	60.4	0.26	53	105
64.6	0.37	54	107	60.3	0.26	53	105
64.5	0.37	54	107	60.2	0.26	53	105
64.4	0.37	54	107	60.1	0.25	53	105
64.3	0.37	54	107	60.0	0.25	53	105
64.2	0.36	54	107	59.9	0.25	53	105
64.1	0.36	54	107	59.8	0.25	53	105
64.0	0.36	54	107	59.7	0.24	52	105
63.9	0.36	54	107	59.6	0.24	52	105
63.8	0.35	54	107	59.5	0.24	52	105
63.7	0.35	54	107	59.4	0.24	52	105
63.6	0.35	54	107	59.3	0.23	52	105
63.5	0.35	54	107	59.2	0.23	52	105
63.4	0.34	53	107	59.1	0.23	52	105
63.3	0.34	53	107	59.0	0.23	52	105
63.2	0.34	53	107	58.9	0.22	52	104
63.1	0.33	53	107	58.8	0.22	52	104
63.0	0.33	53	107	58.7	0.22	52	104
62.9	0.33	53	107	58.6	0.22	52	104
62.8	0.33	53	107	58.5	0.21	52	104
62.7	0.32	53	106	58.4	0.21	52	104
62.6	0.32	53	106	58.3	0.21	52	104
62.5	0.32	53	106	58.2	0.21	52	104
62.4	0.32	53	106	58.1	0.20	52	104
62.3	0.31	53	106	58.0	0.20	52	104
62.2	0.31	53	106	57.9	0.20	52	104
62.1	0.31	53	106	57.8	0.20	52	104
62.0	0.31	53	106	57.7	0.19	52	104
61.9	0.30	53	106	57.6	0.19	52	104
61.8	0.30	53	106	57.5	0.19	52	104
61.7	0.30	53	106	57.4	0.19	52	104
61.6	0.29	53	106	57.3	0.18	52	104
61.5	0.29	53	106	57.2	0.18	52	104
61.4	0.29	53	106	57.1	0.18	52	104
61.3	0.29	53	106	57.0	0.18	52	104

(a)	(b)	(c)	(d)	(a)	(b)	(c)	(d)
56.9	0.17	52	103	52.6	0.06	51	101
56.8	0.17	52	103	52.5	0.06	51	101
56.7	0.17	52	103	52.4	0.06	51	101
56.6	0.16	52	103	52.3	0.06	51	101
56.5	0.16	52	103	52.2	0.05	51	101
56.4	0.16	52	103	52.1	0.05	51	101
56.3	0.16	52	103	52.0	0.05	51	101
56.2	0.15	52	103	51.9	0.05	51	101
56.1	0.15	52	103	51.8	0.04	50	101
56.0	0.15	52	103	51.7	0.04	50	101
55.9	0.15	52	103	51.6	0.04	50	101
55.8	0.14	51	103	51.5	0.04	50	101
55.7	0.14	51	103	51.4	0.04	50	101
55.6	0.14	51	103	51.3	0.03	50	101
55.5	0.14	51	103	51.2	0.03	50	101
55.4	0.13	51	103	51.1	0.03	50	101
55.3	0.13	51	103	51.0	0.03	50	101
55.2	0.13	51	103	50.9	0.02	50	100
55.1	0.13	51	103	50.8	0.02	50	100
55.0	0.12	51	103	50.7	0.02	50	100
54.9	0.12	51	102	50.6	0.01	50	100
54.8	0.12	51	102	50.5	0.01	50	100
54.7	0.12	51	102	50.4	0.01	50	100
54.6	0.11	51	102	50.3	0.01	50	100
54.5	0.11	51	102	50.2	0.00	50	100
54.4	0.11	51	102	50.1	0.00	50	100
54.3	0.11	51	102	50.0	0.00	50	100
54.2	0.10	51	102	49.9	0.00	50	100
54.1	0.10	51	102	49.8	0.00	50	100
54.0	0.10	51	102	49.7	−0.01	50	100
53.9	0.10	51	102	49.6	−0.01	50	100
53.8	0.09	51	102	49.5	−0.01	50	100
53.7	0.09	51	102	49.4	−0.01	50	100
53.6	0.09	51	102	49.3	−0.02	50	100
53.5	0.09	51	102	49.2	−0.02	50	100
53.4	0.08	51	102	49.1	−0.02	50	100
53.3	0.08	51	102	49.0	−0.03	50	99
53.2	0.08	51	102	48.9	−0.03	50	99
53.1	0.08	51	102	48.8	−0.03	50	99
53.0	0.07	51	102	48.7	−0.03	50	99
52.9	0.07	51	101	48.6	−0.04	50	99
52.8	0.07	51	101	48.5	−0.04	50	99
52.7	0.07	51	101	48.4	−0.04	50	99

(a)	(b)	(c)	(d)	(a)	(b)	(c)	(d)
48.3	−0.04	50	99	44.0	−0.15	48	97
48.2	−0.04	50	99	43.9	−0.15	48	97
48.1	−0.05	49	99	43.8	−0.15	48	97
48.0	−0.05	49	99	43.7	−0.16	48	97
47.9	−0.05	49	99	43.6	−0.16	48	97
47.8	−0.05	49	99	43.5	−0.16	48	97
47.7	−0.06	49	99	43.4	−0.16	48	97
47.6	−0.06	49	99	43.3	−0.17	48	97
47.5	−0.06	49	99	43.2	−0.17	48	97
47.4	−0.06	49	99	43.1	−0.17	48	97
47.3	−0.07	49	99	43.0	−0.18	48	96
47.2	−0.07	49	99	42.9	−0.18	48	96
47.1	−0.07	49	99	42.8	−0.18	48	96
47.0	−0.07	49	99	42.7	−0.18	48	96
46.9	−0.08	49	98	42.6	−0.19	48	96
46.8	−0.08	49	98	42.5	−0.19	48	96
46.7	−0.08	49	98	42.4	−0.19	48	96
46.6	−0.08	49	98	42.3	−0.19	48	96
46.5	−0.09	49	98	42.2	−0.20	48	96
46.4	−0.09	49	98	42.1	−0.20	48	96
46.3	−0.09	49	98	42.0	−0.20	48	96
46.2	−0.09	49	98	41.9	−0.20	48	96
46.1	−0.10	49	98	41.8	−0.21	48	96
46.0	−0.10	49	98	41.7	−0.21	48	96
45.9	−0.10	49	98	41.6	−0.21	48	96
45.8	−0.10	49	98	41.5	−0.21	48	96
45.7	−0.11	49	98	41.4	−0.22	48	96
45.6	−0.11	49	98	41.3	−0.22	48	96
45.5	−0.11	49	98	41.2	−0.22	48	96
45.4	−0.11	49	98	41.1	−0.22	48	96
45.3	−0.12	49	98	41.0	−0.23	48	95
45.2	−0.12	49	98	40.9	−0.23	48	95
45.1	−0.12	49	98	40.8	−0.23	48	95
45.0	−0.12	49	98	40.7	−0.23	48	95
44.9	−0.13	49	97	40.6	−0.24	48	95
44.8	−0.13	49	97	40.5	−0.24	48	95
44.7	−0.13	49	97	40.4	−0.24	48	95
44.6	−0.13	49	97	40.3	−0.24	48	95
44.5	−0.14	49	97	40.2	−0.25	47	95
44.4	−0.14	49	97	40.1	−0.25	47	95
44.3	−0.14	49	97	40.0	−0.25	47	95
44.2	−0.14	49	97	39.9	−0.25	47	95
44.1	−0.15	48	97	39.8	−0.26	47	95

(a)	(b)	(c)	(d)	(a)	(b)	(c)	(d)
39.7	−0.26	47	95	35.4	−0.37	46	93
39.6	−0.26	47	95	35.3	−0.38	46	92
39.5	−0.27	47	95	35.2	−0.38	46	92
39.4	−0.27	47	95	35.1	−0.38	46	92
39.3	−0.27	47	95	35.0	−0.39	46	92
39.2	−0.27	47	95	34.9	−0.39	46	92
39.1	−0.28	47	94	34.8	−0.39	46	92
39.0	−0.28	47	94	34.7	−0.39	46	92
38.9	−0.28	47	94	34.6	−0.40	46	92
38.8	−0.28	47	94	34.5	−0.40	46	92
38.7	−0.29	47	94	34.4	−0.40	46	92
38.6	−0.29	47	94	34.3	−0.40	46	92
38.5	−0.29	47	94	34.2	−0.41	46	92
38.4	−0.29	47	94	34.1	−0.41	46	92
38.3	−0.30	47	94	34.0	−0.41	46	92
38.2	−0.30	47	94	33.9	−0.41	46	92
38.1	−0.30	47	94	33.8	−0.42	46	92
38.0	−0.31	47	94	33.7	−0.42	46	92
37.9	−0.31	47	94	33.6	−0.42	46	92
37.8	−0.31	47	94	33.5	−0.43	46	91
37.7	−0.31	47	94	33.4	−0.43	46	91
37.6	−0.32	47	94	33.3	−0.43	46	91
37.5	−0.32	47	94	33.2	−0.43	46	91
37.4	−0.32	47	94	33.1	−0.44	46	91
37.3	−0.32	47	94	33.0	−0.44	46	91
37.2	−0.33	47	93	32.9	−0.44	46	91
37.1	−0.33	47	93	32.8	−0.44	46	91
37.0	−0.33	47	93	32.7	−0.45	45	91
36.9	−0.33	47	93	32.6	−0.45	45	91
36.8	−0.34	47	93	32.5	−0.45	45	91
36.7	−0.34	47	93	32.4	−0.46	45	91
36.6	−0.34	47	93	32.3	−0.46	45	91
36.5	−0.35	46	93	32.2	−0.46	45	91
36.4	−0.35	46	93	32.1	−0.47	45	91
36.3	−0.35	46	93	32.0	−0.47	45	91
36.2	−0.35	46	93	31.9	−0.47	45	91
36.1	−0.36	46	93	31.8	−0.47	45	91
36.0	−0.36	46	93	31.7	−0.48	45	90
35.9	−0.36	46	93	31.6	−0.48	45	90
35.8	−0.36	46	93	31.5	−0.48	45	90
35.7	−0.37	46	93	31.4	−0.48	45	90
35.6	−0.37	46	93	31.3	−0.49	45	90
35.5	−0.37	46	93	31.2	−0.49	45	90

(a)	(b)	(c)	(d)	(a)	(b)	(c)	(d)
31.1	−0.49	45	90	26.8	−0.62	44	88
31.0	−0.49	45	90	26.7	−0.62	44	88
30.9	−0.50	45	90	26.6	−0.62	44	88
30.8	−0.50	45	90	26.5	−0.63	44	87
30.7	−0.50	45	90	26.4	−0.63	44	87
30.6	−0.51	45	90	26.3	−0.63	44	87
30.5	−0.51	45	90	26.2	−0.64	44	87
30.4	−0.51	45	90	26.1	−0.64	44	87
30.3	−0.52	45	90	26.0	−0.64	44	87
30.2	−0.52	45	90	25.9	−0.65	43	87
30.1	−0.52	45	90	25.8	−0.65	43	87
30.0	−0.52	45	90	25.7	−0.65	43	87
29.9	−0.53	45	89	25.6	−0.66	43	87
29.8	−0.53	45	89	25.5	−0.66	43	87
29.7	−0.53	45	89	25.4	−0.66	43	87
29.6	−0.54	45	89	25.3	−0.66	43	87
29.5	−0.54	45	89	25.2	−0.67	43	87
29.4	−0.54	45	89	25.1	−0.67	43	87
29.3	−0.54	45	89	25.0	−0.67	43	87
29.2	−0.55	44	89	24.9	−0.68	43	86
29.1	−0.55	44	89	24.8	−0.68	43	86
29.0	−0.55	44	89	24.7	−0.68	43	86
28.9	−0.55	44	89	24.6	−0.69	43	86
28.8	−0.56	44	89	24.5	−0.69	43	86
28.7	−0.56	44	89	24.4	−0.69	43	86
28.6	−0.56	44	89	24.3	−0.70	43	86
28.5	−0.57	44	89	24.2	−0.70	43	86
28.4	−0.57	44	89	24.1	−0.70	43	86
28.3	−0.57	44	89	24.0	−0.71	43	86
28.2	−0.58	44	88	23.9	−0.71	43	86
28.1	−0.58	44	88	23.8	−0.71	43	86
28.0	−0.58	44	88	23.7	−0.72	43	86
27.9	−0.59	44	88	23.6	−0.72	43	86
27.8	−0.59	44	88	23.5	−0.72	43	86
27.7	−0.59	44	88	23.4	−0.73	43	85
27.6	−0.59	44	88	23.3	−0.73	43	85
27.5	−0.60	44	88	23.2	−0.73	43	85
27.4	−0.60	44	88	23.1	−0.74	43	85
27.3	−0.60	44	88	23.0	−0.74	43	85
27.2	−0 61	44	88	22.9	−0.74	43	85
27.1	−0.61	44	88	22.8	−0.75	42	85
27.0	−0.61	44	88	22.7	−0.75	42	85
26.9	−0.61	44	88	22.6	−0.75	42	85

(a)	(b)	(c)	(d)	(a)	(b)	(c)	(d)
22.5	−0.76	42	85	18.2	−0.91	41	82
22.4	−0.76	42	85	18.1	−0.91	41	82
22.3	−0.76	42	85	18.0	−0.91	41	82
22.2	−0.77	42	85	17.9	−0.92	41	82
22.1	−0.77	42	85	17.8	−0.92	41	82
22.0	−0.77	42	85	17.7	−0.93	41	81
21.9	−0.77	42	85	17.6	−0.93	41	81
21.8	−0.78	42	84	17.5	−0.93	41	81
21.7	−0.78	42	84	17.4	−0.94	41	81
21.6	−0.78	42	84	17.3	−0.94	41	81
21.5	−0.79	42	84	17.2	−0.95	40	81
21.4	−0.79	42	84	17.1	−0.95	40	81
21.3	−0.79	42	84	17.0	−0.95	40	81
21.2	−0.80	42	84	16.9	−0.96	40	81
21.1	−0.80	42	84	16.8	−0.96	40	81
21.0	−0.80	42	84	16.7	−0.97	40	81
20.9	−0.81	42	84	16.6	−0.97	40	81
20.8	−0.81	42	84	16.5	−0.97	40	81
20.7	−0.82	42	84	16.4	−0.98	40	80
20.6	−0.82	42	84	16.3	−0.98	40	80
20.5	−0.82	42	84	16.2	−0.99	40	80
20.4	−0.83	42	83	16.1	−0.99	40	80
20.3	−0.83	42	83	16.0	−0.99	40	80
20.2	−0.83	42	83	15.9	−1.00	40	80
20.1	−0.84	42	83	15.8	−1.00	40	80
20.0	−0.84	42	83	15.7	−1.00	40	80
19.9	−0.84	42	83	15.6	−1.01	40	80
19.8	−0.85	41	83	15.5	−1.01	40	80
19.7	−0.85	41	83	15.4	−1.02	40	80
19.6	−0.86	41	83	15.3	−1.02	40	80
19.5	−0.86	41	83	15.2	−1.03	40	79
19.4	−0.86	41	83	15.1	−1.03	40	79
19.3	−0.87	41	83	15.0	−1.04	40	79
19.2	−0.87	41	83	14.9	−1.04	40	79
19.1	−0.87	41	83	14.8	−1.05	39	79
19.0	−0.88	41	82	14.7	−1.05	39	79
18.9	−0.88	41	82	14.6	−1.05	39	79
18.8	−0.89	41	82	14.5	−1.06	39	79
18.7	−0.89	41	82	14.4	−1.06	39	79
18.6	−0.89	41	82	14.3	−1.07	39	79
18.5	−0.90	41	82	14.2	−1.07	39	78
18.4	−0.90	41	82	14.1	−1.08	39	78
18.3	−0.90	41	82	14.0	−1.08	39	78

(a)	(b)	(c)	(d)	(a)	(b)	(c)	(d)
13.9	−1.08	39	78	9.6	−1.30	37	74
13.8	−1.09	39	78	9.5	−1.31	37	74
13.7	−1.09	39	78	9.4	−1.32	37	74
13.6	−1.10	39	78	9.3	−1.32	37	74
13.5	−1.10	39	78	9.2	−1.33	37	73
13.4	−1.11	39	78	9.1	−1.33	37	73
13.3	−1.11	39	78	9.0	−1.34	37	73
13.2	−1.12	39	78	8.9	−1.35	36	73
13.1	−1.12	39	78	8.8	−1.35	36	73
13.0	−1.13	39	77	8.7	−1.36	36	73
12.9	−1.13	39	77	8.6	−1.37	36	73
12.8	−1.14	39	77	8.5	−1.37	36	73
12.7	−1.14	39	77	8.4	−1.38	36	72
12.6	−1.15	38	77	8.3	−1.38	36	72
12.5	−1.15	38	77	8.2	−1.39	36	72
12.4	−1.16	38	77	8.1	−1.40	36	72
12.3	−1.16	38	77	8.0	−1.41	36	72
12.2	−1.17	38	77	7.9	−1.41	36	72
12.1	−1.17	38	77	7.8	−1.42	36	72
12.0	−1.18	38	76	7.7	−1.43	36	71
11.9	−1.18	38	76	7.6	−1.43	36	71
11.8	−1.19	38	76	7.5	−1.44	36	71
11.7	−1.19	38	76	7.4	−1.45	35	71
11.6	−1.20	38	76	7.3	−1.45	35	71
11.5	−1.20	38	76	7.2	−1.46	35	71
11.4	−1.21	38	76	7.1	−1.47	35	71
11.3	−1.21	38	76	7.0	−1.48	35	70
11.2	−1.22	38	76	6.9	−1.48	35	70
11.1	−1.22	38	76	6.8	−1.49	35	70
11.0	−1.22	38	76	6.7	−1.50	35	70
10.9	−1.23	38	75	6.6	−1.50	35	70
10.8	−1.23	38	75	6.5	−1.51	35	70
10.7	−1.24	38	75	6.4	−1.52	35	70
10.6	−1.25	37	75	6.3	−1.53	35	69
10.5	−1.25	37	75	6.2	−1.54	35	69
10.4	−1.26	37	75	6.1	−1.55	34	69
10.3	−1.26	37	75	6.0	−1.55	34	69
10.2	−1.27	37	75	5.9	−1.56	34	69
10.1	−1.28	37	74	5.8	−1.57	34	69
10.0	−1.28	37	74	5.7	−1.58	34	68
9.9	−1.29	37	74	5.6	−1.59	34	68
9.8	−1.29	37	74	5.5	−1.60	34	68
9.7	−1.30	37	74	5.4	−1.61	34	68

(*a*)	(*b*)	(*c*)	(*d*)		(*a*)	(*b*)	(*c*)	(*d*)
5.3	−1.62	34	68		2.6	−1.94	31	61
5.2	−1.63	34	67		2.5	−1.96	30	61
5.1	−1.64	34	67		2.4	−1.98	30	60
5.0	−1.64	34	67		2.3	−2.00	30	60
4.9	−1.65	33	67		2.2	−2.01	30	60
4.8	−1.66	33	67		2.1	−2.03	30	59
4.7	−1.67	33	67		2.0	−2.05	29	59
4.6	−1.68	33	66		1.9	−2.07	29	59
4.5	−1.70	33	66		1.8	−2.10	29	58
4.4	−1.71	33	66		1.7	−2.12	29	58
4.3	−1.72	33	66		1.6	−2.14	29	57
4.2	−1.73	33	65		1.5	−2.17	28	57
4.1	−1.74	33	65		1.4	−2.20	28	56
4.0	−1.75	32	65		1.3	−2.22	28	55
3.9	−1.76	32	65		1.2	−2.26	27	55
3.8	−1.77	32	65		1.1	−2.29	27	54
3.7	−1.79	32	64		1.0	−2.33	27	53
3.6	−1.80	32	64		0.9	−2.37	26	53
3.5	−1.81	32	64		0.8	−2.41	26	52
3.4	−1.83	32	63		0.7	−2.46	25	51
3.3	−1.84	32	63		0.6	−2.51	25	50
3.2	−1.85	31	63		0.5	−2.58	24	48
3.1	−1.87	31	63		0.4	−2.65	23	47
3.0	−1.88	31	62		0.3	−2.75	22	45
2.9	−1.90	31	62		0.2	−2.88	21	42
2.8	−1.91	31	62		0.1	−3.09	19	38
2.7	−1.93	31	61					

SQUARES AND SQUARE ROOTS OF NUMBERS FROM 1 TO 1,000.

Number	Square	Square root	Number	Square	Square root
1	1	1.0000	41	16 81	6.4031
2	4	1.4142	42	17 64	6.4807
3	9	1.7321	43	18 49	6.5574
4	16	2.0000	44	19 36	6.6332
5	25	2.2361	45	20 25	6.7082
6	36	2.4495	46	21 16	6.7823
7	49	2.6458	47	22 09	6.8557
8	64	2.8284	48	23 04	6.9282
9	81	3.0000	49	24 01	7.0000
10	1 00	3.1623	50	25 00	7.0711
11	1 21	3.3166	51	26 01	7.1414
12	1 44	3.4641	52	27 04	7.2111
13	1 69	3.6056	53	28 09	7.2801
14	1 96	3.7417	54	29 16	7.3485
15	2 25	3.8730	55	30 25	7.4162
16	2 56	4.0000	56	31 36	7.4833
17	2 89	4.1231	57	32 49	7.5498
18	3 24	4.2426	58	33 64	7.6158
19	3 61	4.3589	59	34 81	7.6811
20	4 00	4.4721	60	36 00	7.7460
21	4 41	4.5826	61	37 21	7.8102
22	4 84	4.6904	62	38 44	7.8740
23	5 29	4.7958	63	39 69	7.9373
24	5 76	4.8990	64	40 96	8.0000
25	6 25	5.0000	65	42 25	8.0623
26	6 76	5.0990	66	43 56	8.1240
27	7 29	5.1962	67	44 89	8.1854
28	7 84	5.2915	68	46 24	8.2462
29	8 41	5.3852	69	47 61	8.3066
30	9 00	5.4772	70	49 00	8.3666
31	9 61	5.5678	71	50 41	8.4261
32	10 24	5.6569	72	51 84	8.4853
33	10 89	5.7446	73	53 29	8.5440
34	11 56	5.8310	74	54 76	8.6023
35	12 25	5.9161	75	56 25	8.6603
36	12 96	6.0000	76	57 76	8.7178
37	13 69	6.0828	77	59 29	8.7750
38	14 44	6.1644	78	60 84	8.8318
39	15 21	6.2450	79	62 41	8.8882
40	16 00	6.3246	80	64 00	8.9443

. Squares and Square Roots of Numbers from 1 to 1,000. .

Number	Square	Square root	Number	Square	Square root
81	65 61	9.0000	121	1 46 41	11.0000
82	67 24	9.0554	122	1 48 84	11.0454
83	68 89	9.1104	123	1 51 29	11.0905
84	70 56	9.1652	124	1 53 76	11.1355
85	72 25	9.2195	125	1 56 25	11.1803
86	73 96	9.2736	126	1 58 76	11.2250
87	75 69	9.3274	127	1 61 29	11.2694
88	77 44	9.3808	128	1 63 84	11.3137
89	79 21	9.4340	129	1 66 41	11.3578
90	81 00	9.4868	130	1 69 00	11.4018
91	82 81	9.5394	131	1 71 61	11.4455
92	84 64	9.5917	132	1 74 24	11.4891
93	86 49	9.6437	133	1 76 89	11.5326
94	88 36	9.6954	134	1 79 56	11.5758
95	90 25	9.7468	135	1 82 25	11.6190
96	92 16	9.7980	136	1 84 96	11.6619
97	94 09	9.8489	137	1 87 69	11.7047
98	96 04	9.8995	138	1 90 44	11.7473
99	98 01	9.9499	139	1 93 21	11.7898
100	1 00 00	10.0000	140	1 96 00	11.8322
101	1 02 01	10.0499	141	1 98 81	11.8743
102	1 04 04	10.0995	142	2 01 64	11.9164
103	1 06 09	10.1489	143	2 04 49	11.9583
104	1 08 16	10.1980	144	2 07 36	12.0000
105	1 10 25	10.2470	145	2 10 25	12.0416
106	1 12 36	10.2956	146	2 13 16	12.0830
107	1 14 49	10.3441	147	2 16 09	12.1244
108	1 16 64	10.3923	148	2 19 04	12.1655
109	1 18 81	10.4403	149	2 22 01	12.2066
110	1 21 00	10.4881	150	2 25 00	12.2474
111	1 23 21	10.5357	151	2 28 01	12.2882
112	1 25 44	10.5830	152	2 31 04	12.3288
113	1 27 69	10.6301	153	2 34 09	12.3693
114	1 29 96	10.6771	154	2 37 16	12.4097
115	1 32 25	10.7238	155	2 40 25	12.4499
116	1 34 56	10.7703	156	2 43 36	12.4900
117	1 36 89	10.8167	157	2 46 49	12.5300
118	1 39 24	10.8628	158	2 49 64	12.5698
119	1 41 61	10.9087	159	2 52 81	12.6095
120	1 44 00	10.9545	160	2 56 00	12.6491

SQUARES AND SQUARE ROOTS OF NUMBERS FROM 1 TO 1,000.

Number	Square	Square root	Number	Square	Square root
161	2 59 21	12.6886	201	4 04 01	14.1774
162	2 62 44	12.7279	202	4 08 04	14.2127
163	2 65 69	12.7671	203	4 12 09	14.2478
164	2 68 96	12.8062	204	4 16 16	14.2829
165	2 72 25	12.8452	205	4 20 25	14.3178
166	2 75 56	12.8841	206	4 24 36	14.3527
167	2 78 89	12.9228	207	4 28 49	14.3875
168	2 82 24	12.9615	208	4 32 64	14.4222
169	2 85 61	13.0000	209	4 36 81	14.4568
170	2 89 00	13.0384	210	4 41 00	14.4914
171	2 92 41	13.0767	211	4 45 21	14.5258
172	2 95 84	13.1149	212	4 49 44	14.5602
173	2 99 29	13.1529	213	4 53 69	14.5945
174	3 02 76	13.1909	214	4 57 96	14.6287
175	3 06 25	13.2288	215	4 62 25	14.6629
176	3 09 76	13.2665	216	4 66 56	14.6969
177	3 13 29	13.3041	217	4 70 89	14.7309
178	3 16 84	13.3417	218	4 75 24	14.7648
179	3 20 41	13.3791	219	4 79 61	14.7986
180	3 24 00	13.4164	220	4 84 00	14.8324
181	3 27 61	13.4536	221	4 88 41	14.8661
182	3 31 24	13.4907	222	4 92 84	14.8997
183	3 34 89	13.5277	223	4 97 29	14.9332
184	3 38 56	13.5647	224	5 01 76	14.9666
185	3 42 25	13.6015	225	5 06 25	15.0000
186	3 45 96	13.6382	226	5 10 76	15.0333
187	3 49 69	13.6748	227	5 15 29	15.0665
188	3 53 44	13.7113	228	5 19 84	15.0997
189	3 57 21	13.7477	229	5 24 41	15.1327
190	3 61 00	13.7840	230	5 29 00	15.1658
191	3 64 81	13.8203	231	5 33 61	15.1987
192	3 68 64	13.8564	232	5 38 24	15.2315
193	3 72 49	13.8924	233	5 42 89	15.2643
194	3 76 36	13.9284	234	5 47 56	15.2971
195	3 80 25	13.9642	235	5 52 25	15.3297
196	3 84 16	14.0000	236	5 56 96	15.3623
197	3 88 09	14.0357	237	5 61 69	15.3948
198	3 92 04	14.0712	238	5 66 44	15.4272
199	3 96 01	14.1067	239	5 71 21	15.4596
200	4 00 00	14.1421	240	5 76 00	15.4919

Squares and Square Roots of Numbers from 1 to 1,000.

Number	Square	Square root	Number	Square	Square root
241	5 80 81	15.5242	281	7 89 61	16.7631
242	5 85 64	15.5563	282	7 95 24	16.7929
243	5 90 49	15.5885	283	8 00 89	16.8226
244	5 95 36	15.6205	284	8 06 56	16.8523
245	6 00 25	15.6525	285	8 12 25	16.8819
246	6 05 16	15.6844	286	8 17 96	16.9115
247	6 10 09	15.7162	287	8 23 69	16.9411
248	6 15 04	15.7480	288	8 29 44	16.9706
249	6 20 01	15.7797	289	8 35 21	17.0000
250	6 25 00	15.8114	290	8 41 00	17.0294
251	6 30 01	15.8430	291	8 46 81	17.0587
252	6 35 04	15.8745	292	8 52 64	17.0880
253	6 40 09	15.9060	293	8 58 49	17.1172
254	6 45 16	15.9374	294	8 64 36	17.1464
255	6 50 25	15.9687	295	8 70 25	17.1756
256	6 55 36	16.0000	296	8 76 16	17.2047
257	6 60 49	16.0312	297	8 82 09	17.2337
258	6 65 64	16.0624	298	8 88 04	17.2627
259	6 70 81	16.0935	299	8 94 01	17.2916
260	6 76 00	16.1245	300	9 00 00	17.3205
261	6 81 21	16.1555	301	9 06 01	17.3494
262	6 86 44	16.1864	302	9 12 04	17.3781
263	6 91 69	16.2173	303	9 18 09	17.4069
264	6 96 96	16.2481	304	9 24 16	17.4356
265	7 02 25	16.2788	305	9 30 25	17.4642
266	7 07 56	16.3095	306	9 36 36	17.4929
267	7 12 89	16.3401	307	9 42 49	17.5214
268	7 18 24	16.3707	308	9 48 64	17.5499
269	7 23 61	16.4012	309	9 54 81	17.5784
270	7 29 00	16.4317	310	9 61 00	17.6068
271	7 34 41	16.4621	311	9 67 21	17.6352
272	7 39 84	16.4924	312	9 73 44	17.6635
273	7 45 29	16.5227	313	9 79 69	17.6918
274	7 50 76	16.5529	314	9 85 96	17.7200
275	7 56 25	16.5831	315	9 92 25	17.7482
276	7 61 76	16.6132	316	9 98 56	17.7764
277	7 67 29	16.6433	317	10 04 89	17.8045
278	7 72 84	16.6733	318	10 11 24	17.8326
279	7 78 41	16.7033	319	10 17 61	17.8606
280	7 84 00	16.7332	320	10 24 00	17.8885

SQUARES AND SQUARE ROOTS OF NUMBERS FROM 1 TO 1,000.

Number	Square	Square root	Number	Square	Square root
321	10 30 41	17.9165	361	13 03 21	19.0000
322	10 36 84	17.9444	362	13 10 44	19.0263
323	10 43 29	17.9722	363	13 17 69	19.0526
324	10 49 76	18.0000	364	13 24 96	19.0788
325	10 56 25	18.0278	365	13 32 25	19.1050
326	10 62 76	18.0555	366	13 39 56	19.1311
327	10 69 29	18.0831	367	13 46 89	19.1572
328	10 75 84	18.1108	368	13 54 24	19.1833
329	10 82 41	18.1384	369	13 61 61	19.2094
330	10 89 00	18.1659	370	13 69 00	19.2354
331	10 95 61	18.1934	371	13 76 41	19.2614
332	11 02 24	18.2209	372	13 83 84	19.2873
333	11 08 89	18.2483	373	13 91 29	19.3132
334	11 15 56	18.2757	374	13 98 76	19.3391
335	11 22 25	18.3030	375	14 06 25	19.3649
336	11 28 96	18.3303	376	14 13 76	19.3907
337	11 35 69	18.3576	377	14 21 29	19.4165
338	11 42 44	18.3848	378	14 28 84	19.4422
339	11 49 21	18.4120	379	14 36 41	19.4679
340	11 56 00	18.4391	380	14 44 00	19.4936
341	11 62 81	18.4662	381	14 51 61	19.5192
342	11 69 64	18.4932	382	14 59 24	19.5448
343	11 76 49	18.5203	383	14 66 89	19.5704
344	11 83 36	18.5472	384	14 74 56	19.5959
345	11 90 25	18.5742	385	14 82 25	19.6214
346	11 97 16	18.6011	386	14 89 96	19.6469
347	12 04 09	18.6279	387	14 97 69	19.6723
348	12 11 04	18.6548	388	15 05 44	19.6977
349	12 18 01	18.6815	389	15 13 21	19.7231
350	12 25 00	18.7083	390	15 21 00	19.7484
351	12 32 01	18.7350	391	15 28 81	19.7737
352	12 39 04	18.7617	392	15 36 64	19.7990
353	12 46 09	18.7883	393	15 44 49	19.8242
354	12 53 16	18.8149	394	15 52 36	19.8494
355	12 60 25	18.8414	395	15 60 25	19.8746
356	12 67 36	18.8680	396	15 68 16	19.8997
357	12 74 49	18.8944	397	15 76 09	19.9249
358	12 81 64	18.9209	398	15 84 04	19.9499
359	12 88 81	18.9473	399	15 92 01	19.9750
360	12 96 00	18.9737	400	16 00 00	20.0000

SQUARES AND SQUARE ROOTS OF NUMBERS FROM 1 TO 1,000.

Number	Square	Square root	Number	Square	Square root
401	16 08 01	20.0250	441	19 44 81	21.0000
402	16 16 04	20.0499	442	19 53 64	21.0238
403	16 24 09	20.0749	443	19 62 49	21.0476
404	16 32 16	20.0998	444	19 71 36	21.0713
405	16 40 25	20.1246	445	19 80 25	21.0950
406	16 48 36	20.1494	446	19 89 16	21.1187
407	16 56 49	20.1742	447	19 98 09	21.1424
408	16 64 64	20.1990	448	20 07 04	21.1660
409	16 72 81	20.2237	449	20 16 01	21.1896
410	16 81 00	20.2485	450	20 25 00	21.2132
411	16 89 21	20.2731	451	20 34 01	21.2368
412	16 97 44	20.2978	452	20 43 04	21.2603
413	17 05 69	20.3224	453	20 52 09	21.2838
414	17 13 96	20.3470	454	20 61 16	21.3073
415	17 22 25	20.3715	455	20 70 25	21.3307
416	17 30 56	20.3961	456	20 79 36	21.3542
417	17 38 89	20.4206	457	20 88 49	21.3776
418	17 47 24	20.4450	458	20 97 64	21.4009
419	17 55 61	20.4695	459	21 06 81	21.4243
420	17 64 00	20.4939	460	21 16 00	21.4476
421	17 72 41	20.5183	461	21 25 21	21.4709
422	17 80 84	20.5426	462	21 34 44	21.4942
423	17 89 29	20.5670	463	21 43 69	21.5174
424	17 97 76	20.5913	464	21 52 96	21.5407
425	18 06 25	20.6155	465	21 62 25	21.5639
426	18 14 76	20.6398	466	21 71 56	21.5870
427	18 23 29	20.6640	467	21 80 89	21.6102
428	18 31 84	20.6882	468	21 90 24	21.6333
429	18 40 41	20.7123	469	21 99 61	21.6564
430	18 49 00	20.7364	470	22 09 00	21.6795
431	18 57 61	20.7605	471	22 18 41	21.7025
432	18 66 24	20.7846	472	22 27 84	21.7256
433	18 74 89	20.8087	473	22 37 29	21.7486
434	18 83 56	20.8327	474	22 46 76	21.7715
435	18 92 25	20.8567	475	22 56 25	21.7945
436	19 00 96	20.8806	476	22 65 76	21.8174
437	19 09 69	20.9045	477	22 75 29	21.8403
438	19 18 44	20.9284	478	22 84 84	21.8632
439	19 27 21	20.9523	479	22 94 41	21.8861
440	19 36 00	20.9762	480	23 04 00	21.9089

Squares and Square Roots of Numbers from 1 to 1,000.

Number	Square	Square root	Number	Square	Square root
481	23 13 61	21.9317	521	27 14 41	22.8254
482	23 23 24	21.9545	522	27 24 84	22.8473
483	23 32 89	21.9773	523	27 35 29	22.8692
484	23 42 56	22.0000	524	27 45 76	22.8910
485	23 52 25	22.0227	525	27 56 25	22.9129
486	23 61 96	22.0454	526	27 66 76	22.9347
487	23 71 69	22.0681	527	27 77 29	22.9565
488	23 81 44	22.0907	528	27 87 84	22.9783
489	23 91 21	22.1133	529	27 98 41	23.0000
490	24 01 00	22.1359	530	28 09 00	23.0217
491	24 10 81	22.1585	531	28 19 61	23.0434
492	24 20 64	22.1811	532	28 30 24	23.0651
493	24 30 49	22.2036	533	28 40 89	23.0868
494	24 40 36	22.2261	534	28 51 56	23.1084
495	24 50 25	22.2486	535	28 62 25	23.1301
496	24 60 16	22.2711	536	28 72 96	23.1517
497	24 70 09	22.2935	537	28 83 69	23.1733
498	24 80 04	22.3159	538	28 94 44	23.1948
499	24 90 01	22.3383	539	29 05 21	23.2164
500	25 00 00	22.3607	540	29 16 00	23.2379
501	25 10 01	22.3830	541	29 26 81	23.2594
502	25 20 04	22.4054	542	29 37 64	23.2809
503	25 30 09	22.4277	543	29 48 49	23.3024
504	25 40 16	22.4499	544	29 59 36	23.3238
505	25 50 25	22.4722	545	29 70 25	23.3452
506	25 60 36	22.4944	546	29 81 16	23.3666
507	25 70 49	22.5167	547	29 92 09	23.3880
508	25 80 64	22.5389	548	30 03 04	23.4094
509	25 90 81	22.5610	549	30 14 01	23.4307
510	26 01 00	22.5832	550	30 25 00	23.4521
511	26 11 21	22.6053	551	30 36 01	23.4734
512	26 21 44	22.6274	552	30 47 04	23.4947
513	26 31 69	22.6495	553	30 58 09	23.5160
514	26 41 96	22.6716	554	30 69 16	23.5372
515	26 52 25	22.6936	555	30 80 25	23.5584
516	26 62 56	22.7156	556	30 91 36	23.5797
517	26 72 89	22.7376	557	31 02 49	23.6008
518	26 83 24	22.7596	558	31 13 64	23.6220
519	26 93 61	22.7816	559	31 24 81	23.6432
520	27 04 00	22.8035	560	31 36 00	23.6643

SQUARES AND SQUARE ROOTS OF NUMBERS FROM 1 TO 1,000.

Number	Square	Square root	Number	Square	Square root
561	31 47 21	23.6854	601	36 12 01	24.5153
562	31 58 44	23.7065	602	36 24 04	24.5357
563	31 69 69	23.7276	603	36 36 09	24.5561
564	31 80 96	23.7487	604	36 48 16	24.5764
565	31 92 25	23.7697	605	36 60 25	24.5967
566	32 03 56	23.7908	606	36 72 36	24.6171
567	32 14 89	23.8118	607	36 84 49	24.6374
568	32 26 24	23.8328	608	36 96 64	24.6577
569	32 37 61	23.8537	609	37 08 81	24.6779
570	32 49 00	23.8747	610	37 21 00	24.6982
571	32 60 41	23.8956	611	37 33 21	24.7184
572	32 71 84	23.9165	612	37 45 44	24.7385
573	32 83 29	23.9374	613	37 57 69	24.7588
574	32 94 76	23.9583	614	37 69 96	24.7790
575	33 06 25	23.9792	615	37 82 25	24.7992
576	33 17 76	24.0000	616	37 94 56	24.8193
577	33 29 29	24.0208	617	38 06 89	24.8395
578	33 40 84	24.0416	618	38 19 24	24.8596
579	33 52 41	24.0624	619	38 31 61	24.8797
580	33 64 00	24.0832	620	38 44 00	24.8998
581	33 75 61	24.1039	621	38 56 41	24.9199
582	33 87 24	24.1247	622	38 68 84	24.9399
583	33 98 89	24.1454	623	38 81 29	24.9600
584	34 10 56	24.1661	624	38 93 76	24.9800
585	34 22 25	24.1868	625	39 06 25	25.0000
586	34 33 96	24.2074	626	39 18 76	25.0200
587	34 45 69	24.2281	627	39 31 29	25.0400
588	34 57 44	24.2487	628	39 43 84	25.0599
589	34 69 21	24.2693	629	39 56 41	25.0799
590	34 81 00	24.2899	630	39 69 00	25.0998
591	34 92 81	24.3105	631	39 81 61	25.1197
592	35 04 64	24.3311	632	39 94 24	25.1396
593	35 16 49	24.3516	633	40 06 89	25.1595
594	35 28 36	24.3721	634	40 19 56	25.1794
595	35 40 25	24.3926	635	40 32 25	25.1992
596	35 52 16	24.4131	636	40 44 96	25.2190
597	35 64 09	24.4336	637	40 57 69	25.2389
598	35 76 04	24.4540	638	40 70 44	25.2587
599	35 88 01	24.4745	639	40 83 21	25.2784
600	36 00 00	24.4949	640	40 96 00	25.2982

SQUARES AND SQUARE ROOTS OF NUMBERS FROM 1 TO 1,000.

Number	Square	Square root	Number	Square	Square root
641	41 08 81	25.3180	681	46 37 61	26.0960
642	41 21 64	25.3377	682	46 51 24	26.1151
643	41 34 49	25.3574	683	46 64 89	26.1343
644	41 47 36	25.3772	684	46 78 56	26.1534
645	41 60 25	25.3969	685	46 92 25	26.1725
646	41 73 16	25.4165	686	47 05 96	26.1916
647	41 86 09	25.4362	687	47 19 69	26.2107
648	41 99 04	25.4558	688	47 33 44	26.2298
649	42 12 01	25.4755	689	47 47 21	26.2488
650	42 25 00	25.4951	690	47 61 00	26.2679
651	42 38 01	25.5147	691	47 74 81	26.2869
652	42 51 04	25.5343	692	47 88 64	26.3059
653	42 64 09	25.5539	693	48 02 49	26.3249
654	42 77 16	25.5734	694	48 16 36	26.3439
655	42 90 25	25.5930	695	48 30 25	26.3629
656	43 03 36	25.6125	696	48 44 16	26.3818
657	43 16 49	25.6320	697	48 58 09	26.4008
658	43 29 64	25.6515	698	48 72 04	26.4197
659	43 42 81	25.6710	699	48 86 01	26.4386
660	43 56 00	25.6905	700	49 00 00	26.4575
661	43 69 21	25.7099	701	49 14 01	26.4764
662	43 82 44	25.7294	702	49 28 04	26.4953
663	43 95 69	25.7488	703	49 42 09	26.5141
664	44 08 96	25.7682	704	49 56 16	26.5330
665	44 22 25	25.7876	705	49 70 25	26.5518
666	44 35 56	25.8070	706	49 84 36	26.5707
667	44 48 89	25.8263	707	49 98 49	26.5895
668	44 62 24	25.8457	708	50 12 64	26.6083
669	44 75 61	25.8650	709	50 26 81	26.6271
670	44 89 00	25.8844	710	50 41 00	26.6458
671	45 02 41	25.9037	711	50 55 21	26.6646
672	45 15 84	25.9230	712	50 69 44	26.6833
673	45 29 29	25.9422	713	50 83 69	26.7021
674	45 42 76	25.9615	714	50 97 96	26.7208
675	45 56 25	25.9808	715	51 12 25	26.7395
676	45 69 76	26.0000	716	51 26 56	26.7582
677	45 83 29	26.0192	717	51 40 89	26.7769
678	45 96 84	26.0384	718	51 55 24	26.7955
679	46 10 41	26.0576	719	51 69 61	26.8142
680	46 24 00	26.0768	720	51 84 00	26.8328

SQUARES AND SQUARE ROOTS OF NUMBERS FROM 1 TO 1,000.

Number	Square	Square root	Number	Square	Square root
721	51 98 41	26.8514	761	57 91 21	27.5862
722	52 12 84	26.8701	762	58 06 44	27.6043
723	52 27 29	26.8887	763	58 21 69	27.6225
724	52 41 76	26.9072	764	58 36 96	27.6405
725	52 56 25	26.9258	765	58 52 25	27.6586
726	52 70 76	26.9444	766	58 67 56	27.6767
727	52 85 29	26.9629	767	58 82 89	27.6948
728	52 99 84	26.9815	768	58 98 24	27.7128
729	53 14 41	27.0000	769	59 13 61	27.7308
730	53 29 00	27.0185	770	59 29 00	27.7489
731	53 43 61	27.0370	771	59 44 41	27.7669
732	53 58 24	27.0555	772	59 59 84	27.7849
733	53 72 89	27.0740	773	59 75 29	27.8029
734	53 87 56	27.0924	774	59 90 76	27.8209
735	54 02 25	27.1109	775	60 06 25	27.8388
736	54 16 96	27.1293	776	60 21 76	27.8568
737	54 31 69	27.1477	777	60 37 29	27.8747
738	54 46 44	27.1662	778	60 52 84	27.8927
739	54 61 27	27.1846	779	60 68 41	27.9106
740	54 76 00	27.2029	780	60 84 00	27.9285
741	54 90 81	27.2213	781	60 99 61	27.9464
742	55 05 64	27.2397	782	61 15 24	27.9643
743	55 20 49	27.2580	783	61 30 89	27.9821
744	55 35 36	27.2764	784	61 46 56	28.0000
745	55 50 25	27.2947	785	61 62 25	28.0179
746	55 65 16	27.3130	786	61 77 96	28.0357
747	55 80 09	27.3313	787	61 93 69	28.0535
748	55 95 04	27.3496	788	62 09 44	28.0713
749	56 10 01	27.3679	789	62 25 21	28.0891
750	56 25 00	27.3861	790	62 41 00	28.1069
751	56 40 01	27.4044	791	62 56 81	28.1247
752	56 55 04	27.4226	792	62 72 64	28.1425
753	56 70 09	27.4408	793	62 88 49	28.1603
754	56 85 16	27.4591	794	63 04 36	28.1780
755	57 00 25	27.4773	795	63 20 25	28.1957
756	57 15 36	27.4955	796	63 36 16	28.2135
757	57 30 49	27.5136	797	63 52 09	28.2312
758	57 45 64	27.5318	798	63 68 04	28.2489
759	57 60 81	27.5500	799	63 84 01	28.2666
760	57 76 00	27.5681	800	64 00 00	28.2843

Squares and Square Roots of Numbers from 1 to 1,000.

Number	Square	Square root	Number	Square	Square root
801	64 16 01	28.3019	841	70 72 81	29.0000
802	64 32 04	28.3196	842	70 89 64	29.0172
803	64 48 09	28.3373	843	71 06 49	29.0345
804	64 64 16	28.3049	844	71 23 36	29.0517
805	64 80 25	28.3725	845	71 40 25	29.0689
806	64 96 36	28.3901	846	71 57 16	29.0861
807	65 12 49	28.4077	847	71 74 09	29.1033
808	65 28 64	28.4253	848	71 91 04	29.1204
809	65 44 81	28.4429	849	72 08 01	29.1376
810	65 61 00	28.4605	850	72 25 00	29.1548
811	65 77 21	28.4781	851	72 42 01	29.1719
812	65 93 44	28.4956	852	72 59 04	29.1890
813	66 09 69	28.5132	853	72 76 09	29.2062
814	66 25 96	28.5307	854	72 93 16	29.2233
815	66 42 25	28.5482	855	73 10 25	29.2404
816	66 58 56	28.5657	856	73 27 36	29.2575
817	66 74 89	28.5832	857	73 44 49	29.2746
818	66 91 24	28.6007	858	73 61 64	29.2916
819	67 07 61	28.6082	859	73 78 81	29.3087
820	67 24 00	28.6356	860	73 96 00	29.3258
821	67 40 41	28.6531	861	74 13 21	29.3428
822	67 56 84	28.6705	862	74 30 44	29.3598
823	67 73 29	28.6880	863	74 47 69	29.3769
824	67 89 76	28.7054	864	74 64 96	29.3939
825	68 06 25	28.7228	865	74 82 25	29.4109
826	68 22 76	28.7402	866	74 99 56	29.4279
827	68 39 29	28.7576	867	75 16 89	29.4449
828	68 55 84	28.7750	868	75 34 24	29.4618
829	68 72 41	28.7924	869	75 51 61	29.4788
830	68 89 00	28.8097	870	75 69 00	29.4958
831	69 05 61	28.8271	871	75 86 41	29.5127
832	69 22 24	28.8444	872	76 03 84	29.5296
833	69 38 89	28.8617	873	76 21 29	29.5466
834	69 55 56	28.8791	874	76 38 76	29.5635
835	69 72 25	28.8964	875	76 56 25	29.5804
836	69 88 96	28.9137	876	76 73 76	29.5973
837	70 05 69	28.9310	877	76 91 29	29.6142
838	70 22 44	28.9482	878	77 08 84	29.6311
839	70 39 21	28.9655	879	77 26 41	29.6479
840	70 56 00	28.9828	880	77 44 00	29.6648

SQUARES AND SQUARE ROOTS OF NUMBERS FROM 1 TO 1,000.

Number	Square	Square root	Number	Square	Square root
881	77 61 61	29.6816	921	84 82 41	30.3480
882	77 79 24	29.6985	922	85 00 84	30.3645
883	77 96 89	29.7153	923	85 19 29	30.3809
884	78 14 56	29.7321	924	85 37 76	30.3974
885	78 32 25	29.7489	925	85 56 25	30.4138
886	78 49 96	29.7658	926	85 74 76	30.4302
887	78 67 69	29.7825	927	85 93 29	30.4467
888	78 85 44	29.7993	928	86 11 84	30.4631
889	79 03 21	29.8161	929	86 30 41	30.4795
890	79 21 00	29.8329	930	86 49 00	30.4959
891	79 38 81	29.8496	931	86 67 61	30.5123
892	79 56 64	29.8664	932	86 86 24	30.5287
893	79 74 49	29.8831	933	87 04 89	30.5450
894	79 92 36	29.8998	934	87 23 56	30.5614
895	80 10 25	29.9166	935	87 42 25	30.5778
896	80 28 16	29.9333	936	87 60 96	30.5941
897	80 46 09	29.9500	937	87 79 69	30.6105
898	80 64 04	29.9666	938	87 98 44	30.6268
899	80 82 01	29.9833	939	88 17 21	30.6431
900	81 00 00	30.0000	940	88 36 00	30.6594
901	81 18 01	30.0167	941	88 54 81	30.6757
902	81 36 04	30.0333	942	88 73 64	30.6920
903	81 54 09	30.0500	943	88 92 49	30.7083
904	81 72 16	30.0666	944	89 11 36	30.7246
905	81 90 25	30.0832	945	89 30 25	30.7409
906	82 08 36	30.0998	946	89 49 16	30.7571
907	82 26 49	30.1164	947	89 68 09	30.7734
908	82 44 64	30.1330	948	89 87 04	30.7896
909	82 62 81	30.1496	949	90 06 01	30.8058
910	82 81 00	30.1662	950	90 25 00	30.8221
911	82 99 21	30.1828	951	90 44 01	30.8383
912	83 17 44	30.1993	952	90 63 04	30.8545
913	83 35 69	30.2159	953	90 82 09	30.8707
914	83 53 96	30.2324	954	91 01 16	30.8869
915	83 72 25	30.2490	955	91 20 25	30.9031
916	83 90 56	30.2655	956	91 39 36	30.9192
917	84 08 89	30.2820	957	91 58 49	30.9354
918	84 27 24	30.2985	958	91 77 64	30.9516
919	84 45 61	30.3150	959	91 96 81	30.9677
920	84 64 00	30.3315	960	92 16 00	30.9839

SQUARES AND SQUARE ROOTS OF NUMBERS FROM 1 TO 1,000.

Number	Square	Square root	Number	Square	Square root
961	92 35 21	31.0000	981	96 23 61	31.3209
962	92 54 44	31.0161	982	96 43 24	31.3369
963	92 73 69	31.0322	983	96 62 89	31.3528
964	92 92 96	31.0483	984	96 82 56	31.3688
965	93 12 25	31.0644	985	97 02 25	31.3847
966	93 31 56	31.0805	986	97 21 96	31.4006
967	93 50 89	31.0966	987	97 41 69	31.4166
968	93 70 24	31.1127	988	97 61 44	31.4325
969	93 89 61	31.1288	989	97 81 21	31.4484
970	94 09 00	31.1448	990	98 01 00	31.4643
971	94 28 41	31.1609	991	98 20 81	31.4802
972	94 47 84	31.1769	992	98 40 64	31.4960
973	94 67 29	31.1929	993	98 60 49	31.5119
974	94 86 76	31.2090	994	98 80 36	31.5278
975	95 06 25	31.2250	995	99 00 25	31.5436
976	95 25 76	31.2410	996	99 20 16	31.5595
977	95 45 29	31.2570	997	99 40 09	31.5753
978	95 64 84	31.2730	998	99 60 04	31.5911
979	95 84 41	31.2890	999	99 80 01	31.6070
980	96 04 00	31.3050	1000	100 00 00	31.6228

SOURCE: J. P. Guilford, "Psychometric Methods," 2d ed., McGraw-Hill Book Company, Inc., New York, 1954.

Index